FOR
MOMENT
OF TASTE

'Through hard-hitting facts and disturbing accounts of farm and slaughterhouse visits, Poorva reveals we can save lives, including our own, and protect the Earth, with our plates.'
—Dr Aditi Govitrikar, actor, model and medical doctor

'The most important book for anyone who cares about animals to read this year.'
—Maj. Gen. R.M. Kharb (retd), veterinarian and former chairman of the Animal Welfare Board of India

FOR A MOMENT OF TASTE

How What You Eat Impacts Animals, the Planet and Your Health

POORVA JOSHIPURA

HarperCollins *Publishers* India

First published in India in 2020 by
HarperCollins *Publishers*
A-75, Sector 57, Noida, Uttar Pradesh 201301, India
www.harpercollins.co.in

2 4 6 8 10 9 7 5 3 1

P-ISBN: 978-93-5357-469-7
E-ISBN: 978-93-5357-470-3

Typeset in 11/15 Minion Pro at
Manipal Technologies Limited, Manipal

Printed and bound at
Thomson Press (India) Ltd

For my grandmother,
who left water out for birds, fed squirrels and
gently placed ants outdoors

CONTENTS

FOREWORD

W hen I was little, I had a dog called Kaalu. He was a stray my family had adopted. We lived in a joint family and all the children were very fond of the ageing and sage-like Kaalu.

I have always been a vegetarian, but when Kaalu died I realized there's no difference between him and the other mammals and birds who end up on our plates. My commitment to vegetarianism has been unwavering despite my own family and friends sometimes eating meat—for me, meat was murder.

Milk was a staple in our food and we had it by itself too. Like most kids, I never questioned why milk had to be had before school or bedtime. I used to eat a lot of paneer, yogurt and almost everything that was made out of milk. To give up milk seemed impossible and almost blasphemous.

Then a naturopath encouraged me to reconsider dairy. Today, I am vegan after looking into the impact of dairy consumption on the animal, the self and the environment at large.

Most of us forget that like any other mammal, for a cow or buffalo to have milk in her udders, she either has to be pregnant or have recently given birth. What does life look like for her then? As a calf she is often given drugs so she can grow faster and is later made pregnant through artificial insemination. Once she delivers a child, if it is female, she will be used as a milk-giver like her mother. If the child is male, something else happens: while working with several animal welfare organizations I realized that most of the calves who were brought in with road traffic injuries were male. Those who work in the milk industry separate young calves from their mothers so that they can monopolize the milk for sale. Often having no use for male calves, dairies routinely throw them out on to the street to be crushed under a heavy vehicle. If not, they are often killed and their skins sold to tanneries for soft leather.

Some say that human beings are at the apex of the food chain and seem to justify this poor way to treat another living being, but the sheer cruelty of keeping one pregnant throughout their lifetime is something I can't digest, literally. Also, look around, where has thinking that way gotten us?

There is enough research today to prove that a primary reason for global warming is the deforestation done to create ample grazing space for cattle as well as gas emissions from cattle itself. A person cannot say he or she is concerned about the environment and the air we breathe and then continue to consume dairy. Unlike dinosaurs and many other extinct animals who were wiped out by natural reasons, our ilk may die because of cow flatulence—what an unglamorous way to go for humankind. And yet, we are closer to the edge than most of us realize.

Dairy is also bad for us in other ways. Consuming it can increase our chances of suffering certain cancers, diabetes or heart disease. This book describes what doctors have to say about this and other effects of the consumption of animal-derived foods.

The milk that our grandparents drank was likely very different from that which is available today in the way it was produced. I remember once, in school, we had to fill in a blank for a test.

'The cow eats _____.'

I wrote 'plastic', because that's what I saw in my immediate surroundings. I saw poor cows sifting through open garbage dumps in Delhi for anything they could find. While I was on a visit to a charitable animal hospital once, a cow was brought in for an urgent operation. Close to thirty-five kilos of plastic was removed from her stomach in order for her to survive, and this, I was told, was very common.

To keep up with the demand for milk, cattle are mass-produced as if they are products and not living beings. Through their milk, we often consume hormones, blood, chemicals and adulterants. A survey has revealed that shampoo has even been added to milk by the friendly neighbourhood milkman in order to thicken its consistency. The health risks from the consumption of milk far outweigh any supposed benefits. I have come to this conclusion after careful research, but also after examining the effect of a vegan diet on my own body for nearly two years now.

So, for me, I decided, why would I continue to consume something that is bad for animals, for the planet and for my body? Veganism is all about living and letting live. But the intent of this book is not to force you to leave any food item but to merely present facts so you can make informed decisions. Perhaps reading it will at least inspire you to try something new.

I personally believe that in this time of accessible information, it is our duty to strive to know the truth and make decisions in accordance with it.

Richa Chadha
Mumbai
January 2020

INTRODUCTION

You could say I first met Soum at the Coimbatore municipal sheep and goat slaughterhouse. Technically, I met him briefly the night before the abattoir visit. But the experience of witnessing bleating, desperate animals being cut into pieces on floors awash with blood and the remains of those who went before them had such a profound effect on him that he became vegetarian overnight and pursued me thereafter, wanting to know more about the work I do, and me. That was in 2004—we got married six years later. Had we not gone to the slaughterhouse that day, or to the Coimbatore municipal cattle slaughterhouse that followed later in the week, had he not been so affected by what he saw to want to do something to help animals, I would have never seen him again. And so, yes, as macabre as it sounds, the story I awkwardly tell when someone asks how we met is, Soum and I met at a slaughterhouse—because we essentially did.

No, I'm not a butcher or meat seller—quite the opposite, though I am a former 'hardcore meat eater', as people often call themselves. I was at these slaughterhouses as part of an animal welfare effort to push the Indian leather industry to address at least those abuses of animals in its supply chain that are especially egregious and criminal under Indian animal protection laws, such as severe overcrowding of cattle in transport and the killing of animals in full view of each other with dull knives. In response, the country's Council for Leather Exports (CLE) had hired Ogilvy & Mather, a globally renowned public relations firm, to deal with the bad publicity the leather industry was facing from the campaign. Ogilvy & Mather, in turn, had hired Soum, a filmmaker, to document visits to slaughter sites and a cattle market.

I have held numerous positions with affiliates of People for the Ethical Treatment of Animals (PETA) at different times over the course of two decades, including working as a corporate liaison—which is how I engaged with the CLE—as well as director and, later, senior vice president of international affairs for PETA Foundation based out of Europe, CEO of PETA India, and other senior functions. The role I have most focused on in this book, however, is my time as an investigator of facilities where animals are used and abused. This work led me to study animal farming systems in depth, make personal visits to Indian animal markets and slaughterhouses, and observe trucks carrying animals to slaughter—experiences I have described in this book. I have also overseen or been involved with other investigators who have extensively documented how animals used for food are raised and handled in India, whose detailed findings I also share.

I have written this book largely because if we consider the sheer numbers of animals used and the harshness of the systems in which they are handled and reared today, if ever there was such a thing as the worst time in all of history to be born a cow, buffalo, sheep, goat, pig, chicken or fish—the species most commonly eaten in India and much of the world[1]—it is now. Yet, there has never been any other comprehensive book, at least to my knowledge, focused on the plight of these animals in India. This is that book.

Globally, we are consuming more than seven times the amount of meat that was eaten in 1950.[2] In India too, the consumption of beef, chicken, eggs, dairy and other animal-derived foods has been on a rapid rise.[3] In just ten years, between 2003 and 2013, meat consumption has *more than doubled* in the country.[4] And so, to meet the highest demand for animal-derived foods that there has ever been, worldwide some 77 billion[5] land animals are farmed a year—ten times the number of humans there are on the planet, most of them in intensive farming systems that deny them their natural behaviours— and up to trillions of fish[6] are killed. And these numbers keep rising.

The animals who have been used or lost their lives for meat, eggs or dairy, however, aren't just numbers. Each was a breathing, thinking, feeling being—an individual whose life was as precious to him or her as our lives are to us, and so I consider it my responsibility to tell you their stories, particularly what I or others I know have personally witnessed or discovered, of what it means to be seen and treated as mere commodities.

But as you know from my meat-eating past, I wasn't always vegan (eating purely plant-based) or an animal rights activist. I did my schooling in the southern American state of Virginia—kindergarten through university. Growing up in the US, in the food culture that was common there then, despite being raised in a Gujarati Hindu family, I ate foods made from any species customarily eaten in that country. Whether it was beef, pork, chicken, fish, eggs, cheese or any other animal-derived food—nothing was off limits.

My father ate meat too. He started doing so after he first travelled to the US from Ahmedabad to study chemistry in 1969. Today views have changed, but eating meat was considered the rational thing to do in the US by nearly everyone there back then. He bought into this narrative, at least partly, I suspect, because being a brown-skinned young man who spoke broken English came with its challenges in the America of the late '60s. Americanizing his diet and telling those he met his name was 'Josh' (short for our surname, Joshipura) seemed among his ways of trying to fit in.

My parents wedded in Rajkot, Gujarat, in the early '70s. Their marriage was an arranged one. Some years later, I was born, following which my father got a job offer to work as a scientist, and they ultimately established our home in Virginia. Initially, my mother didn't speak a word of English, though of course learnt it over time, but unlike my father, instead of trying to embrace American culinary customs, she found sanctuary in what was familiar, and her diet largely continued to be typical Gujarati khana like sabzi, daal and roti using whatever Indian spices she could muster—not an easy feat in the States all those decades ago. She stayed lacto-vegetarian and, at some point, also started to eat eggs.

My childhood was somewhat strange. The part of Virginia I grew up in is rural and while today more people originating from various parts of the world are moving in, in the '80s and early '90s, when I did my schooling, we were the only non-white and non-black family for miles around. My sister and brother are considerably younger than me, which meant I was the only Indian person my school peers knew throughout the many years of elementary, middle and high school. I had friends, but also faced either inadvertent, subtle or overt racism nearly every day from my classmates, teachers and sometimes even friends. Back then, I thought facing routine bigotry would just be how I'd always have to live.

The offences ranged from relatively minor, such as mocking my name or never making the effort to learn how to say it properly, to more serious, including a group of white high-school students showing up dressed like members of the Ku Klux Klan at a party I attended. They thought being threatening to the few of us who were not white there would be fun. I attended another event during those years at a white family's home who had named their black dog a derogatory word I cannot repeat. The African American kids we went to school with often faced worse mistreatment than what I did. In fact, I was regularly told by white friends that I am 'almost white'—of course they were trying to say I'm accepted by them and intended this prejudiced statement to be a compliment. Life only changed when I started university, which was in a larger Virginian city than where I grew up and had a culture of embracing, rather than rejecting, diversity.

Consider that non-white children were not even always allowed to attend the same schools that white kids did less than two decades before I joined the school system there and the racism I faced becomes less surprising. In Virginia, efforts were still being made to allow children of different races to study in the same schools together in the 1960s, public schools were opened to Native American children only in 1964, and it wasn't until 1968 that all public colleges were admitting both black and white students.[7]

All of this said, life wasn't wholly grim. I made a great friend in school aged thirteen, Natalie, who continues to be one of my best friends today. I looked different from the other kids, and she sounded different—she had just moved into our town from England with her mother and spoke with a British accent. Natalie was far more popular and accepted than I was, but still sometimes faced others' ignorant jokes because of how she spoke.

One day, at a mall food court, after I got a McDonald's chicken burger and she got something vegetarian from somewhere else we met back at a table. She looked at my sandwich, wrinkled her face in disapproval and asked me, 'Are you really going to eat that?' I asked her what she meant. She replied, 'It's a dead animal.' I said, 'Yes I am, I'd never give up eating meat,' and ate the chicken that day. But the truth is, her remark made me feel guilty and respond defensively, and although my own mother was an ovo-lacto vegetarian, Natalie's comment eventually led me to consider, for the first time, the possibility of being vegetarian too.

After all, we treat animals the way we often do because they are different—having four legs, feathers or fins. I understood from my school days what it feels like for the focus to always be on differences, rather than similarities, and to be cruelly treated for those perceived dissimilarities. Indeed, the experiences of that time set the stage to allow my heart and mind to be opened to the plight of those who seem unlike us, animals, but who are similar to us in important ways, such as their ability to feel pain and the desire to live.

When I told Natalie some weeks after our outing how what she said really made me feel, she shared that the lyrics of the song, 'Meat is Murder', by Morrissey's former English rock band The Smiths, first made her think. They go, *Heifer whines could be human cries/Closer comes the screaming knife/This beautiful creature must die …/And death for no reason is murder*. And a brochure she had been handed by an animal rights activist during a visit to London made her think some more.

Natalie invited me to join her in learning about the plight of animals. I agreed. We contacted PETA US and other animal protection outfits for literature, read and discovered together that rabbits suffer from chemical burns on their skin from the testing of consumer products, elephants are jabbed with weapons to be forced to perform in circuses, foxes are commonly killed by anal electrocution for fur. There was a lot more.

We also read about factory farming systems used for rearing animals for food that are now common in India and all over the world and that I describe in detail in this book. On these farms, animals are raised in vast warehouses by the hundreds, thousands or even millions in severe confinement—crammed into the tiniest spaces, cages or crates—to help create and meet the growing demand for cheap meat, egg and dairy foods. These systems use automation, mechanization as well as less area and a reduced workforce compared to what should be needed to manage such huge numbers of animals, so as to allow companies to reduce costs and achieve the highest possible profits, while mass-producing animal-derived products.

In factory farm systems, animals are typically denied natural movement, or often any movement at all. They are frustratingly deprived of the expression of behaviour that is basic and important to their species, like building nests or raising their young. If chickens or other animals who are unfortunate enough to be born on an intensive farm get to feel the sun on their backs or breathe fresh air, it is usually brief—on the day they are loaded on to trucks to be taken to slaughter. Animals who are not reared on factory farms do not escape misery. In India, cows, buffaloes, goats and other animals face other horrors common to its livestock industry too, such as severe and deadly overcrowding in transport and being hacked at with dull knives while still conscious.

Photos and videos Natalie and I came across taken by animal protection advocates, such as of sick chickens used for eggs in cages so small they could not even spread a wing, pigs screaming as they were loaded on to vehicles through beatings and force, and wide-eyed cows awaiting slaughter made clear to us that these animals did not want to be in the horrendous situations they were in any more than we would like to be.

Over and over, as we spoke of our growing concern for chickens, pigs, fish and other animals commonly used for food to our classmates, many of whom had dogs or cats at home they loved, they shared their beliefs that animals reared for food were stupid, and that fish especially could not feel pain—popular notions ethologists and other scientists tell us today are false.

Having endured our own share of mockery for looking or sounding different to other schoolmates, we saw similarities between the bias against animals typically used for food and the unfair depiction of certain human beings in history—those who are female, have dark skin, are homosexual or unlike the majority in other ways. This includes the once widely held views by Caucasians in the US that black people did not feel pain the same way as them (shockingly, a recent University of Virginia study shows many American medical students still think this[8]) or that women are not as smart as men— such biases were encouraged to keep people in oppression.

The bulk of my focus in this book is on animals commonly used for food—who they are, and what happens to them, mainly in India—but it also comprises of the wisdom passed on to me from pioneering medical doctors I have been fortunate enough to meet through the course of my work about the health consequences of eating either animal-derived or plant-based foods, and the learnings obtained through study of the production of meat, eggs and dairy on the planet.

I also know something about the health outcomes of dietary choices first-hand. I decided to go vegetarian before my seventeenth birthday, and stopped consuming cheese, milk and other animal-derived foods to become dietary vegan by age twenty. As described, what moved me to consider changing how I ate was concern for animals, but I quickly experienced the health benefits of eating plant-based foods, as have members of my family now.

Growing up, my mother would ply me with cow's milk, as many moms do. All throughout childhood, I struggled with stomach cramps. This didn't happen every day, but it occurred often, and occasionally the discomfort would become nearly unbearable. During these times I'd lie in a foetal position on my bed until the pain subsided. When I got sick, such as with a cold or fever, I would usually develop a persistent cough. The coughing would be uncontrollable, especially at night. No cough drops or medicine could ever stop or sufficiently soothe it. Thinking about it now, it seems strange that my parents and I thought this, but we simply considered these problems a part of my genetic make-up, something I'd have to endure my whole life because that's just how I was built. We were wrong.

It's only when I stopped having dairy and foods containing it, now more than twenty years ago, that I realized I must have been unable to properly digest milk (as is the case for most people after weaning). After choosing to eat vegan, I never experienced the stomach upset nor that horrendous coughing again. I never got tested for these conditions since the ailments disappeared, but the symptoms of a milk allergy and lactose intolerance include stomach cramps. The symptoms of a milk allergy also include coughing and wheezing. If only my parents and I realized that I am likely lactose intolerant, allergic to milk or both, we could have saved me years of misery.

My father suffered a stroke in his late thirties and a heart attack in his early fifties, while my mother has high blood pressure and osteoporosis—all ailments linked to dietary habits. Today, because I would regularly share my findings about eating vegan with my family, my mother stopped eating eggs and both she and my sister are lacto-vegetarian, my brother is vegan, and my father is nearly so. My parents are now in their mid-seventies, look about sixty, and are extremely busy, active and independent. My father has never faced a major health problem since he stopped eating animals. My mother sadly still lives with osteoporosis and hypertension, conditions thought to be aggravated by dairy consumption, as explained in Chapter 13 of this book, but is a lively and otherwise healthy individual.

Soum, who since the age of eighteen had suffered from a kidney condition called minimal change disease, which resulted from a bout of strep throat (an infection that can cause reactions that result in damage to the kidneys), is also vegan. He was born in Jamshedpur, is Bengali, and yes, as the stereotype of Bengalis goes, he used to love eating fish and also happily ate other meats. For years after becoming vegetarian, to my displeasure, he continued to occasionally eat eggs and have milk or cheese and would face regular flare-ups of the disease, which involved large amounts of protein leaking from his urine.

The relapses of the disease were visible—his ankles and fingers would swell, his face would look puffy and he would appear to gain weight as his body retained fluid and his kidneys failed to properly work. During such times, he'd have to take steroids to get his kidneys back on track. The trouble with this treatment, however, apart from having to experience some of the many negative side effects of taking steroids, is that one's body eventually gets used to the drug, the steroids therefore become less effective, and the flare-ups appear at an increasing frequency. Where once upon a time he would have the relapses once or twice a year, it got to the point where if he was not taking steroids, he was laid up.

After reading about the dietary experiments of others also suffering from minimal change disease on various online forums, he decided to become fully vegan and gluten-free. The disease appears to have gone into remission because he has not had a relapse for three years since making this change—nothing short of a miracle.

Meat, egg and dairy production also come with environmental costs, as they are incredibly polluting: the world's top five meat and dairy corporations alone are responsible for more greenhouse emissions that exacerbate climate change—particularly through the methane emitted from cattle and other ruminant animals bred for food—than major oil and gas companies ExxonMobil, Shell or BP.[9] The production of animal-derived foods to meet the world's tremendous appetite for them is, in fact, so environmentally disastrous that the Food and Agriculture Organization of the United Nations describes animal agriculture as 'one of the top two or three most significant contributors to the most serious environmental problems, at every scale from local to global'.[10]

Cynics would point out it's hard to pin specific weather events to climate change, but scientists tell us global warming brings on extreme weather. I was in Mumbai on that fateful day, 26 July 2005, trapped in a flat, without electricity and with no way of knowing whether the people I loved were alive or dead, when the city was submerged from the highest-recorded rainfall in a hundred years, causing the deaths of more than 1,400 people and countless animals and destroying more than 14,000 homes.[11] I was in Delhi, almost unable to breathe from the oppressive heat, on one of India's hottest days, when the temperature reached nearly 47 degrees Celsius; in Phalodi, Rajasthan, the temperature climbed to an unbearable 51 degrees.[12] I was in England during the 2018 heatwave that resulted in 1,000 more people dying in the UK that summer than average.[13]

In fact, we will all remember, that year saw numerous extreme weather events including Kerala floods that killed hundreds (Soum luckily had left Thiruvananthapuram just before the heavy rains hit), wildfires on multiple continents and a Japanese heatwave that killed dozens.

And so, while meat, egg and dairy consumption are at an all-time high, vegetarian and vegan eating are also increasing over ethical and health concerns. In India, between 2004 and 2014, there was a 5 per cent growth in the number of vegetarians above the age of fifteen,[14] and today it is said 70 per cent of the world population is now either working on reducing their meat intake or going vegetarian.[15]

I have also written this book because I consider it consumers' right to be aware of the full extent of what these concerns are and the potential to make a positive difference in animals' lives (it is estimated that we can save up to a hundred animals a year by not eating them[16]), better their own health (not eating meat is said to cut heart disease risk by 32 per cent[17]) and improve the state of the planet (eating plant-based is calculated to have the potential to reduce a person's carbon footprint by up to 73 per cent[18]) with their wallets and plates should they so choose.

Most of all, I have written it because I believe we owe it to animals to at least understand what it means to spend one's entire life in a farming system to satisfy the human desire for what is, after all, just a fleeting moment of taste.

1

THE INDIVIDUAL ON YOUR PLATE

The fact that they may not understand us, while we do not understand them, does not mean our 'intelligences' are at different levels, they are just of different kinds. When a foreigner tries to communicate with us using an imperfect, broken, version of our language, our impression is that they are not very intelligent. But the reality is quite different.[1]

—Professor Maciej Henneberg on animal intelligence, University of Adelaide

The dog who adopted Soum and me is called Mehboob, which means beloved in Urdu. He was found bone-thin and running helter-skelter near Mehboob Studios in Mumbai, Maharashtra. He appeared to have ended up in a territory that was not his own, and it looked like he had been struggling to find food. His plight melted our hearts, and we took him in.

Mehboob gets visibly happy when we take him for walks on Mumbai's Juhu Beach. He develops a little pep in his step, prances

1

and makes playful gestures towards us—like the classic 'play bow', bending forward on his two front paws and doing a little twirl, as if to say, 'C'mon!'

Mehboob is blind in one eye. We do not know exactly how he got that way, but veterinarians tell us it seems the result of an injury he suffered during his life on the street. He is afraid of certain objects, presumably because of bad experiences, and these things include gas cylinders. Though he is visually impaired, when we go out for a walk, he will spot not only gas cylinders, but a gas cylinder-wallah, much before I do, with his one good eye. He recognizes them by their trucks and uniforms. He can also recognize gas cylinders by the clanging sound they make when being moved around, even without seeing one. Any sign of a gas cylinder makes him panic, tremble and pull me by his leash in the opposite direction.

Mehboob responds to his name, sniffs through the gap under the door to figure out who is on the other side when the doorbell rings, behaving differently depending on who it is (jumping excitedly, for example, if it is Soum versus acting alert and cautious if it is someone he doesn't know), softly barks and lightly kicks his paws while dreaming, and pulls us towards our car when he feels like going on a jaunt. When he wants to go for a walk, he stomps his feet and stares into our eyes. If we don't act right away, he whimpers. In other words, he 'talks'.

Two cats have adopted us too. They are called Tim and Mil. They were found in the Dharavi slums, in separate places, alone, as kittens by a colleague. In the process of cleaning them up, giving them care and building their strength, Soum and I fell in love with them and they now stay with us.

Tim and Mil are the best of friends, but, like any two human beings, they have distinct personalities. Tim is energetic and adventurous; Mil is relaxed and calm. Tim is immediately curious about visitors, whereas Mil is initially scared and needs time to warm up to them.

The cats have different food and sleeping preferences. Tim likes to sleep under covers; Mil likes to cuddle up to me or Soum.

They both, however, like to have fun, and spend most of their days playing games of chase and hide-and-seek. Tim has chosen a plastic curtain clip as his favourite toy because it slides on the floor. I throw it and he runs after it and bats it around and then waits patiently for me to pick it up and start again. He recognizes the fairly sophisticated idea that we are playing a game.

Tim and Mil also 'talk'. They let us know when they want us to wake up by meowing, and if we don't listen, Tim will follow that up with light nibbles of our faces or feet. Mil shows us love by licking (grooming) our hair, skin and clothes.

But it is not only dogs and cats who communicate, show affection, enjoy play, remember good and bad experiences, distinguish and remember humans and other animals, and do other things they can do. Animal behaviourists, or ethologists, who study them in laboratories and in the field as well as caretakers who have the opportunity to spend time with them, such as sanctuary workers, tell us species of animals commonly raised for meat, eggs or dairy also demonstrate deep emotions and are just as smart or smarter than the animals most of us call friends, not food. We can see that cows, buffaloes, sheep, goats, pigs, chickens and fish are feeling, thinking, bright beings when we look at them with open minds and observe them in their natural surroundings.

A Cow Hides Her Calf

Perhaps one of the strongest emotions cows and other animals reared for food commonly demonstrate is motherly love. In India, it may be more generally acknowledged that cows are good mothers as compared to in other countries. Generally, Hindus are known to regard cows as the very symbol of motherhood.

Karma is a cow who was rescued from awful conditions on a farm, but she bellowed and cried. Her rescuers were sensitive enough to realize she may have had a calf who was left behind. They went back and luckily managed to find him just before he was sent for slaughter. The Dodo, a website that puts out news and true tales of animals, shared their story, and described that upon seeing each other again, Karma and her calf excitedly bolted towards each other. When both were finally reunited, Karma gently nudged and fed her hungry baby.[2]

The Dodo also shared the story of a mother cow on an American dairy farm who frantically hid her calf when she saw the approach of a truck that she knew, from previous experience and observation, took calves away. The calves were collected and sent to be reared and killed for veal. By the time the farmer found the calf, the truck had already left. Not wanting to 'waste' the mother's milk on the calf, he left him alone outside the farm. A woman walking by inquired about the calf and upset that he wasn't being fed, managed to convince the farmer to let him be taken to a sanctuary. Today, he lives at Poplar Spring Animal Sanctuary in Maryland, US and is called Moses, based on the baby whose mother in the Bible puts her trust in God for her child's well-being.[3] Tragically, Moses' mother would never know what happened to him, but she saved his life.

Buffaloes are good mothers too. A popular video that can be found on YouTube and that you may have seen is called 'Battle at Kruger'[4]. It shows the moment a herd of African buffaloes rescues a calf from a pride of lions, at great personal risk to themselves. The calf had been drinking at a watering hole. Suddenly the pride emerges and attacks the calf who falls in the water. As if things weren't bad enough for the young one already, crocodiles appear and engage in a toothy tussle for the calf with the lions. Instead of fleeing and leaving the calf behind to die, the herd made the collective decision to stop running, turn around and challenge the lions, surrounding them. The buffaloes can be seen carefully taking turns charging at and chasing away the lions, even hurling one up in the air, ultimately rescuing their cherished calf.

In Uttar Pradesh's Pilibhit, a farmer had his life saved by his herd of buffaloes when they took on a tiger who surfaced nearby while they grazed. The herd had a calf with them who was killed. The buffaloes had, however, put up such a ferocious fight that the tiger left the mauled body behind.[5]

Chickens are also great moms. In one ethological experiment, shots of air were used to deliberately upset baby chicks. On seeing the babies distressed, the mother hens panicked—their heart rates shot up and their calls to the chicks intensified.[6] This is not unlike how my sister reacts when my nephew falls and hurts himself on the playground—she becomes distraught and remains so as long as her son is upset. Mother hens, like us, also teach their chicks the ways of the world, including which foods are fine to eat and other lessons on safety.[7] Also, like human mothers, they do their best to protect their kids from harm such as by hiding their babies in their feathers or guarding them with their wings.

Farm Sanctuary, an animal protection organization based in the United States, which houses animals rescued from food industries, reports that chickens also seem to 'adopt' the babies of other birds if necessary. At their sanctuary, they noticed hens will sometimes take care of chicks who are obviously not theirs as is evident by the chicks' different ages and sizes.[8] This is kind of like how neighbours will keep an eye out for the well-being of other people's kids, not only their own.

Buffaloes care for the babies of other buffaloes too. During a recent visit I made to India Project for Animals and Nature (IPAN), a vast sanctuary for rescued animals based in the Nilgiris, Tamil Nadu, all of the adult buffaloes had gone off to graze, except one who stayed back and nuzzled up to a calf from the opposite side of a fence. The calves there are initially kept in a large fenced-in area for their safety. I commented on how doting a mother she seemed for refusing to leave her child. Nigel Otter, who runs the refuge with his veterinarian wife Ilona, told me to my surprise that this, in fact, was not his mother, but an aunt who has adopted the calf. He said this particular female buffalo had never borne children but had developed a deep attachment to this baby. I bet his biological mother was grateful for the help.

Can a mother-child, or aunt-child, emotional connection between animals be genuine love? Some people will say it's merely instinct. But couldn't our parental love be described as 'instinct' too? And it would be hard to argue for even the biggest sceptics that the grieving killer whale who made global headlines for refusing to let go of the dead body of her calf for seventeen days[9] didn't love her child. As authors Dr Jeffrey Masson and Susan McCarthy discuss in *When Elephants Weep: The Emotional Lives of Animals*, we can't surely know when someone else loves their baby whether that someone is an ape or a human because we are not them. They point out that in the case of both, the mother will feed, nurture, play with and protect the baby—in humans, we say these are demonstrations of love, but are not always ready to accept the same proof as love when it comes to animals.[10]

The Cow Who Chases Bus KA-31F 857

Like killer whales, as Karma's constant wailing until she was reunited with her calf showed, mother cows and buffaloes experience unmistakable grief when it comes to upsetting matters involving their children.

A video taken in the Uttara Kannada district of Karnataka that went viral shows a cow attempting to stop the state transport bus numbered KA-31F 857—something she has been observed doing just about every single day for years since her calf died. This is the bus that ran over her calf and the heartbroken mom spends her days near the spot where she lost her baby. The cow does not try to stop any other buses, trucks or cars. Just this one. Even a person who can be seen in the video trying to hit her with a stick cannot deter this anguished mother from chasing the bus. The bus owner changed the colour of the bus, but the cow was not fooled.[11]

John Avizienius is the deputy head of the UK Royal Society for the Prevention of Cruelty to Animals (RSPCA) farm animals' department. He recalls a cow shaken for nearly two months after her calf was taken away from her on a dairy farm, so that her milk could be sold instead of any being fed to her baby, describing, 'When the calf was first removed, she was in acute grief; she stood outside the pen where she had last seen her calf and bellowed for her offspring for hours. She would only move when forced to do so. Even after six weeks, the mother would gaze at the pen where she last saw her calf and sometimes wait momentarily outside the pen. It was almost as if her spirit had been broken and all she could do was make token gestures to see if her calf would still be there.'[12]

Calves mourn being separated from their mothers too. Daniel Weary is an applied animal biologist at the University of British Columbia, Canada. He and his co-researchers have been observing how being separated from their mothers, as is common on dairy farms, effects calves. He told *Wired* that when this happens, 'The calves will engage in repetitive crying … and sometimes you'll see a decline in their willingness to eat solid food.'[13]

The Power of Loving Touch

When allowed, both cows and buffaloes demonstrate love and protect their young through touch. We've all seen cattle moms lick their young. Being able to engage in this behaviour is important to these mothers as it means being able to do what's best for their kids. For instance, when a calf is just born, the mother will try her best to hide the scent of the birth to protect her newborn from possible predators. Licking also provides her baby comfort and helps solidify their bond, while seeming to aid in vital body functions like breathing and circulation for the calf.[14] Being denied this nurturing behaviour would undoubtedly impact both the mother and calf's well-being.

Cattle will also lick (groom) their friends. Rescued bulls at Animal Rahat's sanctuary in Sangli, Maharashtra, which exists mainly for bulls who were formerly used for work, can be seen doing exactly that. Animal Rahat is an organization dedicated to providing free veterinary services and other relief to animals used for work, as well as other animals in their community. The bulls at their sanctuary don't just lick any bullock, but the one they consider their best friend. Their best friend will also reciprocate the gesture, increasing their connection.

Animal Rahat's sanctuary workers gain the trust of these bulls— who, before being rescued, have only known a hard life in which they were made to haul tons of sugarcane at the threat of being hit—by grooming them daily with a brush that mimics licking. This calms them and, gradually, these bulls, who once distrusted humans, will even approach visitors for a scratch between the horns, much as a dog would approach someone for a pat.

A Fish's Loyal Friend

Some species of animals choose to be alone at times, even for long periods when not mating or raising the young, like tigers and polar bears. However, friendships and having regular contact with others of their own species is important to most animals. This includes fish.

A video of a porcupine fish trapped in a net and being delicately freed by a snorkeler attracted global attention. That's because the porcupine fish's concerned fish friend hovered by, despite the potentially dangerous human around, and waited patiently for the porcupine fish to be cut free of the net.[15]

I do not use the word 'friend' lightly—pigs and fish, and other animals, have friends too. Pigs are less upset when their food doesn't arrive if they are with a friend. It *has* to be a friend, because if they are with a pig they do not know, they can behave in an even more disturbed manner than they would have otherwise.[16] This is not unlike when a person asks a friend to go with her to hospital because she is worried about receiving bad news. Somehow being with that friend makes bad news seem more bearable.

Social isolation is, therefore, a terrible a punishment for pigs, as it is for us. Pigs form close bonds with each other. Like dogs, they welcome each other with gusto, and enjoy being physically close to their friends and family members. So much so that they often sleep touching noses.

Like pigs who are comforted by their friends, and the person who asks her friend to go to see the doctor with her, sheep are similarly comforted by other sheep. In a study by the Babraham Institute in the UK in which sheep were made to suffer separation anxiety, as proven by their measured heart rate and scientific observation of other physiological and behavioural changes upon being put into a darkened room alone, merely showing a photograph of another sheep on a screen reduced the stress of the isolated sheep.[17] Sheep are herd animals who protect each other from predators and other danger, and so it should come as little surprise really that being alone is traumatic for them.

Pigs Who 'Talk' To Humans

Sheep are in fact so sensitive, they can read emotions, including those of human beings. Neuroscientist Dr Keith Kendrick and his team of researchers at Cambridge University found that sheep prefer pleasant, smiling human faces to ones that appear cross. And how does one judge a sheep's preference? The scientists put equal amounts of food behind two doors the sheep were able to open. On one door, they put a picture of a cheerful-looking human or calm sheep, on the other an irate-looking human or an upset sheep. The sheep strongly preferred going through the door with the photo of the human or sheep who looked content.[18]

Pigs are perceptive too and show empathy. When pigs in one study were put together with other pigs who had been trained to expect either rewards (such as raisins) or punishment (social isolation), the untrained pigs took on the same behaviour as their trained companions did despite not knowing what specifically to expect. In other words, trained pigs who behaved nervously led to untrained pigs picking up their tense mannerism despite having no idea a punishment was coming up. Likewise, trained pigs who displayed happy behaviour resulted in untrained pigs acting similarly even though the untrained pigs did not know something good was coming up.[19] One can only imagine the toll that seeing a companion being killed in a slaughterhouse takes on a pig who is waiting and watching then, and knows he or she is next in line.

Pigs and all animals 'tell' each other and humans how they feel by way of their behaviour, but pigs have even been taught to explain how they feel in ways humans can more easily understand. Pigs were trained by researchers in the UK (much of the work on studying the emotional and intellectual capacities of animals commonly used for food happens there) to show a particular action when they felt at ease, and another when they felt anxious. The researchers already knew that the anxious pigs felt that way because they had been given an anxiety-inducing drug. The pigs could correctly 'tell' the researchers how they felt, and then later the pigs could 'tell' the researchers when they felt anxious again, such as when exposed to a new environment—by using the same anxiety response.

Professor of animal behaviour and welfare Dr Michael Mendl of the University of Bristol has been studying pigs for decades. His work shows that pigs get stressed by routine farming practices, such as being handled to have their weight recorded, and that this results in them becoming forgetful.[20] I can certainly relate to this. On days when my mind is preoccupied with some worry or the other, I am much more likely to lock myself out of my flat or leave my phone behind at a coffee shop.

When treated poorly, animals, like us, can be resentful. We already know, thanks to the cow mom who chases the bus that killed her calf, that cows can hold a grudge against humans who have treated them badly. Researchers studying herd behaviour have found that cows will show preferences that make clear who is a friend and who is a foe, remembering which other cows have treated them badly too.[21]

Goats remember when they have been treated kindly. IPAN is home to several goats who have been rescued from being forced to perform tricks in circuses. Despite having lived lives of hardship, they recognize their rescuers, know they are not harmful and trot up to them to be stroked. One black goat who had been precariously made to walk on a tightrope in a circus appears to understand he is never going to encounter a dangerous person again so long as he is in the sanctuary. When I visited IPAN, he was my guide—curiously greeting me and others at the gate when our car arrived, following us wherever we went, and then walking us back to the exit when we left.

Goats, when not abused, are joyous souls who love to have fun. Anyone who has ever seen kid goats leaping about know their fondness for play and mischief. They gallop, play fight, run, tumble around, hop, jump and delight in being silly.

Alice, the Purring Turkey

Chickens and other birds are social, too. In fact, chickens and turkeys who have been treated kindly usually enjoy and even seek out the company of humans.

Years ago, when I visited Poplar Springs Animal Sanctuary, where Moses lives, I was greeted by an extremely curious, friendly, large-sized turkey called Alice who had been rescued from the meat industry. I was carrying a handbag that contained little mirrors in its design, and Alice was fascinated by it, and me, a potentially new friend. I knelt down to help her have a better look at the bag and she made little clucking sounds to communicate, as if to say something like, 'Your bag is interesting. Welcome, hello!' Alice was so sociable, she loved it when I stroked her feathers. I know this because she began to make a sound that is the turkey version of a cat purr—a wonderful noise turkeys make when they are pleased.

Some of the chickens at the sanctuary were just as curious and inquisitive as Alice. Others, like Mil, were more cautious and shyer. Some appeared to be leaders, others not. Each bird expressed his or her own unique personality.

However, whatever their nature, each one of them was busy. Some were taking dust baths, others were sunbathing. Some were approaching me to be stroked like Alice, others were foraging for food. They were also 'talking' constantly to each other.

Chickens, in fact, like turkeys, have a language. Chickens have dozens, if not more, distinct vocalizations, including one to alert flock members that a predator, for example a hawk, is approaching by air, a different one if the predator, such as a snake, is coming by land.[22] Chicks and mother hens will chirp at each other even before the chicks hatch.[23]

Fish also communicate through gestures, movements, electric pulses, bioluminescence, the release of chemicals or sounds.[24] Crustaceans 'talk' to each other too. In the book *Chemical Communication in Crustaceans*, the authors describe that lobsters use chemicals to relay all sorts of things, such as sexual status, or their place in a social hierarchy.[25] Scientists have also found that lobsters establish relationships with one another and take long-distance journeys together by using complex signals.[26]

The Fish Who Likes to Play

Fish, like goats, dogs, cats and other animals like to play! James Murphy is a herpetologist who kept fish in a tank. He noticed that a cichlid, presumably bored, appeared to play with the tank's thermometer. The fish would hit the thermometer, let it spring back, hit it again and so on—sort of like how Tim bats around the curtain hanger.

Of course, as fish seem so different from humans, it would be easy to argue that the fish was perhaps doing something else. So, to be sure, Murphy got together with other scientists from the University of Tennessee in the US to check this out further.

They first defined play. They said it is behaviour that occurs voluntarily without an exact purpose (other than entertainment), appears gratifying, is repeated and happens when the animal does not seem to be stressed. The scientists put other fish of the same kind in different tanks to avoid them learning from each other and three of them struck the thermometer repeatedly too, but in slightly different ways. The scientists decided that what they observed was, in fact, play.[27]

Fish are not only playful, they're brainy. In a paper published in *Animal Cognition*, Dr Culum Brown, who specializes in the study of fish, explains fish learn from each other, cooperate on tasks, have complex societies, recognize each other and themselves, build involved structures and more.

The pervasive myth that fish have three-second memories reveals our stupidity, not theirs. Dr Brown says fish actually have very impressive memories. They are so smart that he says in many cognitive areas, like memory, fish match or even surpass other vertebrates, including nonhuman primates.[28] For example, in an experiment Dr Brown showed that the Australian crimson-spotted rainbowfish recalled how they escaped from a net nearly a year afterwards. As they do not live very long in comparison to humans, it would be like us remembering a task from decades ago. And as fish have to navigate their complex marine environments, they remember their way and create mental maps to do so.[29]

Pigs Who Play Video Games

Considering that stray cows and buffaloes can commonly be seen having to find their way through crowded cities in India, it should come as no surprise then that cows in Australia did exceptionally in an experiment involving going through a maze.[30] And really, city streets are mazes, aren't they? Anyone who feeds stray cattle their dinner leftovers know that not only can cows and buffaloes remember where to get this food, they also seem to be able to show up at the time it is normally given. They do this without a watch or a mobile phone! They recognize who is the food giver too.

And like cows and buffaloes, University of Cambridge neuroscientist Dr Jenny Morton has found that sheep create mental maps and use memory for navigation.[31] Common sense would tell us, like humans, animals need to be able to steer themselves through and so require the mental capacities to do so.

These animals' strong memories mean they can remember faces. Sheep have been found to be able to recognize at least fifty unique sheep and ten humans[32] and remember them from photographs for years. That's what's been found so far, but it's likely they can recognize far more. If you think this is no big deal, consider whether you are always easily able to distinguish sheep. Sheep can, and they can tell us apart too. Contrary to what some people may think, sheep do not all look the same—especially not to sheep.

Intelligent animals like to use their minds. That's why we humans engage in problem-solving games. We feel a sense of achievement after having figured out a puzzle.

Cows feel pleased when they've solved a problem too. In an experiment, cows were observed jumping for joy when they figured out how to unlatch a gate to reach food. The researchers described this as the cows' 'eureka' moment.[33]

Goats and sheep are good problem-solvers as well. In a test, goats had to solve a puzzle in order to reach fruit. Two out of a dozen of them were barred from the test when they tried to use their horns instead of playing along, one was unable to solve it, but the remaining nine nailed it. After ten months, the same nine goats were able to solve the puzzle within sixty seconds, showing they have great memories too.[34]

Farmers in England have reported that clever sheep were able to figure out that they could simply roll on their backs to get past a cattle grid—a series of bars placed over a depression in the road—something animals are generally reluctant to walk over since their legs could get caught in the gaps.[35]

Dr Morton has conducted various tests on sheep that showed their performance as at a level comparable to monkeys and humans in the preliminary tasks. The task involved their having to learn which type of bucket food could be found in, depending on the bucket's colour or shape. When the rules changed, they still performed as well as monkeys.[36]

Pigs are so good at puzzles that they have been taught to play video games. They used their snouts to control a joystick to move a cursor on the screen and hit targets. They could understand the complex cause-and-effect relationship between what they were doing and what was appearing on screen. Dogs, as clever as they are, in comparison, did not do well with this.[37]

Lori Marino and Christina Colvin are researchers at Emory University in the US. They reviewed numerous studies of pigs and other animals in a paper published in the *International Journal of*

Comparative Psychology, entitled, 'Thinking Pigs: A Comparative Review of Cognition, Emotion, and Personality in *Sus domesticus.*'

The studies show, among other things, that pigs like dogs love to play, like cows are great at mazes, and like fish learn from each other. They also have exceptional memories, advanced social abilities, can use a mirror as a tool to find food that is concealed and can comprehend a basic symbolic language.[38]

The researchers concluded, 'We have shown that pigs share a number of cognitive capacities with other highly intelligent species such as dogs, chimpanzees, elephants, dolphins and even humans. There is good scientific evidence to suggest we need to rethink our overall relationship to them.'[39]

The Wily Rooster Casanova

Chickens' intelligence too has been compared to that of nonhuman primates by ethologists.

Chickens are, in fact, so clever that they can be deceptive. A rooster may move his head horizontally and vertically, pick up food and drop it and call in a particular way to a hen when he's found something good to eat, and she'll dart over. Sometimes, however, he will just make the call, even when there's nothing there. This behaviour reminds me of a joke I saw on Twitter about some men's deceitful efforts to woo ladies, 'When he asks if you wanna "Netflix and chill" but he doesn't even have a TV.' Like with women, after a point, faking it stops working with hens too.

Roosters also use their wiliness and smarts to attract females in other ways. When there's an alpha rooster around, other males will only make the head movements and deliberately leave out the verbal sounds. This way, they can secretly entice the hens away.[40]

Chickens are also sharp in other ways. It has been found that even baby chicks can count, perform basic math and geometry, recognize something exists even when they are unable to see it (human babies can't do this until half a year old or older). Chickens can also remember people and other chickens, learn from other chickens, have a sense of time, develop expectations based on past experiences, anticipate the future and demonstrate self-control. They will wait for tastier food in the future if they know it is coming, rather than accept a little food now. They can also reason—they have been found to be proficient at basic transitive inference, that is figuring out a connection between things that have not previously been explicitly compared, something we develop an ability to do around age seven.[41]

Our Personal Biases

We have long regarded ourselves as the most intelligent and emotional animal in the animal kingdom. But is this an inaccurate, biased view? University of Adelaide researchers think so.

Professor Maciej Henneberg, a professor of anthropological and comparative anatomy from the School of Medical Sciences at this university, explains animals often have capabilities different to our own. These are commonly misread or unappreciated by humans. But that does not necessarily mean, he says, that our cognitive acumen is at different levels to other animals, but rather they are of differing types. And so, always measuring animals by how well they fare at human-like tasks is unfair. Each species of animal has proficiencies to excel in their own natural environment, and that means many species of animals have incredibly remarkable abilities we do not.

Professor Henneberg shares, for example, that gibbons produce diverse sounds to allow them to communicate across forest cover—an ability humans do not need to have—and that animals like dogs and tigers leave complex olfactory marks in their environment that we probably cannot begin to fully understand since our sense of smell is poor in comparison.[42] Similarly, around fifty species of animals including birds and reptiles are thought to navigate using Earth's magnetic field[43] while dolphins and whales use echolocation, which would give them a completely unique view of their environment than what we have, and scientists believe elephants may be able to communicate over long distances through seismic signals they feel in their feet.[44] As we observe animals commonly used for food more, what else will we learn about their abilities?

Already, knowing what we now know about the emotional and intellectual capabilities of animals, more and more people agree species used for meat, eggs and dairy deserve our critical examination of how the production of these foods affects them and an analytical review of the merits of the reasons we commonly give on why we eat them.

2

WHY DID I EAT ANIMALS?

~

*Do you eat chicken because you are familiar with the scientific
literature on them and have decided that their suffering doesn't
matter, or do you do it because it tastes good?*[1]

—*Jonathan Safran Foer, author of* Eating Animals

When I consumed animal-derived foods, it would have
been normal for me to have a day with a menu like this:
a glass of milk with a masala omelette for breakfast; pork meat
deli sandwich slathered with mayonnaise and taken along with
potato chips for lunch; tacos with ground beef and cheese for
dinner; and a milk chocolate candy bar as a snack. Our family
friend, Heera auntie knew I loved spicy food and had fiery
chicken or fish masala dishes ready for me whenever we visited.
Similarly, my friend Jessica's mother would be ready with
another favourite dish of mine, chicken parmesan (an Italian–
American dish that consists of chicken, spaghetti, tomato sauce
and cheese), for my stays.

Yet, when I ate meat, if someone were to have asked me if I loved animals, I would have said an enthusiastic 'yes!' After all, I adored playing with dogs and cats I would come across, enjoyed feeding squirrels and birds with my grandmother and liked watching wildlife documentaries with my father.

However, eating animals requires someone ripping them from their families and butchering them—this is something everyone knows, even if they do not know the details of how it is done, and I knew that much too. Yet, I ate meat anyway. What allowed me to do so? What might allow others to do the same?

The Brazilian Supermarket Prank

Scientists have been studying this conflict, between caring for animals and killing them to eat them. This phenomenon has been labelled 'the meat paradox' by University of Kent and Université Libre de Bruxelles researchers Steve Loughnan, Boyka Bratanova, and Elisa Puvia.[2]

And we generally do care for animals. That's why countries have laws protecting animals, why societies for the prevention of cruelty to animals (SPCAs) and other animal protection groups exist, why there was such national outrage when tigress Avni was killed, why the global horror when Cecil the lion and later his son Xanda were killed by trophy hunters in Zimbabwe, and it is likely why you are reading this book. In fact, many of us find what has to happen to animals to produce meat wrong, at least in principle, what little we may know about it, even if we eat meat.

A prank that was set up at a supermarket in Brazil, in which a man pretending to be a butcher offered samples of free fresh pork sausages to the store's customers, proves this point. Shoppers would visit the counter, eat and admire the pork. Then, the butcher would offer to make more, but to do so he would bring out a live piglet and put the animal in a machine that appeared to instantly grind her up and turn her into fresh meat. In reality, another prankster was sitting in the machine safely collecting each baby pig. Although customers had just readily eaten pork, they were aghast when they thought a live pig was about to be killed. One woman spat out pork from her mouth, others pleaded with the butcher not to kill the young pig and even tried to physically stop him from doing so. None of them picked up another piece of the free fresh pork that they had eagerly eaten before seeing the live pig.[3] If you were one of the customers, what would you have done?

Ranking Species on Worthiness of Moral Concern

While many of us are perturbed by the thought of slaughter of any animal, several studies[4] found people who choose to eat animals are inclined to reject the thought that animals are capable of complex emotions and are likely to draw a further line between the emotional capacities of animals usually used for food (such as chickens) versus those who are not typically eaten by humans (like parrots). Both are birds, but the findings of these scientists indicate that people who eat meat are prone to believe parrots can feel more deeply than chickens, even though there's no scientific support for such a view. Refusing to acknowledge animals, especially animals used for food, have the ability to experience deep emotions, appears to let many of us dismiss what happens to them in the production of food.

Through studies conducted by Loughnan and his colleague Brock Bastian of the University of Queensland, the pair describes how vegetarians tend to compare with meat eaters in thinking about the mental faculties of animals when told they will be killed. Vegetarians did not alter their view of that animal's acumen when told an animal, such as a lamb, was set for slaughter. When meat eaters were told the same thing, it was found that they generally reduced their view of the animal's mental abilities. This, the researchers surmise, may be a 'defensive way' to allow us to consume animals without much guilt or remorse.[5]

Another experiment shows merely categorizing an animal as 'food' effects how most people perceive the animal's rights. In this study, researchers introduced a tree kangaroo to participants—an animal the participating individuals were not familiar with. They were given general information about tree kangaroos and then some were told that the animals were for eating while others were not. Those individuals who were told the species was food considerably regarded tree kangaroos as less deserving of concern than the other participants.[6]

Labelling an animal 'friend' has an effect too, but an opposite one—doing so tends to increase our respect for the friend species. This labelling of animals as 'friend' versus 'food' and the psychological effect it has on how we then view them is surely what helped me, when I consider it in hindsight, to simultaneously love animals like dogs and cats and eat animals like cows, chickens and pigs.

If this is the effect one study had on people's minds, imagine the result of being told repeatedly, like we usually are from a young age, that certain animals are for 'food' by authority figures, like our parents, or members of our community or people we want to be accepted by, like our friends. What if these individuals would have instead categorized those same animals as 'friend'? Would we have thought differently?

Today there are many vegetarians and vegans in the United States, but in the '80s and early '90s, the repeated messaging to me as a youngster from most people was speciesist: Animals like cows, sheep, pigs, chickens and fish merely existed to be eaten and animals like dogs and cats are friends. In other words, particular species are worthier of respect than other animals just by way of being. Indeed, though I happily ate what I considered to be the 'food' members of the animal kingdom, I would have eaten my own foot before I ate a dog. If we are raised in a meat-eating family, or if our families engage in rituals or customs that involve killing or eating certain animals, something similar is usually the repeated messaging we hear too.

Labelling of Dogs in China, Cows in India

Dogs are not 'friend' animals everywhere. As we Indians know well, cows are not 'food' animals everywhere too. People may not consider whales exactly friends, probably having never met one, but many certainly put these animals in the inedible category. Perhaps their label is somewhere between 'friend' and 'wild' in most people's minds, and many of us think of most non-domesticated animals as not to be eaten. Plus, whales have had the advantage of their intelligence being made well-known, which may help us think of them more as 'friends'. (Those who consider wild animals inherently inedible and domesticated animals edible may be forgetting that domesticated animals come from wild ancestors and that dogs and cats are domesticated too.)

In certain parts of India, and elsewhere in Asia, dogs are labelled 'food'. Those of us who have been raised with the idea that dogs are 'friend' animals tend to be appalled by this. There are huge global protests every year against China's dog meat festival that takes place in the city of Yulin. Yet those protesting this event are often not vegetarian themselves and would not think twice about eating meat from a species they consider socially acceptable to eat. Some might call that a hypocritical stance. Many Hindus are staunchly against cow slaughter, regarding cows as 'mother', a status even higher than 'friend', yet beef is widely consumed around the world and numerous Hindus eat other types of meat. While many find the idea of eating whale meat abhorrent, it is eaten by some Japanese.

The American television channel Animal Planet featured a hugely popular documentary-style show called *Whale Wars*, which followed the organization Sea Shepherd's efforts to obstruct the illegal poaching activities of Japanese whaling ships. I wonder if Animal Planet would be willing to dedicate a show to, say, PETA US's work to save the lives of marine animals more commonly eaten in the West, such as lobsters, tuna, crabs and salmon. Capturing these animals is not usually illegal, but sometimes it is, as fishing quotas are often set to control the depletion of marine life from the sea—quotas which are regularly ignored as enforcement measures are often inadequate. Sea Shepherd's actions recently resulted in the detainment of the world's largest fishing vessel by Peruvian authorities, a vessel that alone catches half a million tons of fish per year, as they investigated its involvement in illegal fishing.[7] Moreover, laws do not mean the marine animals more popularly eaten than whales do not suffer.

The inconsistency of which animals are called 'friend' versus 'food' shows labelling is largely determined by culture, or as American social psychologist Dr Melanie Joy would perhaps more scientifically call it, our schema—mental classifications based on our beliefs and experiences.[8]

The Children Who Refuse to Eat Meat

As a teenager, when I ate meat, I knew I was eating animals. But young children who are fed meat are frequently not told they are being fed animals, or are not given the full truth about what they are eating should they enquire, and so they have not developed a personal categorization of certain animals as 'food' by the time they figure out they are being asked to eat them. These kids offer a window into how we might react to news that certain animals are being killed for food without the repeated messaging that these animals are food.

In a video that went viral, a little boy called Vitor is seen crying and begging his mother not to cook a chicken. He pleads, 'Please leave her alone.' She tells him the chicken is already dead and that she needs to cook it for lunch. He responds, 'I'm telling you not to cut her.' His mother explains she has already cut the bird's wings and thrown away the head. Vitor is visibly traumatized and becomes relentless in urging his mother not to cook what remains of the bird. He places his hand protectively on the bird's body and says he will take care of the bird, in his innocence not understanding that bird cannot be restored to life. His mother finally gives in, moved by her son's unwavering position, and says she will not cook the fowl.[9]

Not just Vitor, many children have a natural fascination with, and admiration for, animals. When they realize *who* is on their plate, many steadfastly and vocally object to eating them.

In another internet video, a young boy questions his mother over the octopus on his plate. He asks, 'This octopus isn't real, is it?' She lies, 'No.' He's not convinced. He asks, 'And it neither speaks nor has a head, right?' His mother says, 'It has no head,' and explains what's on his plate are only the octopus's 'little legs, chopped'. The little boy asks, 'Is his head in the sea?' His mother says, 'It's at the fisherman's.' The little boy then asks if the fisherman hacked the octopus's head off and why it was done. The mother explains, 'So we can eat, dear, just like they hack the ox, the chicken.' At this moment, the young boy expresses shock and disbelief at hearing chickens and oxen are eaten as well and protests. He tells his mother that he only wants to eat the potato and the rice on the plate. He says, 'When we eat the animals, they die,' declaring, 'I don't like that they die. I like that they keep standing and happy,' and, 'Those animals are for us to take care, not to eat them.' This young boy's natural compassion moves his mother to tears. She assures him they will not eat animals any more.[10]

There are numerous videos online of children refusing to eat animals, and one tearjerker is of a three-year-old Nepali boy who fights, successfully, to saves his goat friend from sacrifice.[11]

Not all parents tolerate such displays of emotions for animals, much less allow their children to eat vegetarian. Often, children who object to eating animals are told that they *must* eat them, and that the dead animal in front of them is indisputably 'food'. When we are told something like this enough times, most of us begin to accept it, but sometimes, someone comes along who makes us question what we have long believed.

As I described in the Introduction, I stopped eating meat after my friend Natalie challenged my eating habits.

But before I could join her in becoming vegetarian, and later, vegan—I had to consider, and examine, the merits of my reasoning for why I ate products made from animals' bodies.

Carnism: A Belief System

One of the biggest reasons why I ate animals was simply that it was normal, that essentially everyone was doing it. Sure, most people eat animals, but my notion that virtually everyone does was not true— Natalie, for example, was proof of that. My own mother was an ovo-lacto vegetarian at that time (now a lacto-vegetarian) and I knew many people in India are vegetarian, but I considered that different, religiously driven, and in the US, had thought of my mother as an exception. Somehow, Natalie becoming vegetarian and the animal rights literature I found through her made me see there are many more vegetarians and vegans—and who are so for ethical reasons or good health—than I had previously known.

Of course, just because most people do something does not make it inherently the way to go. The author of *Meat Logic: Why Do We Eat Animals*, Charles Horn argues that the number of people holding a belief or engaging in an action cannot determine if it is the sounder or just option. We already know this, but many of us tend to forget it when it comes to decisions regarding eating animals. Horn gives certain examples: Christianity is the world's most popular organized religion,[12] but that need not mean those of us who are not Christian need to turn so. Nor, as he writes, must we choose our political leanings purely based on the party in power.[13]

The question parents use to discourage kids from being swayed by their friends—'If all of your friends jumped off a bridge, would you?'—comes to mind.

I thought of eating meat as natural. Dr Joy coined the term 'carnism'. Carnism, as defined on Joy's website *Carnism.org*, is 'the invisible belief system, or ideology, that conditions people to eat certain animals'. She notes belief systems not held by the majority, such as vegetarianism or veganism, are those readily pointed out but argues carnism is a belief system too: just one that is prevailing. That most people eat meat leads to the common conviction that consuming certain species and animal-derived foods, is natural, the way of the world, rather than the outcome of popularly held attitudes in society.[14]

Eating animals and products of animal origin is also normalized by meat, egg and dairy industry messaging, and that of fast food and other companies, for their monetary gain. For instance, McDonald's spends about two billion US dollars each year in advertising[15] their beef and chicken burgers and other food products.

Today, thanks in part to such promotions, global meat production and consumption is on a rapid rise, but as news about the benefits of eating plant-based foods spreads, so is vegetarian- and vegan-eating. There are now 375 million vegetarians worldwide[16] while another survey shows there are 3.5 million vegans in the UK.[17] In the United States, there were 600 per cent more vegans in 2017 than there were in 2014, just three years before.[18] In 2003, a survey commissioned by grocery chain Safeway revealed that so many people in Britain go vegetarian each week that the whole country could be vegetarian by 2047.[19] Already, a third of Britons are vegetarian, vegan or have reduced their meat intake.[20]

Carnism may be the leading belief system in most places around the world, but in Gujarat, for example, where less than 40 per cent of the population eats meat, being vegetarian dominates.[21]

The Carnivore's Jaw

While many humans are choosing to eat animals or animal-derived foods, many are opting not to for a variety of reasons. Unlike for carnivorous animals like lions and hammerhead sharks—where their genetic make-up leaves them no such choice—humans, as is evident by the huge numbers of us who elect not to do so, do not *have* to eat other animals to survive.

Though the term 'carnism' wasn't yet invented when I became vegetarian, meeting other vegetarians and hearing their stories about how refraining from eating meat helped them achieve a healthy weight and gave them more energy led me to view eating animals as a product of a belief system rather than the inherent human state of being. If you think about how carnivorous animals are built versus humans, it's hard not to at least question what those differences mean for the commonly held notion that we are innately meat-eating.

Carnivorous animals easily eat meat raw, and are attracted to, rather than disgusted or dismayed by, killing and the sight of blood, and they do not *disguise* meat as we commonly do. If you think about it, humans often hide meat in various ways: by having someone else do the killing; calling it 'pork' versus 'flesh of butchered pig', 'beef' versus that of 'slaughtered cow' and so on; chopping it up or processing it so that it no longer resembles the animal it came from; packaging it attractively; cooking it; hiding what happens inside slaughterhouses and referring to them, if at all, as 'processing plants' instead of a more honest term and so on.

Dr Joy calls rationalizations used by individuals who eat meat despite otherwise being against cruelty to animals 'carnistic defenses'.[22] Denial is considered one such defence, and hiding slaughter from public view, as it commonly is, a type of mass denial of the fact that slaughter even occurs.

Carnivorous animals are also equipped from birth with the means to rip into and properly digest flesh. Unlike human beings, they have sharp claws, a large stomach volume, shorter, small intestines, the ability to swallow chunks of meat whole and thus a lack of digestive enzymes in their saliva, extremely sharp teeth, and a wide mouth. Their facial features and claws allow them to kill their prey without snares, guns, knives and other external weapons. Their large stomach volume helps them remain nourished between infrequent kills, and their short, small intestine is equipped to digest meat quickly.

Humans, on the other hand, have bodily features that are better suited to processing plants. We have to considerably chew our food—we can't just swallow chunks whole. Our teeth are best suited for use on softer materials (which is a reason why humans usually cook meat), our intestines are long and twisting and our saliva contains enzymes that allow plant foods to be broken down, while our fingernails are essentially so useless some of us use them primarily for beautification.

Even when we compare our anatomy to that of omnivorous animals, who though they eat plants must still retain an ability to catch, slay and digest animals, like most bears, we find differences in mouth and intestine sizes, stomach volume, teeth, ingestion, digestive saliva enzymes, claws and so on.[23]

The Psychology of a Carnivore

Humans and carnivorous animals also appear to differ psychologically in how we see other animals, and how we typically desire to engage with them. We can witness this difference easily by observing domesticated cats who are still hardwired to hunt and can digest raw meat (though it is not recommended they be fed this due to bacteria and potential food poisoning). There are examples of domesticated cats who defy stereotypes and live comfortably with other animals, like 'pet' rats, rabbits or birds, in the same house, but my two rescued cats, Mil and Tim, as sweet as they are, *enjoy* hunting and killing animals. Perhaps even more than liking the chase, they seem to have no choice but to do it—automatically getting into stalking mode when they see a small being flying around or running by.

If not stopped, they would pounce on the animal, claw the creature, and kill them with their bared paws and teeth—motions they act out on their stuffed toys. Soum and I, therefore, have to keep an eye out for lizards, moths and other small creatures who may enter our flat because if Mil or Tim see them first, they go into attack mode and strike. While some people kill the animals they consider 'pests', and though some of us take up hunting or fishing as a form of entertainment, most of us do not long to kill animals or get any satisfaction out of doing so. Imagine how distracting it would be if our automatic desire upon seeing a pigeon or squirrel was, 'Kill!'

(For those interested, vegan cat food brands exist where the foods have been fortified with nutrients cats usually get from meat.)

Challenging the Notion of Meat and Dairy Foods as Human Necessities

When I consumed animal-derived foods, I thought drinking milk especially was necessary. Society ensures most of us think this but these days, study after study shows not only do we not need to eat animals, consume eggs or drink milk to survive, we must not eat these foods if we want to thrive: a study published in *JAMA Internal Medicine*, for instance, found that vegans live longer than people who are not vegan.[24] Because the health consequences of eating animals or being vegetarian or vegan is a topic deserving of in-depth analysis, it is covered further in Chapter XIII of this book.

The health benefits of being vegan were not as widely studied as they are today, however, when I was considering going dairy-free— at least I was not aware of any such information about it. Though I stopped eating animals at sixteen, Natalie and I both didn't become vegan until about four years later because of our shared belief that drinking milk was a human requirement. It was only when it was highlighted to us by vegans we met that humans are the only species that drinks the milk of another species, and that too, the only species to drink milk at all after infancy, that we started seeing us drinking cow's milk as weird as the idea of humans drinking dog's, cat's or rat's milk. The dairy industry would rather we not ponder this basic fact, but biologically, cows, buffaloes and goats produce milk specifically for their own children, just as humans and other mammals produce milk for theirs.

Dr Michael Klaper who focuses on nutrition-based medicine explains it on his website this way, 'Cow's milk IS baby calf growth fluid. No matter what you do to it, that is what the stuff is. Everything in that white liquid—the hormones, the lipids, the proteins, the sodium, the growth factors like IGF-I—[is] all there to start that calf growing into a great big cow, or else they would not be there.'[25]

In other words, cow's milk exists specifically to turn a thirty-kilo calf into a 200-kilo or more cow quickly. When you take that into account, dairy no longer fits neatly into the definition of people food.

Since mammalian species produce milk for their own species, that too only for consumption during infancy, it's no surprise then that about 75 per cent of the world's human population loses their ability to digest milk after weaning.[26] These individuals have been historically called lactose intolerant, but this condition is now considered the norm. Symptoms of lactose intolerance include bloating, stomach cramps, gas, vomiting and diarrhoea but commonly lactose-intolerant individuals write these symptoms off as something else, or simply consider it just how their bodies are built since they would have usually been drinking animal milk their entire lives.

The Unappetizing Labrador Retriever

Finally, and perhaps primarily, I ate meat, eggs and dairy foods because I thought they tasted good. Many people think so. It is a taste, however, that lasts just a few seconds in our mouths, and so, like I did, more and more people are doing the cost/benefit analysis of whether they consider it acceptable to put thinking, feeling animals through a lifetime of misery; negatively impact their health; and put an extra burden on the planet, since the production of animal-derived foods is far more inefficient, resource-intensive and environmentally polluting as compared to plant-foods, for this fleeting moment of taste.

Thankfully for those who have turned vegetarian or vegan, tastes change. Indeed, many vegetarians and vegans say that after they stopped eating animals or products of animal origin, they lost the desire for it, and now find the idea of eating it revolting. I certainly do.

Dr Joy offers one possible explanation for this shift. Her book *Why We Love Dogs, Eat Pigs and Wear Cows* starts with an exercise asking the reader to imagine they are at a dinner party where the host brings out a delicious smelling pot of meat stew. The reader is then asked to imagine the host sharing her recipe saying, 'You begin with five pounds of golden retriever meat, well marinated, and then …'[27] This would stop most people in their tracks, and they would suddenly find the stew sickening and inedible. They may even begin picturing a playful golden retriever.

When people stop eating animals, eggs or dairy foods out of empathy for what the animals suffer, they can often picture a baby chick, mother buffalo, happy pig or fish in the vast ocean—each of them a conscious, feeling individual full of life and none of them wishing to suffer and die—thereby making the food as undesirable as that golden retriever stew.

It turns out that I wasn't the only one using rationalizations to eat meat, eggs and dairy foods. Dr Jared Piazza of Lancaster University and his team of researchers from around the world describe justifications commonly used by people who eat animals as the '4Ns': that doing so is 'natural', 'necessary', 'normal' and 'nice'.

Dr Piazza explains, 'The 4Ns are a powerful, pervasive tool employed by individuals to diffuse the guilt one might otherwise experience when consuming animal products.'[28] If we are using any of these or other reasons, like I once did, then we must inspect their merit and consider how 'natural' it seems to rear animals the way we do today.

3

FAST FOOD AND FACTORY FARMS

We are not encouraged, on a daily basis, to pay careful attention to the animals we eat. On the contrary, the meat, dairy, and egg industries all actively encourage us to give thought to our own immediate interest (taste, for example, or cheap food) but not to the real suffering involved. They do so by deliberately withholding information and by cynically presenting us with idealized images of happy animals in beautiful landscapes, scenes of bucolic happiness that do not correspond to anything in the real world. The animals involved suffer agony because of our ignorance. The least we owe them is to lessen that ignorance.[1]

—*Jeffrey Moussaieff Masson, author of*
The Face on Your Plate: The Truth About Food

Oh, how I loved to go to McDonald's as a child! My parents would take me there to use their playground, for my classmates' birthday parties, and to meet their famous clown, Ronald McDonald, whenever he was scheduled to be around. I'd use the company's toy pails to collect Halloween candy from neighbours and keep an eye out for new toys on offer in its Happy Meals (little boxes for children's meals). In the US, Christian holidays are commonly celebrated by people of all religions, and so I would visit McDonald's for Easter egg hunts, and around Christmas go meet whoever they had recruited to dress up like Santa Claus there too. McDonald's is so genius at marketing to kids, and adults, they have long played a significant role in the lives of many families.

When I was growing up, kids were enthralled by the company's 'McDonaldland' fantasy world. McDonaldland was a bizarre concept designed for children that appeared in the company's advertisements and messaging, where, among other things, McDonald's beef hamburgers grew out of the ground like cabbages, and burgers spoke and sang along with Ronald McDonald. Characters from McDonaldland such as Ronald as well as Mayor McCheese and Officer Big Mac—who both had beef burgers for heads, and later the McNugget Buddies—who were a group of happy, talking chicken pieces, featured in McDonald's commercials, as part of the playsets on McDonald's playgrounds that adjoined the restaurants, and as toys in Happy Meals. Of course, anyone who is familiar with McDonald's in India or anywhere else in the world knows they still offer Happy Meals and continue to attract families through playgrounds, by providing facilities for children's birthday parties and by giving out toys (McDonald's is the largest toy distributor in the world).[2]

As a result of its family-friendly image and the myth that was created through its fun promotions that the company's meat foods are produced in benign ways, I ate beef burgers or chicken nuggets every time my parents relented to my begging and took me there to play. In my young mind, eating foods like burgers was all part of the McDonald's experience that I absolutely had to have, and as it was possible to fill a child's stomach for less than a US dollar there then, my parents were fine with letting me have it.

McDonaldland no longer exists, but the company's 'I'm Lovin' It' catchphrase and other advertisements used to build their fan base in India and elsewhere worldwide remain so clever and happy it is easy to forget McDonald's is responsible for the butchering of billions and billions of animals, none of whom volunteered to die or grew out of the ground. Americans alone are said to cause the deaths of five and a half million cattle for the beef they eat at McDonald's in just one year.[3]

Masters of Distraction

McDonald's, of course, isn't the only master of distraction. You're unlikely to ever see an advertisement from KFC, thought to kill over 850 million chickens a year,[4] that says, 'Our chicken buckets are full of the body parts of intelligent birds who were raised in crowded sheds and did not want to die,' or from Burger King that says, 'Our Mutton Whoppers are produced by treating goats in ways that would cause a furore if they were dogs or cats.' Instead, if the sentiments of their commercials are to be believed, you might suppose you can fall in love while eating a KFC Chick'n Fried Roll or be able to use your Whopper as a substitute for a partner on Valentine's Day—or at least that's what I think Burger King India was trying to relay with its strange #FlirtyWhopper campaign.

In fact, instead of honesty, sometimes the animal-derived foods industry releases an advert that goes beyond just trying to equate good times with fast food by being deliberately deceptive. For instance, a February 2018 front-page *Times of India* ad by All India Poultry Development and Services, a subsidiary of VH Group of which Venky's is a part, gave consumers misleading assurances about the Indian poultry industry's antibiotic use. Venky's supplies to outlets such as McDonalds, KFC and Pizza Hut in India. The Centre for Science and Environment, an Indian think tank, slammed this poultry firm for misrepresenting facts to the public, while the Advertising Standards Council of India also upheld complaints made to it about claims in the ad being disingenuous,[5] but most of us would have only seen the prominently placed promotion and not news of the firm having distorted the truth.

This has been the case in the West for decades, but increasingly today, the fast-food industry impacts how people in India and other countries eat—through its advertisements, affordability and availability, and it largely determines how the food it sells is produced globally too. The industry is famous for processing its menu items on assembly lines, and in its pursuit of cheap, mass-produced meat, eggs and dairy foods, it uses suppliers who handle live animals comparatively too.

Today, with no small thanks to the influence of McDonald's and food businesses like it, and to meet the rising demand for animal-derived foods, which is already the highest it has ever been, 99 per cent of animals in the US are raised on factory farms while globally almost 70 per cent of land animals[7] and even most fish[8] are reared on factory farms too.

Life on a Factory Farm

Take a moment right now to close your eyes and picture a farm. What did you see? When many people imagine how animals are raised in India, they think of small backyard facilities where chickens are free to scratch at the ground to find morsels to eat and cows have calves in tow. However, times have changed, and family-run farms are being rapidly replaced by intensive animal-farming operations in India and around the world for convenience, mass production, low costs, profit and corporate greed. Already today, factory farms are the most common method of egg and chicken meat production in India[9] and plans are afoot to intensify the farming of other animals too.

Often, when we discuss the ethics of eating meat, eggs or dairy foods, we focus on whether and how the animals die. I couldn't possibly guess how many times people have said to me, 'But chickens do not die for eggs' or 'Cows don't die for milk'—neither of which is actually true. However, factory farms raise a bigger concern about how these animals live.

Factory farms are industrialized farms that house huge numbers of animals, up to millions per farm, usually indoors, in the least amount of space; and use machinery and technology for most farming operations. The idea is to use minimal resources—manpower, employees, area—to produce the most amount of cheap meat, eggs and dairy foods possible for maximum profits. Lax environmental controls allowing these farms to get away with enormous levels of pollution, such as by not properly treating the huge amounts of faeces they generate, help keep costs low.

On factory farms, which I describe in-depth in chapters that follow, animals are crammed into tiny cages, metal or wooden crates, plastic hutches or filthy sheds. The purpose of this severe confinement is to have each animal use the least amount of resources and space, and avoid them 'wasting' energy so that they can be more easily fattened up for slaughter; or in the case of veal production abroad, to produce tender meat from the butchered bodies of calves forced to live nearly stationary.

Though they live together, up to tens of thousands in the same shed, animals on these farms are commonly kept either restrained individually or in such maddeningly crowded conditions that it is impossible for them to make even a single friend, forget about developing any type of social structure. The animals become so upset by the overcrowding, imprisonment and lack of social order that, when they can, some injure each other and fight. In the case of chickens, they even commonly cannibalize their cage or shed mates. These animals' lives are unimaginably painful, miserable and lonely.

Factory-farmed animals are born thanks to artificial insemination, a usually crude and painful process, have in most cases never met their mothers, are separated from their children, cannot build nests or engage in virtually any behaviour that is natural and important to them—not even freely move. Most never get to learn what it feels like to have grass beneath their feet, sun on their backs or fresh air to breathe. If they do get to experience any of these things, it's usually not pleasant and just brief, when they are loaded on to trucks to be taken to slaughter.

In such harsh detention, the animals' muscles atrophy and bones deteriorate from lack of use, they develop wounds and sores from the wires of their cages or being unable to shift their weight, and most are forced to live mired in their own urine and faeces and the waste of other animals.

To make matters worse, animals raised in this way are often castrated or suffer other mutilations without anaesthesia or painkillers, are fed unnatural diets and their bodies are commonly bred and drugged to make them grow faster and larger so as to produce more meat, eggs or milk than their bodies naturally can. The pressure of this unnatural production is hard on their bodies, resulting in ailments ranging from heart failure to broken bones. Or their bodies are manipulated in other ways, such as being temporarily starved to 'trick' them into producing more eggs.

If aliens took over Earth and started rearing humans the way we raise most animals used for food, even if all a person could remember from birth is being imprisoned or crammed by the thousands in a shed, he would still—at a minimum—long to stretch his limbs, move about, have personal space and engage his mind. Similarly, animals on factory farms long to do what their species is naturally meant to do too, even if they have not known any other life.

The Basics: What an Animal Needs

A critical person may say, sure we know what humans need for our well-being because we are human, but how do we really know what animals need? What defines good welfare for them? The chances are that if you wouldn't want to suffer it, it would be safe to assume that animals wouldn't either. However, because it is legal to raise at least certain species of animals for food, basic welfare, as it relates to animals under human use, had to be defined.

In 1964, Ruth Harrison wrote *Animal Machines*, which described factory farming practices and resulted in a hue and cry in Britain over how bad things were for animals there. The British government responded by creating a committee to look after farmed animals. Shortly after its formation, the committee, chaired by Professor Roger Brambell, offered its report which stated that animals should have the freedom 'to stand up, lie down, turn around, groom themselves and stretch their limbs'. Notice these *extremely basic* freedoms do not even require an animal to be able to walk around.[10]

Later, in 1979, the UK Farm Animal Welfare Council (FAWC) established the Five Freedoms, which consider the animal's physical and mental state, as below:

- Freedom from hunger and thirst: by ready access to fresh water and a diet to maintain full health and vigour.
- Freedom from discomfort: by providing an appropriate environment including shelter and a comfortable resting area.
- Freedom from pain, injury or disease: by prevention or rapid diagnosis and treatment.
- Freedom to express normal behaviour: by providing sufficient space, proper facilities and company of the animal's own kind.
- Freedom from fear and distress: by ensuring conditions and treatment which avoid mental suffering.[11]

Even if we look at the more basic freedoms from the Brambell report, the treatment of animals in today's farming systems—decades after those simple freedoms were formed—usually falls short. For instance, chickens used for eggs are commonly kept in cages so small around the world that they cannot fully stretch their wings, cattle used for dairy in India are often tied so tightly to a railing or post they are unable to shoo away a crow pecking at a wound, and pregnant pigs are commonly kept in crates so cramped they cannot turn around.

The Five Freedoms established by the FAWC are recognized as a good set of guidelines by veterinarians and other experts worldwide. They are referred to by the World Organisation for Animal Health (OIE),[12] an intergovernmental organization of 181-member countries, including India, focused on animal health and disease control, as the basis by which to measure animal welfare. Yet, on factory farms in India and around the world, they are mostly disregarded altogether.

India's 'Scientific' Plans

The Indian government has included promoting pig farming 'on scientific lines', as a pig meat industry website describes it, under its five-year plans.[13] Regarding commercial goat farming, the Indian Council for Agricultural Research (ICAR) reports, 'Due to its good economic prospects, goat rearing under intensive and semi-intensive system for commercial production has been gaining momentum for the past couple of years,'[14] while the Tamil Nadu Agricultural University describes how to keep sheep and goats in a 'zero grazing' system.[15] Zero grazing means just that—animals would be 100 per cent confined so to be used for dairy or fattened up for meat.

The Indian central Department of Animal Husbandry, Dairying and Fisheries,[16] numerous Indian state animal husbandry departments,[17,18] and agriculture universities such as Kerala Veterinary and Animal Sciences University[19] and Tamil Nadu Agricultural University (TNAU)[20] all refer to farrowing enclosures on their websites and other material on pig rearing. The Coimbatore-based supplier of factory farm equipment Royal Livestock Farms[21] sells, among other contraptions, farrowing crates. All this provides a window into what plans for pig farming on 'scientific lines' in India likely entails.

There are varieties of farrowing pens with varying degrees of restriction, but farrowing crates are the most commonly used abroad and exist to keep mother pigs in place and to stop them from accidentally crushing their piglets. On farms that use them, mother pigs are moved into farrowing crates shortly before giving birth and are kept there for a month while they nurse. Ironically, it is the space restriction and conditions of the factory farm that put piglets at risk of being killed in the first place—in nature, a mummy pig would carefully build a nest before giving birth.[22]

Farrowing crates are so narrow that a mother pig is denied performing any natural behaviours whatsoever, and she can only stand and get back down with some struggle. Lying on their sides on concrete while nursing, pigs often develop pressure sores that can become infected from filth. A small concrete or metal barred area is provided for the piglets to nurse, but the space is so cramped that it does not allow the mother pig to nuzzle, clean or see her piglets well. It doesn't even allow her to move to protect herself if they nibble while nursing.[23]

Coimbatore's Royal Livestock Farms sells gestation stalls too, also known as sow stalls. This is despite the director of animal husbandry for Punjab and Chandigarh issuing a letter in 2014 to his subordinates asking them to ensure gestation crates are not used by pig farms in the region referencing the Prevention of Cruelty to Animals (PCA) Act 1960[24]. This central government law, applicable India-wide, prohibits putting animals in restraints that do not allow a reasonable opportunity for movement—a requirement routinely ignored in the rearing of animals for food. Gestation stalls are similar to farrowing crates but are used to keep pigs in severe confinement for the entire duration of their four-month pregnancy until they are moved into farrowing crates.

Imagine being forced to live on concrete and confined to metal stalls hardly larger than the size of your own body during your pregnancy, birth of your child and even as you try to nurse. There would be no soft pillows to lean on, no way to shift around to get comfortable, no way to stretch to get some circulation going, no way to move about. For humans, a pregnant woman needing cushions and exercise is a matter of common sense. Similarly, there is no reason to believe a pregnant pig could not do with some hay and at least a basic allowance for movement.

Yet, female pigs on farms in many parts of the world live mind-bogglingly bleak lives, of going between the gestation stall and farrowing crate over and over until they are killed. Affected by the stress of unyielding imprisonment, pigs commonly exhibit strange behaviours they never would in nature, like biting continuously at the enclosure bars or chewing constantly but without any food in their mouths.[25]

Libby was one such pig reared on a factory farm in the US. Her rescuer describes, 'When I first met Libby ... she had no name, only a number stamped on the metal tag in her ear. She was a breeding sow. Her purpose in the factory was to produce piglets to be turned into more breeding sows if they were healthy girls or else pork products if they were boys. She lived on cement floors. She lived crowded by the metal bars surrounding her body. She could stand or lie down, but she could never walk around. She didn't have sweet earth, didn't have grass and didn't have a soft bed of hay. She was fed a limited amount once a day and the rest of her day was spent doing nothing. She was a pork producer, nothing more.'[26]

Libby would have been turned into sausage, but her fate changed—she was rescued. She spent her remaining days at a sanctuary near the American city of Seattle eating blackberries and apples, greeting children who visited and eagerly rolling over for belly rubs like a dog. When her health was failing, she touchingly chose a patch of ground under a sign at the sanctuary that read 'Pigs are friends not food' to die.

Dairy and fish farming in India is also on an intensive trend. Parag Milk's farm in Pune houses 4,000 Dutch Holstein cows,[27] who are made to take turns stepping on to a rotating platform to be milked by machines,[28] while Chitale Dairy in Bhilawadi, Maharashtra boasts about having 2,00,000 cows and Chennai's Hatsun says it has 2,20,000.[29]

Meanwhile, on fish farms, aquatic species are confined to cramped, filthy enclosures underwater in conditions comparable to how factory farmed animals are kept on land. Parasitic infections, diseases and injuries on fish farms are common. Aquaculture, as this farming is called, is classified into freshwater and brackish water production in India. Today, freshwater fish farming is so common, it makes up more than half of total fish production in the country.[30]

Drugs to Keep Animals Alive Contribute to Humans' Deaths

Drugs, in particular antibiotics, are the primary reason factory farms, including fish farms, can exist. Crowded, filthy conditions mean diseases can spread quickly. So, animals on these farms are fed a regimen of antibiotics—so much so that antibiotics are used more widely on factory farmed animals than directly by humans.[31] Animals are also fed antibiotics for other reasons. Feeding them these drugs to encourage growth was banned in the European Union in 2006, but it remains common in India.[32] Animals may also be given antibiotics to require less food for the desired milk or other output ('feed efficiency' as the industry calls it).[33] The residue from antibiotics can end up in the meat, eggs and milk that is consumed.[34] What's that, waiter? How would you like bread with that antibiotic soup, you say? This overuse of drugs in animals used for food is contributing to drug-resistance in humans—and, of course, in the animals too.

Antibiotic resistance is exactly what it sounds like: It's when bacteria that infect humans or animals become unresponsive to them. As the World Health Organization (WHO) explains,[35] when this happens, it increases the risk of death and means antibiotics for numerous infections like pneumonia and tuberculosis in humans are becoming less effective, making these conditions difficult to treat. Bacteria that become resistant to antibiotics in humans and animals have contributed to the emergence of 'superbugs'—new, aggressive pathogens. And superbugs can kill: More than 58,000 newborn babies died in India in 2013 because cures for bacterial infections stopped working.[36] Superbugs are also estimated to kill 33,000 Europeans each year.[37]

In its 2016 exposé of indiscriminate antibiotic use in the Indian poultry industry, Bloomberg described visits to numerous Indian poultry farms in Telangana stating antibiotics were put in the animals' food, water and given to them by injection.[38] Most of India's egg production and much of its chicken meat production takes place in Andhra Pradesh and Telangana.[39]

Bloomberg's reporters examined records on site at various farms and reported that colistin and numerous other antibiotics necessary for treating potentially life-threatening human ailments were being fed to the animals, including those banned from use in chickens in numerous other countries. Disturbingly, Bloomberg also found that most farmers they met did not even understand what they were using or the gravity of the consequences of feeding chickens antibiotics used for human consumption, sometimes referring to these drugs as mere 'vitamins'.

The use of antibiotics can quicken growth in animals, but researcher Ramanan Laxminarayan, director of the Center for Disease Dynamics, Economics & Policy, says that in India antibiotics are often used instead of cleanliness.[40] It's no surprise then that India has among the highest rates of antibiotic resistance in the world[41] and no wonder VH Group wants to downplay the chicken meat industry's role in this public health crisis.

On 8 August 2019, the Food Safety and Standards Authority of India (FSSAI) finally issued a draft regulation to be immediately implemented to add at least colistin on the banned list for use in the production of meat and meat products in India.[42] In addition to what Bloomberg's reporters found, in 2018, the Bureau of Investigative Journalism exposed Venky's was giving colistin to farmers to boost chicken size.[43] Colistin is a final hope drug used to treat certain infections in severely sick human patients.

Ripe Time for a Pandemic of Deadly Flu

Factory farms also greatly increase our risk of contracting zoonotic diseases, or animal diseases that can also infect humans. Bob Martin, former executive director of the Pew Commission on Industrial Animal Farm Production, which was established to recommend ways to address problems caused by factory farms, calls them 'super-incubators for viruses'.[44]

Bird flu, or avian flu, is a disease that can spread easily on a crowded farm. There are at least 144 different strains of this flu.[45] A dead chicken found at a meat shop in December 2017 tested positive for H5N1 in Bengaluru,[46] just months after India declared itself free of the virus.[47] H5N1 kills most birds and is potentially deadly to humans, killing about 60 per cent of people who catch it.[48] Humans can get this flu from being around infected birds, but improperly cooked meat and eggs are also a risk.[49] Because of its often disastrous health effects, when a chicken on a farm is found to be infected with bird flu, all of the chickens on the farm are killed. Some countries do this by suffocating struggling birds under litres of white foam.[50]

Swine flu, which as the name suggests is linked to pigs, has killed thousands of people in India.[51] Its H1N1 strain is thought to have developed on a US factory farm.[52] It can be passed on from pig to person or person to person.

If that sounds bad, Dr Jonathan Quick, chair of the US-based non-profit Global Health Council, warns things may get worse. He says conditions are currently right for a deadly flu pandemic and bird flu is the potentially most dangerous. He cautions if an extremely contagious strain of H5N1 were to develop, the human death toll could be catastrophic.[53]

Paying High Costs

One of the highest costs of factory farming faced by the public is damage to human health and hospital bills—not only because of viruses, superbugs and drug resistance, but by way of environmental pollution and the effects of consuming meat, eggs and dairy themselves, especially in the quantities they are consumed now.

A study by the Institute of Health Metrics and Evaluation at the University of Washington, the most thorough carried out on this matter, found that poor diet causes one out of five deaths worldwide.[54] While diets rich in animal-derived foods are regarded as aggressors for cardiovascular disease, doctors have shown heart disease can be arrested and even reversed with healthy plant-based foods (described in detail in Chapter XIII). Looking at heart disease alone, including costs for direct healthcare and loss of productivity, the World Heart Federation reports that by 2030 the total global cost of cardiovascular disease is expected to rise by over 20 per cent to US$1,044 billion.[55]

Other costs are paid by the rural community. As you can imagine, it is not nice living next to a factory farm. Yet the power of corporate money often means rural families have no choice. Apart from the constant nauseating stench of untreated waste, which contain microbes that make people ill (in the US, it was found the stink from pig farms was even increasing neighbours' blood pressure),[56] there are problems like flies. Residents in Raipur Rani and Barwala in Haryana who live near poultry farms complain of being plagued by houseflies and mosquitoes.[57] This is not unique to India. In the US, residents near factory farms complain of throngs of flies that force them indoors. These residents also complain of a variety of health ailments thought to be linked to the farms, such as headaches, eye irritation, respiratory problems, sore throats and diarrhoea.[58]

And when it comes to pollution and other dangers, health-wise, the workers on the farms are the worst off. These are the individuals who are directly inhaling gases and other dangerous matter emitted by factory farms, or are in close contact with sick animals. They inhale particles from feathers, faecal matter, dead skin cells of often thousands of animals, fungi and more. They commonly inhale massive amounts of ammonia, from the animals' combined waste, and hydrogen sulphide, from liquid manure. As a result, they frequently suffer from respiratory complications and worsening of asthma, eye problems, cough, damage to their throats and even premature death.[59]

A study published in *Clinical Infectious Disease* of pig farmworkers in the US state of Iowa found they are six times more likely than those not involved in the trade to be carriers of the aggressive *Staphylococcus aureus* group of bacteria.[60] Carriers of *S. aureus* are at risk of staph infections that they can pass on to their family and friends. Those who become sick can have reactions ranging from relatively mild skin ailments to more invasive bodily infections in their blood, lung or heart, and can even die. These infections are hard to treat because they are resistant to numerous drugs. This is not a new problem, but it is a widespread one—about ten years ago, it was reported that hospital-acquired staph infection methicillin-resistant *Staphylococcus aureus* (MRSA) causes more deaths in the US than AIDS.[61]

MRSA is now considered a major global health threat.[62] Pig farms are not the only culprit for staph bacteria, they are common in chicken and other factory farms too.[63] In India, a new clone of MRSA has been found in Kochi through routine laboratory testing of fish used for seafood. It is called t15669 MRSA. This is considered a potential hazard for anyone who handles the fish.[64]

Exploitation and Disturbed Workers

Workers at municipal slaughterhouses in India can usually be found wading through urine, faeces and blood without wearing any protective gear whatsoever. They work with dirty knives and amongst the filth of the slaughterhouse with bare feet and bare hands. There are often no washing provisions in these facilities or even any drinking water. The workers live in poverty and typically don't have any channel through which to get care if they become sick or injured from the gruelling and dangerous work conditions.[65] PETA India investigations have also found children working on some farms rearing animals for food and in slaughterhouses.

I met an old butcher at a Coimbatore municipal slaughterhouse some years ago who had nine daughters. His daughters were married, and presumably not helping him, so he had no choice but to continue to toil to take care of himself. He must have been over eighty, or at least he looked that way, and with his curved back and frail body, he slit animals' throats for a few meagre rupees a day.

It seemed he was trapped in this unfortunate life of cutting up animals. I didn't spend enough time with him to really get to know him, but for many workers, the challenges of factory farm work and seeing animals chopped to pieces has a damaging psychological effect.

In undercover video after undercover video by animal protection groups, disturbed factory farm and slaughterhouse workers have been filmed being deliberately cruel to animals who already face the inherent harshness of these systems. PETA US caught workers at a pig breeding farm in the American state of North Carolina administering daily beatings of pregnant sows with a wrench and an iron pole. They also documented the skinning of pigs alive and sawing off a conscious animal's legs.[66] In British Columbia, Canada, Mercy for Animals captured footage of workers at a farm ripping live chickens open; tearing limbs off of their bodies; throwing, kicking and stomping on chickens; even forcing the animals into sexual acts with each other.[67] In the UK, slaughterhouse workers were filmed kicking a pig and slamming the animal against a wall.[68] In India, transporters were filmed walking on top of baby chicks, with feathers and guts stuck to the soles of their feet.

An American study of non-metropolitan counties with slaughterhouses found that these towns have higher arrest rates for domestic violence, rape and murder.[69] In Australia, a study found that slaughterhouse workers are likely to become insensitive to suffering, which can result in violence towards humans too. There, it was found that female slaughterhouse workers were even more aggressive than men. These individuals, both men and women, were described by Flinders University sociology professor and author Dr Nik Taylor as extremely angry.[70] In an article that appeared in the *Bihar Times* several years ago, former Union Minister Maneka Gandhi wrote, 'Which are the most dangerous cities in India? I would put Rampur on top of my list … Murders and other forms of violent crime are common. It also has the last number of illegal slaughterhouses killing cows and buffaloes by the thousands every day. The Mewat region of Haryana, where police refuse to go, is the largest illegal slaughter centre in north India, and the centre of the wildlife parts smuggling trade as well.'[71]

In India, massive corporations like VH Group, Skylark Hatcheries, Godrej Agrovet and a few others make up more than 70 per cent of the total output from the poultry sector in the country.[72]

Increasingly, small, family-run farms are unable to compete with farming giants like these in India, the US and around the world. As a result, farmers are typically left with hardly any bargaining power and little choice but to enter into contractual arrangements with corporations. Usually in these arrangements, the farmers raise animals for the large companies. The costs the corporations pay may be set, while farmers can usually be expected to make their own investments to match the corporations' requirements and assume the risks—naturally this imbalanced set-up doesn't always work out in the contract farmers' benefit.[73] Not too long ago, it was reported, more than 71 per cent of all contractors raising chickens for corporations in the US earned pay so low they were considered living in poverty.[74]

Meat Promoters to Veggie Burger Sellers

The silver lining in this dark cloud of a factory farm world, however, is that while companies like McDonald's promote meat products globally, they also amend their practices when there's enough consumer pressure—sometimes marginally, other times more significantly—and aim to sell consumers the products they think they want. And so, half the McDonald's menu is vegetarian in India, and vegetarian and McVegan and other vegan burgers and vegan nuggets are being gobbled up at its outlets in an increasing number of countries.

Also responding to consumer demand, KFC has trialled meat-free chicken-like, but plant-based, options in select UK and US stores, selling out in record time,[75] and it offered vegan options in Vietnam apparently for those Buddhists who are sometimes vegetarian there.[76] Burger King offers vegetarian options in India and a vegan Whopper has been rolled out in stores across America.[77] Also in the US, White Castle now offers a vegan slider sandwich,[78] Pizza Hut and Papa John's offer vegan (that is non-dairy, plant-based) cheese pizzas in the UK,[79] Domino's sells vegan cheese pizzas in Australia and New Zealand,[80] and Pizza Express launched vegan cheese pizzas in India for a limited time.[81] Subway is offering a meat-free 'meatball' sub in the US and Canada also for a limited time (for now) to the delight of those who want interesting and delicious plant-based meals.[82] Almost all major coffee chains operating in India also offer soya or almond milk as an alternative to dairy.

And so, just like how Domino's in Gujarat removed meat from its menus because it finds most Gujarati customers prefer to eat at places that don't serve meat,[83] with the right consumer demand, the contents of the burgers sold by McDonald's of the future may indeed grow out of the ground.

Until such times, animals need us to consider their plight.

4

BORN TO DIE

The question is not, 'Can they reason?' nor, 'Can they talk?' but 'Can they suffer?'[1]

—*Jeremy Bentham*

Even newborn and juvenile animals make unmistakably known that they do not want to suffer and die.

Some years ago, a buffalo calf escaped Mumbai's Deonar slaughterhouse. After he and other cattle were unloaded there, he sensed trouble and made a run for it, out of the exit and into a scrapyard. The butchers tried to get him, but he was so clever, he managed to evade them for twenty hours! Finally, someone called the Bombay SPCA. They initially couldn't get the feisty, terrified calf either, but after a great deal of struggle, he was caught and transported to their shelter.[2] By bolting, he saved his own life.

Bonnie, a baby cow, saved her own life too. She ran away from a farm that reared cows for beef in the American state of New York and into the woods when she was just four months old. She had become frightened by the cries and sight of other cows being corralled for slaughter. She too became a master evader and though she would be spotted at times, nobody was able to catch her. People wondered how this young calf managed to survive on her own. Finally, cameras revealed Bonnie had been adopted by a herd of deer. She moved with them, slept with them, ate with them and they looked after her. However, knowing Bonnie may eventually succumb to the harshness of the winter, a kind woman, Becky Bartels, slowly befriended Bonnie by taking food into the forest. Farm Sanctuary, which houses animals rescued from the food industry, also stepped in, and after being on the run for eight months, Bonnie was caught, given care and taken to the sanctuary where she will live out her days with other rescued friends.[3]

Calf Herbie is another survivor. Also, at just four months old, he managed to escape a truck headed to slaughter by bolting down a busy New York City street. Upon hearing about Herbie's will to survive, many people pleaded to authorities that he be allowed to live. Herbie was finally captured, and police handed him over to a sanctuary saving his life. When he was moved to his new permanent home, he was lovingly welcomed with toys and a vegan cake.[4]

Baby chickens try to avoid trouble too. When taken to be fed live to fish from a facility run by a Telangana-based egg farm, a tiny chick managed to evade falling into the water and hid behind a stone. Secretly filmed video footage reveals a transporter spotted him but let him be. Cruelly, he remarked, rats would get him.[5]

These are rare cases. Tens of billions of young animals used by the egg, meat and dairy industries each year are left with no chance of escape.

'Surplus' Living Beings

Hens used for eggs are ultimately slaughtered, but nowadays chickens used commercially for meat and those used for eggs are not the same—those used for meat are bred to have 'meatier', heavier upper bodies and to grow to full size in just about six weeks. Those used for eggs are selectively bred to lay an abnormal number of eggs, often hundreds per year.

So, what does the egg industry do with most male chicks (minus those used for breeding), since they aren't used by the meat industry and can't produce eggs? What does it and the meat industry do with chicks who are sick, deformed or weak?

Similar to how chickens are bred to either be 'meatier' or to produce more eggs, today cattle are commonly bred to produce more milk than nature intends, and so those breeds used for tilling fields and carting loads versus milk are often different. And with increasing use of farming technology, cattle are also used less for work than in the past. Like humans, cows and buffaloes only lactate when they are pregnant or upon giving birth in order to feed their calves. Thus, as dairies generally have no use for male calves as they can't produce milk, how do they deal with them?

Thanks in large part to a sensitive young man who spent a considerable amount of time at major facilities involved in egg and chicken meat production in Andhra Pradesh and Telangana a short while ago, we know how key industry players handle baby chicks from the time they are born. He provided vast and powerful footage taken over months to PETA India via another group: Anonymous for Animal Rights (now called Animals Now). PETA India publicized the video footage he obtained with his permission and prepared a detailed report[6] of his findings but, for his safety and at his request, has not released his identity. However, for the sake of avoiding awkward writing, I will call him by a false name, Arun.

In fact, it is mostly thanks to brave, compassionate people like Arun—whistle-blowers, investigators, rescuers and the like—that we know what *really* happens in any industry using animals, whether it is animals used for food, clothing, experiments, entertainment or any other purpose, and not just what the industries want the public to know. And so, similarly, it is thanks to such individuals, combined with official government and industry documentation, that we know what happens to calves at the hands of the dairy industry too.

A Chick's Life

As Arun observed, chickens used for meat and eggs on factory farms in India are not born in nests, but on trays in a machine—an incubator with temperature and other controls—nowhere near their mothers. Remember the foetus fields in the science-fiction film *The Matrix* where humans were grown, maintained in pods and kept alive by machines? The machines in which chickens are born are comparable conceptually—except, for chicks, this is real life.

Incubators can be huge. A Hyderabad-based company advertises machines with capacities ranging from 2,000 to 30,000 eggs.[7] This artificial process doesn't always go right due to reasons such as the incubator temperature or other settings being wrongly fixed, a lack of appropriate machine maintenance, not filling the incubator to capacity which effects air flow and so on.[8] Chicks are, therefore, sometimes born with damage to their organs—like those Arun filmed being born at a hatchery to be used by the meat industry. When things go wrong, they are also born with deformities or other problems.

Chicks are adept early on—far more capable and advanced than human babies in many ways, standing and walking soon after birth, but they are babies after all, small and vulnerable, and they react to pain and express fear. If they were born as nature intended, they would spend their early days in the security of their mum's protection, pressed up to her side or sitting beneath her for warmth and she would do her best to guard them from predators and other harm. If they got upset, her presence would comfort them. In a factory farm system, newborn birds are left to face frightening and painful procedures with nobody around but their abusers and other panicked chicks, having never met their mothers.

Even procedures that may initially sound benign, such as gender determination, are immensely distressing for nervous, helpless chicks—partly because, like for most birds, humans are huge and scary, and largely because the process is usually rough. Arun filmed how this is done on a farm. It's not easy to see if a young chick is male or female. So, this process tends to involve a 'sexer' squeezing bodily waste out of the wriggling chick for a proper look. Then, the sexer uses his or her fingers to spread open the cloaca (opening on the underside of the chick), expose the genitals, and check for a small bump that would indicate the chick is male.

Imagine how it must feel for chicks to have their tiny bodies squeezed so hard that faeces falls out of them, and then to be handled by a giant. In the video that Arun shot, they can be seen wincing, struggling to get away and chirping in fear. Some breeds of chicks can be sexed in other ways, such as by separating their feathers to check for their length, but this wasn't the case at this farm and industry-wide it is less common.

On farms that produce chicks to be used by the egg or meat industries, the ones considered undesirable are separated from those that are useable. This is an even harsher process. Arun documented workers on farms callously setting aside rejected chicks they see not as living, feeling individuals—but as problems to get rid of. They mindlessly smash and step on them; roughly handle the boxes, crates or bins they are in and throw them. Just one farm can produce lakhs of 'waste' chicks per month.

The chicks to be used by the egg industry or for breeding face other horrors, including having part of their beaks seared off when they are about a week old. Chicks to be used for meat may also be maimed, but those used for eggs live longer and so are often re-mutilated later in life. This process is called debeaking, and it is commonly done through the use of mechanical blades or a heated blade machine.[9]

Arun videotaped birds defecating in fear and cheeping in pain as the blade is taken to their faces. They are then tossed aside together in a box or crate with other birds, all with stunted, bloody beaks. The debeaking procedure doesn't always go as planned, and if the cut is later deemed insufficient, the chick is put through the traumatic process again.

You may wonder, does this really hurt the birds though? Well, yes. In a paper on the topic, the American Medical Veterinary Association (AMVA) explains neuromas, or masses of nerve tissue, form following debeaking with a hot blade and that, 'These neuromas have spontaneous discharge patterns similar to those seen in human amputees who experience chronic phantom limb pain.'[10] Phantom limb pain is pain felt where a limb has been amputated in human patients, and it can be agonizing. It could thus very well be that the birds experience sensations similar to human amputees in their heads. Indeed, after debeaking, chicks rest for long periods of time, and hide what remains of their beak under their wings as if to protect it from the infliction of more pain.

A beak has a purpose. In nature, it is used for foraging, eating, fighting, protecting, preening and making nests, among other things. Hens in battery cages—the cramped enclosures egg-laying hens in India and other countries are usually kept in—do not have opportunities to engage in most natural behaviours, but just as a human amputee needs to adapt to life without an arm or a leg, chickens need to try to learn how to live without a portion of their beaks. This doesn't always work out. Many chicks initially have trouble eating and drinking, become weak and drop weight. But even as they grow, unable to groom themselves properly, many live harassed by lice.[11]

Debeaking is done to address some of the damage caused by frustrated birds, when they peck at each other or each other's wounds, often to death, or engage in cannibalism, in a battery cage. The space in these cages is so restrictive that the birds who are jam-packed together in each contraption cannot even spread a wing. It is thought the pecking, which can lead to cuts and escalate to cannibalism, comes from the birds not being able to engage in natural behaviours such as foraging or exploring.[12] Debeaking does not, however, stop this pecking behaviour nor does it effectively prevent serious injury or death. But the industry performs this mutilation instead of giving the birds more space or making other changes, such as allowing them time with their mothers (studies have found chicks who spend time with motherly hens have reduced occurrence of feather pecking and cannibalism and associated death[13]) to maximize financial gains.

A Chick's Death

What to do with huge numbers of male and other rejected chicks is a dilemma hatcheries face and different companies in India opt to get rid of them in different, disturbing ways.

Some chicks end up in pet shops or sold as toys to children on the street, often stuffed into plastic bags[14] or dyed bright colours, like pink, blue, green and so on. To be painted, dozens of these chicks are dumped from a box or crate into a plastic bucket full of chemical dye and tossed around like leaves of a salad. That the dye gets into the chicks' eyes, mouths and so on as they cry appears of no concern to those colouring them.[15] Such 'pet' animals would then usually die of the dye, suffocation in the heat, mistreatment by a child or starvation, become lost or be abandoned and left to their fate.

The majority of male chicks, however, in hatcheries that cater to the egg industry, are born, just to be killed on their first day of life or soon after. Since they are considered 'waste', they die without ever tasting food, having water or experiencing any kindness. According to one estimate, 180 million male chicks are destroyed each year in India,[16] but countless chicks would be killed unaccounted for too.

Arun spent a long time at a facility that raises chickens to be used for meat. The video he captured shows hundreds of rejected chicks piled on top of each other in large bins. Workers then drown these chicks in a soapy water solution.

The footage is incredibly distressing—witnessing it in person, Arun says, was devastating. The chicks can be seen peeping in terror and desperately clamouring on top of each other to try to escape as more solution is poured into the bins. Those underneath the others die more quickly, but it takes a surprisingly long time for many of them to succumb to death, even up to a half an hour, the workers say, and some actually survive. Those who survive suffer the next stage in this process, which is to be burnt. Arun described that here again, the burning is slow and many chicks escape this too, are left half burnt and suffer and die slowly. The video shows chicks panting, and one burnt chick trying hard to get up and walk, another lying on top of burnt waste, and yet another hatching in the fire.

Other companies skip the drowning and go straight to burning. This tends to involve setting a fire in a pit dug for 'trash', such as reject chicks, chicks who hadn't come out of their shells fast enough, egg shells and so on.

The footage shows various rubbish and chicks together in a pit at one farm with a slow burning fire. One worker laughs at the struggling babies' plight and refers to them as 'zombies'. These chicks, however, had no chance of escape. In the footage, a man can be heard instructing another to throw chicks trying to run away back into the fire.

Another major producer of chickens uses a different method. Arun's video shows rejected chicks piled on top of each other in drums with broken eggshells. Workers callously crush tiny chicks under the drums when they are moving them, or when they pile one drum on top of another. Chicks at the bottom of the pile inside the drums suffocate. Among those visible in the footage, some are dead, others weak or injured, yet others deformed with their organs visible, while some still hatching.

This company then tosses live rejected birds, eggs shells and dead birds together in a grinder. The material which comes out of this process is used to create food for animals (likely even for chickens themselves).[17]

Other companies simply allow the chicks to be taken to be fed to fish direct. Arun and his friend temporarily stopped a truck leaving a hatchery on its way to a fish farm. It was full of thousands of chicks laid in rows on top of each other.

Arun's friend caught the incident on a mobile phone camera. The video clip shows many chicks dead, some dying and all who still could, peeping in panic. The rows of chicks were separated by black cloth in the bed of the truck. Chicks underneath the cloth would have suffocated or been crushed by the weight of other chicks. The driver said he would be collecting more chicks from other farms to dump on top of those already in the truck and take them to fisheries.

Video footage of another company, captured by Arun, shows drums full of rejected chicks being dumped in a truck. There are approximately 70,000 chicks in the truck, and, almost unbelievably, another one lakh was to be put on top of them. Transporters can be seen emptying bins full of the baby birds inside the truck while one man steps in and walks on top of the sea of chicks. Many chicks are crushed either by his weight or by the other chicks piled on top of them. His bare legs and feet can be seen covered in blood, feathers and guts.

Upon reaching the fish farm, a transporter once again climbs into the truck, on top of the chicks, to prepare for unloading. Most of the chicks are dead by then, but some are still alive. The man pushes the chicks with his feet, and body parts get stuck to his legs. The bed of the truck is then gradually toppled to unload thousands of chicks. These animals fall together in a yellow, fluffy, almost solid-looking mass into water. On closer look, smashed chicks with their organs visible can be seen among the accumulation of the other dead. One chick who is still alive, on top of a pile of dead little birds, can be spotted for a few tragic moments on camera—exhausted, blinking, gasping.

What work Arun had in these facilities cannot be revealed as it could disclose his identity, but he desperately wanted to protect the chicks from harm. Witnessing their handling and killing in the most dreadful ways was a deeply harrowing experience for him. Today, he takes solace in knowing his extensive and powerful footage is being used by PETA India to help the public see what supporting the egg industry means, while also campaigning for industry-level change. Should you be interested, the video PETA India released to the public of this footage, including names of companies implicated, can be seen on its official YouTube page.[18]

PETA India is a pro-vegan group but so long as the public continues to eat eggs, it is aggressively pushing that industry to pledge to use new in-ovo sexing technology, which has been developed abroad, and a form of which is slowly becoming commercially available.[19] This new technology is designed to determine the gender of the chick soon after incubation so that the egg—instead of a hatched, fully formed, animal—can be destroyed. The group is also urging the Indian government to require the industry to at least implement methods to deal with unwanted baby chicks for now as recommended by the World Organisation for Animal Health (OIE), such as the use of a mixture of gases,[20] to alleviate some suffering. The draft Prevention of Cruelty to Animals (Egg Laying Hens) Rules, 2019, published by the Ministry of Agriculture and Farmers Welfare on 29 April 2019, if passed without change, would require the handling of male chicks as prescribed in the OIE guidelines. But so far, the Indian egg industry has not itself publicised any change, and PETA India has escalated the matter via a petition filed in the Hyderabad High Court.

The Plastic Cow

Many unwanted male calves are handled differently; they are simply abandoned. Some end up at cow sanctuaries (*gaushalas*) or other such centres—many of which, sadly, despite best intentions, suffer severe overcrowding by being faced with more animals than they can reasonably handle and lack resources to keep the animals well themselves. As a result, these facilities can be either safe havens for animals when well-equipped or unable to provide adequate food, water, shelter, veterinary care or space to them when not.

Most abandoned cattle however end up on the street. As per the latest Indian government livestock census, India has over five million stray cattle.[21] This figure would largely be made up of males deemed worthless by the dairy industry and females who stopped producing milk at the levels the farmers desire.

Envision being a baby who still needs and longs for his mother, being tossed out like litter on to the street. How would you know what to eat and where to find food? Where would you find water? How would you avoid getting hit by a car? Hungry, thirsty and desperate, how would you feel when you approached people who you hope are kind—only to be hit, or shooed away? Seeing a young calf, all alone, calling for his mother is not an unusual sight on Indian roads.

There are thought to be thousands of unregistered dairies throughout India that contribute to the crisis of cows and buffaloes on the streets. These facilities are also notorious for letting the animals they use out to eat from garbage instead of paying to feed them properly.[22] These and other stray cattle must scrounge for food and water, often suffer being struck by vehicles, and some are picked up to be imprisoned in municipal pounds or for slaughter. To make matters worse, countless suffer the consequences of ingesting plastic and other garbage.

The Plastic Cow Project (PCP) is an initiative that was set up to try to address the issue of the ingestion of plastic by cows and tries hard to encourage the public not to use plastic bags. Supporters of the effort explain how our takeout trash might be hurting animals. Hungry cows and buffaloes, unable to get to the food, eat knotted bags with food inside whole. Over time, these bags accumulate inside the bodies of the cattle, and as PCP says, 'get entangled and become hard like cement'.

The fate of such cattle, without surgery, is usually a slow, painful death. Karuna Society for Animals & Nature based in Puttaparthi, Andhra Pradesh regularly removes plastic from the stomachs of cattle. The group routinely surgically takes out up to 70 kilos of plastic from each cow![23]

Prime Minister Modi's goal to stop single-use plastics in India by 2022 should greatly help cows and other animals. [24]

Other male calves are discarded in other ways.

Calves 'Allowed to Die'

The late Dr Verghese Kurien was known as the father of India's 'white revolution' for his involvement in Operation Flood. Operation Flood was the world's largest dairy development programme in terms of the area it spanned and longevity. In his 16 December 1972 lecture, 'Dairying as an Instrument of Change,' Dr Kurien explained the Mumbai dairy industry as it was back then. He described each year one lakh buffaloes would be brought into the city as soon as they gave birth along with their calves from various rural places, as far away as Punjab. He said, 'Then the first thing they do to the buffalo which reaches the city is to teach it to let down milk without the calf. This takes 15 days. No sooner has this been done than the calf is allowed to die. Sometimes they help it to die. The calf mortality is 100 per cent in 15–20 days from arrival in the city of Bombay.'

He also described the dairy industry in Kolkata, West Bengal, stating, 'They have decimated the finest of the cow population in Punjab, by taking the cows from there along with the calf, killing the calf and ultimately making the cows dry. And these cows cannot be then killed because under the laws of the land you cannot kill a useful cow; therefore, they break its leg—now it is a useless cow—then they kill it.'[25]

The Indian Meat Industry Red Meat Manual, which can be found on the Agricultural & Processed Food Products Export Development Authority (APEDA) website, reveals that things have not changed much since. It reads, 'When dairy animals are retired from productive age, they are utilized for meat production in addition to the male progeny born.' It further says, 'Most of the buffalo calves, generally males, are allowed to die intentionally by the owners for economic reasons. The buffalo cows also end up in slaughter house after they go dry.'[26]

This odd choice of words by Dr Kurien and in the Red Meat Manual, 'allowed to die', is deliberate. It is not uncommon to see buffalo calves waiting to be killed at slaughterhouses. However, as it is illegal to slaughter young animals under the Prevention of Cruelty to Animals (Slaughter House) Rules, 2001, and perhaps to avoid various state-wise legislation protecting cattle from slaughter, many dairy farmers get to the same end result without selling them to the butcher: They starve them to death instead.

Khalbacchas Only Fooling Farmers

Some years ago, several colleagues from PETA India visited dairy farms in Delhi, Maharashtra, Punjab, Haryana, Madhya Pradesh, Bihar, Uttar Pradesh and Rajasthan.

A PETA India report describes what they found in Mumbai: '[M]ale calves have their feet tied, so they cannot try to go over to their mothers for milk, and their mouths tied shut with ropes, so they cannot cry out when they are hungry (this is done so the residents of buildings near the *tabelas* do not come to investigate why they hear the babies' cries). These babies are then left to die a slow, agonising death in a corner. Once or twice a week, a *haath gaadi wala* comes by and picks up the dead and sometimes dying bodies of the calves and takes them to Deonar [Mumbai's municipal slaughterhouse], where they are skinned for calf leather. Other male calves are abandoned on the roads to fend for themselves. Very often, live calves are sold to slaughterhouses for their meat.'[27]

Family is dear to cows and buffaloes, and cattle will fiercely protect their children if given a chance. How must these animals feel when they see the corpses of their babies being dragged off the farm right in front of them? How must they feel when the decapitated head of a calf is hung by their side? This hideous practice is so common; the decapitated head has a name. It is called a *khalbaccha*.

Recently, Federation of Indian Animal Protection Organisations (FIAPO) conducted investigations in forty-nine dairies across Rajasthan.[28] They found *khalbacchas* used on some farms to try to fool the mothers' bodies to keep lactating for their babies. Hay and balm is used to get rid of any stench, and the calf head or head and tail are hung or propped up with sticks near the mother cattle while the rest of the body is used for leather and veal. While we cannot ask the mother cows and buffaloes what they think, some benefit of the doubt seems in order here: That farmers believe these mothers would not recognise there is something very wrong with the calf by their side seems to me a show of their idiocy and not the animals'.

Veal is the meat of calves. While veal is consumed less domestically (it can occasionally be found on a restaurant menu),[29] India appears to include calf meat (particularly from buffaloes) in its beef export trade. Official beef and veal export figures are presented as combined.[30] Calves are used by the Indian leather industry too, including calves from both buffalos and cows. The Council for Leather Exports website includes a searchable database where buyers can get a listing of Indian suppliers who sell what they call 'cow calf leather' or 'buffalo calf leather'.[31]

The Meat of an Anaemic Cow

Things are horrendously bad for male calves, but they could get worse. Should any domestic and export interest in veal continue, it is possible that we may even see India move towards the veal production method still common in the US. There, calves used for veal also originate from the dairy industry. These babies are taken from their mothers, made to endure stressful and even injurious transport, and forced into individual crates, about 76 cm wide and 168 cm long, on farms. These crates prohibit movement and normal muscle growth in order to produce tender meat. The calves are fed a milk substitute that is purposely low in iron and given little or no solid food to make them anaemic and their flesh desirably pale.[32]

Calves raised in this way are unsurprisingly susceptible to poor health conditions, including joint and digestive problems, pneumonia and diarrhea.[33] Many confined calves also exhibit repetitive abnormal behaviours from stress, such as tongue rolling, eye-rolling and 'sham-chewing' (going through the motions of chewing without food in the mouth).[34]

After enduring eighteen or so weeks in these torturous conditions, many of these babies can barely walk because their muscles have wasted away, or due to sickness, or both. They are then crowded on to trucks and taken to be killed.

In the European Union, veal crates are banned, but space allowances remain low, and calves are still forced to endure stressful transport and kept on a low-iron diet for the product they refer to as 'white veal'. For 'rose veal', also referred to as 'young beef', the animals' iron and food intake may not be so restricted, but they are still usually raised in systems that give rise to serious welfare concerns.[35]

There is hope for reduced male births as sexing technology exists that allows cattle farmers to give higher chances to the birth of a female, but it is currently considered too expensive at Rs 1,500 for a dose of sexed semen versus Rs 50 for regular semen and would still involve invasive artificial insemination. This is partially because US company Sexing Technologies (ST Genetics) holds the patents for choice technology. That means if anyone wants to set up a sexed semen laboratory using their technique, they have to play by this company's rules.[36] Maharashtra's Bharatiya Agro Industries Foundation and the Uttarakhand Livestock Development Board have signed agreements with this American company to set up centres dealing with sexed semen.[37] In Uttarakhand, with significant central and state government subsidies, it is hoped the price of the semen can be reduced to Rs 350 per dose.[38] The Deep Frozen Semen Production Centre in Rishikesh, Uttarakhand has been chosen for the project at a cost of Rs 47.5 crore.[39] Meanwhile, Uttar Pradesh officials recently laid the foundation stone of a sexed semen facility working with US-based Genus Breeding Pvt Ltd[40] and Union Animal Husbandry and Dairying Minister Giriraj Singh recently announced the government hopes to have all cows born through sex-selection semen by 2025.[41] But for now, abandoning and killing male calves remains the standard industry method.

Eating Children

Many people assume that animals who are consumed for meat are adults. Except for cattle sent to slaughter after their milk production wanes or after a lifetime of work, or egg-laying hens, this is not usually the case. However, even in the case of animals who are permitted to reach adulthood, their lifespans are typically significantly shortened.

For instance, there are different breeds with varying lifespan expectancies, but generally chickens can live between about five to fifteen years if allowed. Chickens raised for meat, however, are killed when they are between just six to eight weeks of age.[42] Egg-laying chickens are killed at about seventy-two weeks of age, or eighteen months, when their egg-production wanes.[43]

For other animals, the age of slaughter may somewhat vary, but as a general rule, if they are not being used for milk, eggs or work first, these animals will be slaughtered when they are considered just fat enough, just young and thus tender enough, to be killed for meat. Farmers do not want to waste time and money on the animals' upkeep beyond this point. Thus, pigs are killed by nine months of age,[44] after they reach their 'slaughter weight', even though their natural lifespan is ten to twelve years or sometimes longer. Sheep and goats may be killed at six months, or by their first birthday, though they would otherwise live between twelve and fourteen years.[45]

For those animals who are allowed to live longer because they are used for dairy, eggs or work, the extended time is a cruelty, not a kindness.

5

MOTHERHOOD ON THE FARM

⮌

They must have separated the calves from the cows this morning. That's not a happy cow. That's one sad, unhappy, upset cow. She wants her baby. Bellowing for it, hunting for it. She'll forget for a while, then start again. It's like grieving, mourning—not much written about it. People don't like to allow them thoughts or feelings.[1]

—*Professor Temple Grandin while observing a bellowing cow*

One of the most gorgeous sights in the world is a happy cow. Cows used on a dairy farm in Germany were let out of a shed they had been kept in all winter. Realising they can finally be outside, free in a field, these four-legged mothers and daughters developed a spring in their step. They ran, jumped and pranced. One cow knelt down and rubbed her face and shoulder on the grass, relishing the moment, like a prisoner who basks in the sun on her first day of freedom. The farmer was facing financial difficulties and the cows were scheduled to be sent for slaughter, but something

70

happened: An organisation called Kuhrettung Rhein-Berg stepped in and spared them the butcher's knife. During the release of these cows into the field, a witness by the name of Hans-Georg Jansenn beautifully remarked, 'I mean everyone who saw how the animals ran into the field today must have to ask oneself, where else does one find something like that? This lust for life, this spontaneity, this enthusiasm. We all saw it here.'[2]

Jansenn and I aren't the only ones who delight from seeing joyful cows. Apparently, at least one other beef farmer does too—or, I should say, former dairy and organic beef farmer. Englishman Jay Wilde had been a vegetarian for twenty-five years, but he still reared cows to be killed. The farm was passed down to him when his father died. For a long time, Wilde was conflicted between the pressure of running the farm out of familial duty, and his concern for cows. He would raise the cows for two or three years, get to know each of them, and then send them off to slaughter—an act that would break his heart. Eventually, his principles got the better of him, and he decided to give the remaining sixty-three cows, thirty of them pregnant, to a sanctuary to live out the rest of their lives.

Wilde could have made tens of thousands of British pounds if he had sold these specially reared cows to slaughter, but he reasoned the price his conscience would have to pay for that would be too high. His brother-in-law called him crazy, but Wilde had made up his mind—he would not send cows he loved to a horrifying death any longer.

The founder of the UK-based Hillside Animal Sanctuary that took them in, Wendy Valentine, knows other farmers who have also experienced a change of heart. The sanctuary helped one couple stop dairy farming and keep their cows as companions instead, like cats and dogs, except the bovines are too big to curl up on the couch![3]

Of course, reverence for cows is so common in India, culturally and religiously, the country is renowned for its compassion for the animal around the world. Idols of Lord Shiva's bull Nandi and Krishna's cows are worshipped in temples across India. Cows, and in fact all animals, are protected by the Indian Constitution. Though not always adhered to, Article 48 calls for the preservation of, and prohibition of slaughter for, 'cows and calves and other milch and draught cattle' while Article 51A(g) makes it the duty of every Indian citizen to protect the environment and 'to have compassion for living creatures'. The slaughter of cows is banned in many Indian states, as is often the slaughter of bulls and beef eating. Buffaloes, especially females, are afforded legal protection from slaughter in some states too. More than 5,000 gaushalas exist in India with the aim of providing shelter to vulnerable cattle.[4]

Many members of the public in India also look out for cows. They feed and give water to those who are stray, and avoid consuming beef. But does today's dairy industry honour the popular desire to protect cows from slaughter and other harm, or has greed taken over?

A Cow's Pregnancy

The only way cows and buffaloes' bodies produce milk is by having calves, just as women only produce milk for their babies. Most cows and buffaloes on today's commercial farms do not mate with other cattle naturally but are forced into repeated pregnancies through artificial insemination administered by farm staff.

The staff first collect semen from a bull. They may do this by using a dummy or restraining a female cow or buffalo and goading a feisty bull to mount her. Just as the bull gets ready to thrust, the worker will catch the bull's penis in an artificial vagina and wait for him to ejaculate. The semen will then be stored.

There are various artificial insemination methods,[5] all of them disturbing. Typically, several men will chain or tie a female cow or buffalo—a skittish prey animal who cannot comprehend why this is happening to her—to a rack and hold her down. A worker will then jam his arm far up into her rectum to locate and position her cervix. Next, he will force a rod-like instrument into her vagina. She will struggle but ultimately be helpless against this act.

Let's pause and think about this for a moment. If this happened to a female human—if she were held in place to allow a man to ram his arm up her insides and crudely insert an object in her vagina— what would we call it? If a man held down a yelping dog to shove something inside her, what would we call that? If a man violated a cow outside of a dairy, it would be considered a crime.

However, because it happens to cattle institutionally, this practice is given a scientific sounding name: the recto-vaginal method of artificial insemination. PETA India's investigators have noted that gloves and sterilized instruments are rarely, if ever, used in this process. In fact, they did not witness any use of gloves at all in their investigations of dairy farms in eight different Indian states, and instead observed workers inseminating the cows with their bare unlubricated hands, shoving their arms up animals' backsides halfway up to their elbows, and then using and re-using filthy instruments as the animals fought helplessly to get away.

In another insemination method, a speculum is rammed into the cow's vagina, then an insemination tube is pushed through the speculum. In the vaginal method, a worker forces his hand up the cattle's vagina to guide the inseminating tube to where the semen is to be left. TNAU warns, 'Here there is a risk of contamination and injury of female genitalia.'[6] However, any artificial insemination method can cause serious injury if performed poorly and by unskilled staff, as is often the case on Indian dairy farms.

When babies are born out of this rough process, as we know from the last chapter, they, especially males, are swiftly taken away so that the least amount of milk is used up by calves—whom nature, of course, meant it for—and can instead be sold to people. Female calves may be allowed to suckle for a short time for strength but are often quickly separated too and fed milk replacer.[7] They are then made to endure the same fate as their mothers.

As a result of this forced separation, as anyone who lives next door to one knows, dairies can be loud. Mother cows and buffaloes call frantically in vain for their babies; and the young ones, when their mouths have not been tied shut and when they haven't yet been thrown out on the street, starved or sent to be killed, call back. It is a heartbreaking cacophony of desperation and grief.

Fractures in Childbirth

Indian breeds of cows do not produce as much milk as foreign cattle who have been deliberately bred for unnatural milk production.[8] The president of Punjab's Progressive Dairy Farmers' Association, Daljeet Singh, described his preference for foreign breeds by explaining that Holstein Friesian cows produce up to four times the amount of milk in a ten-month period than an Indian cow. Holstein Friesians also reach puberty, and are thus able to have calves and produce milk, quicker than Indian breeds.[9]

For these reasons, the Indian dairy industry has over time focused on the cross breeding of Indian cattle with foreign breeds like the Holstein Friesian, Jersey, Red Dane and Brown Swiss and the use of pure foreign breeds.[10] This shift has resulted in a whole host of problems.

As any mother knows, it's painful enough to give birth. Imagine then trying to give birth to a baby that's as big as, say, a four-month-old child. An attempt at such a feat may tear a person wide open, even break bones. Many cows are being forced to endure something comparable to that or worse.

Artificial insemination is used to cross-breed Indian cattle with foreign breeds. This kind of mixing of breeds means sometimes embryos or semen from large cattle breeds are put into smaller ones. This can result in a bigger calf developing inside of a cow than what the animal is naturally built to give birth to. As a result, these small cows can suffer pelvic fractures, severe nerve damage and other serious injuries during calving. Calving complications exist around the world. They are the cause of nearly half of the cases where cows are not able to stand on British dairy farms.[11]

Foreign breeds of cattle are not suited to the Indian climate. It is recommended they be kept essentially on life support when in the country—inside expensive, temperature-controlled, weather-proof sheds.[12] This would be a miserable, confined life that in itself would be wrought with welfare issues—but it's a system that might at least help prevent the animals from succumbing to disease from being unable to bear India's tropical conditions. They also need specialized feeding and, of course, like all animals, veterinary care. Most Indian farmers are unable or unwilling to meet these needs, which results in even more suffering. And when their milk production wanes, the cattle are often abandoned. A Punjab Gau Sewa Board study revealed that 80 per cent of stray cattle are cross-breeds.[13] Despite these major problems, many farmers in India are hell-bent on using cross-breeds or foreign breeds of cattle to maximize milk production and, therefore, their profits.

Drugged for Milk

Milk production is also manipulated in other ways. FIAPO recently conducted a survey of 451 dairies across ten Indian states.[14] They reportedly found that cattle are often genetically manipulated, drugged with antibiotics and injected with oxytocin to enhance milk production. During PETA India's investigations, they too found vials of oxytocin on dairy farms. The use of oxytocin on cattle for this purpose is prohibited in India, but many dairies pay no heed.

Antibiotics used by the dairy sector are at risk of being passed on in the animals' milk to consumers and are thought to be capable of causing allergies and other severe health problems, such as bone marrow aplasia[15], in some people. But doctors are also concerned about the possible effects of oxytocin in milk drinkers while veterinarians are concerned about its effect on the animals themselves.

Dr V.L. Deopurkar of the Maharashtra Animal & Fishery Sciences University shares commercial dairy farmers are sometimes using oxytocin injections twice a day[16] on cattle, while veterinary expert Dr A.K. Varshney reveals the injections cause pain similar to being in labour in the animals and leads to eventual damage of their reproductive systems.[17] Ludhiana-based endocrinologist Dr Parminder Singh believes hormones like oxytocin in milk are linked to gynaecomastia (breast enlargement) in male children and the early onset of puberty. Endocrinologist Dr Shashank Joshi of Lilavati Hospital in Mumbai has shared similar concerns.[18]

The illegal use of oxytocin by dairy farmers is recognized as so rampant and problematic that the Indian government had made radical moves to restrict its manufacture and sale, with only Karnataka Antibiotics and Pharmaceuticals being allowed to produce it in the country. This had led to doctors who use oxytocin in human patients to raise concerns, and the decision was challenged by pharmaceutical companies that wanted to sell it in the Delhi High Court. In December 2018, the court quashed the government order allowing only one company to produce it and the case is now in the Supreme Court.[19] Dairy farmers, however, have long been used to getting oxytocin vials in clandestine ways, so chances are that no matter what happens in court, they will continue to stock farms with oxytocin through a black-market trade.

Relentless Pregnancies

The time between giving birth and being made pregnant again is referred to by the dairy industry as the 'service period'. TNAU recommends, 'For cattle the optimum service period is 60–90 days.'[20]

This means the animal is forced into pregnancy only two to three months after giving birth and is re-impregnated while still lactating from the previous pregnancy.

This frequency, the unnaturally heavy quantities of milk they are forced to produce, and the cows' and buffaloes' living environment on dairy farms put an enormous burden on their bodies and results in lameness and other misery.

Cattle's hooves and legs are made for standing and walking on soft earth and grass; if allowed, cows would spend about ten–twelve hours of their day lying down.[21] Visit just about any dairy in India today, and you'll find most cattle spend their lives essentially chained or tied in place next to each other on concrete. Out of the 451 dairies FIAPO observed, nearly 80 per cent of them kept cattle on hard floors.[22]

It's not just India: cattle lameness is widespread in dairies around the world. It is an awfully painful condition for the animals.[23] Lameness can be caused by any one or a combination of foot and leg problems ranging from injury to disease, resulting in animals' having an abnormal limp or stance.

Most cattle on Indian farms are secured with ropes around their necks or through their pierced noses.[24] Workers often do not even allow them the ability to stand or sit normally, with ropes or chains often kept so short that they must maintain uncomfortable postures, sometimes making even sleeping difficult (cattle cannot get deep sleep standing up). The restriction is often so severe that animals are helpless against crows that pick at wounds caused from prolonged chaining.

Visualize for a moment if someone tied you by your neck to a post in a dirty dairy in a way that you could not sit down or hardly move your head. In one position, hour after hour, day after day, how much would your neck and legs ache? Standing in piles of your own excreta and next to those of your neighbours', you might try your best to shift a bit. In doing so, you might slip. Perhaps you'd manage to get some sleep leaning against the post, but how miserable would you be?

Cows and buffaloes kept tightly tied are miserable too. Abnormal behaviours they often express, like tongue rolling (repetitively moving their tongue out of the mouth and side to side) and continuously swaying tell us so.[25] Tying results in other troubles too: during its investigations, PETA India found calves tied away from their mothers, alone, who had strangled themselves trying to get free. And during floods, up to thousands of animals die in dairies because they are tethered in place and cannot escape.[26]

No Sick Leave

Hunger is also a common problem for cattle used for milk. In its extensive study, FIAPO found, 'The quality and quantity of fodder depends on the economic status of the dairy owner. 57.8% farms feed less than half of the desired minimum quantity (20 kg) to their cattle per day.'[27]

This situation may be even worse for certain breeds used for dairy. The Holstein, a breed that's popular globally and now also in India, is one such type of cow. In its report, 'The Dark Side of Dairy', Viva!, a vegan charity, explains, 'The high-yielding Holstein cow is a large animal who simply cannot consume enough food at pasture to sustain her enormous milk output as well as her other bodily functions, leaving her in a constant state of 'metabolic hunger'. This means when she eats she feels full but simultaneously starved for nutrients.[28]

Imagine how horribly unwell such a cow feels when she's abandoned on the roads to eat from garbage. About one lakh Holstein–Friesian (mix between the large Holstein and Friesian breeds) can be found abandoned on Punjab roads. Kulwinder Singh, who runs the Baba Gau Hira Hospital there, reports finding a variety of waste, including even iron objects, that have been swallowed by these hungry cows during treatment. Singh also reports people who find them a nuisance and have been attacking them with acid, chili pepper, fire and swords.[29]

Diarrhoea is another common ailment for cattle on dairy farms. The causes of diarrhoea are countless. It can be from inadequate food, parasites, bacteria like *E. coli*, viruses, poor physical surroundings and more.[30]

The accumulation of faeces creates a breeding ground for bacteria. Cattle used for dairy in India and around the world routinely suffer mastitis, a painful bacterial infection of the udder that leads to inflammation and the hardening of the infected udders. Milk from cattle who are suffering from mastitis can contain blood, pus or clots.[31] Cows forced to produce unnaturally high quantities of milk are especially susceptible to mastitis, not only from bacteria that thrive in dairy farm muck, but also the heavy pressure on their sensitive tissues from the milk. Mastitis can spread between animals via poorly maintained milking machines.[32]

Today, more and more cows and buffaloes in India are milked by machines. PETA India's investigators report, 'Workers often do not pay attention while the machines are on; even after milk has been taken out, the machines often keep sucking the animals' dry udders, causing them a lot of pain.'[33] It is almost unimaginable how much agony cattle suffering from mastitis would be forced to endure due to this negligence.

Numerous other diseases and disorders are also common in mother cattle because of the heavy demands that dairy production and relentless calving put on their bodies. They include ketosis, fatty liver syndrome and milk fever.[34] Symptoms for these conditions range from lack of appetite, weight loss, fever, agitation, muscle tremor and more, including going into a coma or even death.

John Webster, emeritus professor in animal husbandry, from the School of Veterinary Sciences, University of Bristol, UK, says the feelings of cattle commonly used for dairy can be described as 'simultaneously hungry, tired, full up and feeling sick'.[35] When we consider the psychological trauma of cows and buffaloes having their children repeatedly taken away from them, we can also add the word 'depressed' to this list.

The Thankless End

Many of these miserable cows and buffaloes get into such terrible physical shape that they are simply too sick or injured to walk. These animals are known to the meat and dairy industries as 'downers'. During visits, investigators have documented numerous downers at Mumbai's Deonar slaughterhouse queued up in trolleys for slaughter. Most markets and facilities just leave them where they collapse to slowly die.

Because it is illegal to slaughter cows in almost all parts of India, and sometimes buffaloes too, if they are not abandoned on the roads or end up in *gaushalas*, they are often trucked to the states where killing them is allowed, across the border to Bangladesh, or are butchered in unregistered facilities.

The TNAU animal husbandry agritech portal explains, 'After [the third] or [fourth] lactation the [milk] production starts declining.'[36] This is similar to what the situation is around the world: Cows are commonly sent for slaughter before their fourth lactation, aged around five, a fraction of the natural lifespan of about twenty years.

The Red Meat Manual put out by an Indian government website admits there are more than 25,000 'unregistered premises where animals are slaughtered'[37]. In all likelihood there are a lot more—as they are unregistered, and thus illegal, they are hard to count. Several states—Uttar Pradesh, Jharkhand, Rajasthan, Uttarakhand, Chhattisgarh and Madhya Pradesh—have called for the closure of such facilities,[38] but the truth remains most slaughterhouses in India are illegal. And when I say most, I mean by a huge percentage. Through a right-to-information query *The Indian Express* obtained a 2014 figure, as reported by states and union territories, which put the total number of licensed facilities at 1,623.[39] The Red Meat Manual puts this figure at 4,000.[40] Either way, as the numbers show, there are plenty of opportunities to turn cows into beef.

Milk and Beef Go Hand in Hand

Pregnant volunteers supporting PETA India have held numerous demonstrations in Indian cities against cow and buffalo slaughter, chaining themselves to stalls like the animals used for dairy and holding out blood-red-painted hands.

That's because in India, unlike in the West, there is no such thing as cattle raised solely for beef. Rather, the beef industry largely exists because it is supplied animals to kill by the dairy sector—male calves considered useless by the industry, as well as females whose milk production has waned. India's rank as both a major dairy producer[41] and beef producer[42] is no coincidence—the industries work hand in hand.

Today, penalties and consequences for cow slaughter in some places have become more severe, and an increasing number of cows are ending up in often overcrowded *gaushalas* after use at dairies. While there are well-run sanctuaries whose existence is vital to aid in law enforcement and subsequent rescue, there are also *gaushalas* run so poorly that many of the housed animals do not fare better than those at dairies or who get sent to the butcher.

In Rajasthan, over 250 contract workers at the then government-run Hingonia *gaushala* that housed 8,000 cows went on a long strike. Nobody stepped into their place to clean, feed the animals or provide them water. In a two-week span, more than 500 cows died.[43] Most of the cows starved to death. Surviving bone-thin cows were filmed by the media stuck in muck that had developed due to heavy rain, often shoulder deep, unable to move. As if that wasn't bad enough, it was later discovered that in 2016, between January and the end of July, 8,122 cows died at this *gaushala* due to poor conditions and upkeep.[44]

More than a year after this shocking news was publicized, the media reported on the continuous struggle to maintain the expense of feeding the animals and to provide them space to live. The mortality rate had dropped, but still thirty cows were dying a day.[45]

Goats are also used in India for dairy. As this industry grows, these animals are increasingly made to bear similar processes as cattle used for dairy, including artificial insemination, being removed from their young, confinement, ailments like mastitis and, of course, slaughter.

How About a Glass of Detergent?

Perhaps unsurprisingly, the general disregard for hygiene and standards by the Indian dairy industry often extends to how the milk is handled too.

In 2011, a National Survey on Milk Adulteration was conducted by the Food Safety and Standards Authority of India (FSSAI) that revealed milk sold in India frequently contained detergents and other contaminants. Detergents appeared to be from improper cleaning, but other substances were found to be added to make the milk thick, viscous or to last longer. These materials included urea, starch, glucose and formalin. Water, which itself could be dirty or contaminated, was commonly added to milk. Upsettingly, *none* of the milk samples from Bihar, Chhattisgarh, Odisha, West Bengal, Mizoram, Jharkhand and Daman & Diu were found to be compliant with food standards.[46]

In recent times, the problem of adulteration continues. A few years ago, two children and a social worker died and 127 other kids were hospitalized after consuming poisonous milk as part of their midday meals in Mathura.[47] And the most recent FSSAI surveys released in November 2018 and then again nearly one year later found 7–10 per cent of milk sold in India is totally unfit for consumption.[48] Ten per cent is a huge proportion, meaning if we go by the November 2018 figures, essentially one in every ten milk packets may be so adulterated that it is unsafe to drink. Yet the FSSAI seems to have put out the latest reports to encourage milk drinking after the 2011 survey, which rightly caused panic. The October 2019 survey puts the figure for wholly unfit milk at 7 per cent but admits 41 per cent of the 6,432 milk samples taken across the country did not meet the safety standard.[49] Would you get in a car if there was an up to 10 per cent chance you would get into an accident?

Attempts at Reform

Indian legislation has not caught up to adequately regulate the dairy sector. As unbelievable as it may sound for a country considered the world's largest milk producer and with the globe's largest cattle population, rules to specifically address the practices of today's factory-like dairies as they relate to animal welfare are severely deficient and enforcement of any rules that exist is nearly non-existent.

The Prevention of Cruelty to Animals (Registration of Cattle Premises) Rules, 1978, say anyone keeping more than five cattle must be registered, but as stated before, there are thought to be thousands of illegal, and thus wholly unregulated, dairies in existence across India.

Animal Equality, an organization that conducted a two-year study of over hundred dairy farms, two semen-collection centres, eleven cattle markets and other related facilities in Haryana, Punjab, Telangana, Kerala, Tamil Nadu, Karnataka, Uttar Pradesh, Gujarat and Maharashtra, found conditions for cattle such as what is described in this chapter. It is among the organizations that has called for animal welfare rules and guidelines for dairy cattle to be introduced, not just related to registration, but to address dairy industry practices as they relate to the animals themselves.[50]

World Animal Protection joined with the National Dairy Research Institute to create a national code of practice for the functioning of dairies in an effort to bring in basic care, but they continue to plead for it to be taken up with due seriousness.[51]

And Dr Chinny Krishna, former vice-chairman of the Animal Welfare Board of India (AWBI), a statutory advisory body established under the PCA Act, 1960, has revealed suggestions were made to the central government to strengthen this Act and municipal rules to protect animals used for dairy, but a will to implement them seems missing.[52]

Milk-Free Human Cultures

The dairy industry works to make sure cow and buffalo milk is thought of as wholesome, pure and essential, and thus many see the horrors of this industry as necessary evils. Cow and buffalo milk are all of these things, when unadulterated—but for calves. Per nature, we have to admit even if we drink it, it is nourishment for four-legged infant animals who have fast-growing, heavy bodies, a multi-chambered stomach and who chew cud.

Historians tell us the chronicle of drinking milk in humans is this: Thousands of years ago when farming started becoming commonplace, some cattle farmers figured out how to reduce lactose in dairy products through fermentation to make cheese or yogurt. Later, a genetic mutation developed in Europe that allowed some people to drink milk in adulthood. Now, the minority who can digest lactose as adults usually have some European lineage.[53] An ability to digest it, however, does not mean its consumption is wholly problem-free for those individuals either.

Some human cultures, such as in parts of Asia and Africa, traditionally consumed little to no milk. China is one such place. This fact helped Professor T. Colin Campbell, a former dairy farmer and previous advocate of a meat, egg and dairy-heavy diet, to survey diseases and lifestyle factors in rural China and Taiwan—known widely as the China Study and the most comprehensive nutritional study ever conducted— as part of a twenty-year partnership of Cornell University, Oxford University and the Chinese Academy of Preventive Medicine. It concluded that a diet consisting of a variety of whole plant-based foods, which is low in fat, salt, sugar and highly processed foods, is best for human health.[54]

While many cultures have now long had dairy as part of their diet, nobody consumed dairy foods at the volumes we do now, especially in India. In India, milk consumption doubled in just a thirty-year period following 1970,[55] and now India's milk consumption is the highest in the world.[56]

India also ranks highest in diet-related ailments like deaths from heart attacks[57] and diabetes,[58] has a high prevalence of osteoporosis in both men and women and has high rates of prostate, breast and ovarian cancers. Coincidence? Doctors think not. More on what Campbell and other medical experts have to say on milk, egg and meat consumption in Chapter XIII of this book.

So, even if more legal protections for animals are passed and miraculously fully enforced, laws will not eliminate dairy consumption's effect on human health. Laws will also not stop the need to keep cows and buffaloes pregnant to produce milk, the issue of 'surplus' male animals, the existence of the beef industry, the problem of housing millions of animals to meet consumer demand, or a bovine's lust for joy, freedom and a quality life.

6

CONFINEMENT

❧

Thus far, our responsibility for how we treat chickens and allow them to be treated in our culture is dismissed with blistering rhetoric designed to silence objection: 'How the hell can you compare the feelings of a hen with those of a human being?' One answer is, by looking at her. It does not take special insight or credentials to see that a hen confined in a battery cage is suffering, or to imagine what her feelings must be compared with those of a hen ranging outside in the grass and sunlight. We are told that we humans are capable of knowing just about anything that we want to know—except, ironically, what it feels like to be one of our victims.[1]

—*Dr Karen Davis in* Prisoned Chickens Poisoned
Eggs: An Inside Look at the Modern Poultry Industry

Many years ago, when I was twenty-four years old, I was arrested in New York for disrupting a Michael Kors fashion show. Michael Kors, as you may know, is a well-known American fashion designer. He has since stopped using fur, but back then he still sold garments using fur ripped from animals' bodies.

With the gift of the gab and youthful audacity, I talked my way into the New York Fashion Week event despite not having a ticket. I had fake blood hidden in small bags in my coat pockets. At the right time, I intended to jump on to the runway and, squeezing the contents of the bags into my hands, shout about how Michael Kors had blood on his hands—in front of the audience and, I had hoped, snapping media cameras. I managed to make a small scene for a few seconds but was quickly pulled away by security. Next thing I knew, I was in handcuffs and being read my rights just like in Hollywood movies by the police.

The cops first took me to a small holding cell in which I was locked up alone while they processed the paperwork. The stench of the exposed toilet was unbearable, and I asked a guard if my cell could be changed. She replied sarcastically, 'You're not at the Marriott, honey,' and left me where I was. It was just as well—all of the cells were probably worse or the same. I didn't have a watch and couldn't see any clock. Having no prior experience of the prison system, I had no idea how long they planned to keep me there. Each minute was excruciating—all I could think about was when might have been the last time the toilet was cleaned.

Finally, some hours later, they released me from there, handcuffed me to other prisoners and moved us together into a police van towards another jail site. I hadn't committed any major offence so I knew that I would be out in no time, but I still couldn't help but look out of the bars of the van, longingly, wishing I were on the other side. I watched people cycling, drinking coffee, walking their dogs, playing with children, listening to music and just living their lives as we drove by. I thought, for the first time, they don't know how good they have it—I don't know how good I usually have it, free.

At the next facility, my mugshot was taken, and I was put into another temporary holding cell, this time with other inmates, where we were to be kept for the night. They included a woman who bragged about how she had attacked someone at a nightclub with the blade of a box-cutter. I watched her interact with other cellmates one by one and saw that she would threaten anyone who didn't look her in the eye when she spoke to them, or who failed to speak to her confidently. So, I decided to stand up and make 'friends' when she approached me and listened to her tell the tale of assaulting her victim as she laughed. I quietly wondered if she knew whether that person was in the hospital, or dead. I also wondered what this attacker must have endured in her own life to make her so violent and seemingly cold-hearted. I apparently passed her test because she moved on from me and on to a timid lady who, for the rest of the night, sadly bore the brunt of this disturbed woman's ire.

The toilet in this cell was only partially hidden by two half walls and a short wooden door in between. A person's head and shoulders would remain visible as they crouched inside. I decided using the bathroom for the duration of my imprisonment would not be for me.

At some point, the guards finally decided to feed us—I got handed a bologna sandwich. It consisted of white bread, a thin slice of meat and a negligible amount of sauce—a miserable-looking meal. I was hungry and would have eaten a dire vegan sandwich had I been provided it, but here I had to tell the guards I don't eat meat. Things are changing for vegan prisoners now, but back then, at least in that moment at that jail, nobody cared about my dietary needs. I gave my sandwich to the bully instead.

The blaring white lights were kept on all night and, as it was just a temporary cell, there was no soft space on which to sleep. We were expected to rest sitting up on a bench or lie on the hard floor. I chose the former, but couldn't get any sleep. Apart from the lights and the sounds of others talking, I was worried about what my new 'friend' might try to do to anyone who wasn't alert. The next day, I appeared in court and was released without charge.

For a long time, following this brief period of incarceration, I couldn't stop thinking about chickens. While all species used for food are increasingly being intensively confined, the extreme imprisonment of chickens, particularly for eggs, is perhaps the most ruthless worldwide. And so, as unpleasant as a night in jail was for me, what egg-laying chickens are forced to endure, not just for a day but for the duration of their lives, is on another scale.

Try to imagine being in the jail I described, but with the cell so small and crowded that there is almost no opportunity to move. Instead of hard ground and with a toilet nearby, envision that you and your cellmates are expected to defecate and urinate where you stand, through the gaps in a wire floor. Picture that you are to eat whatever slop the prison decides to feed you through the cell bars, but only if you can get to it first. Visualize the prison being made up of countless and never-ending rows and columns of cells. Imagine that you've been in this jail for as long as you can remember, despite having committed no crime, and that your only escape is death.

What would the bully do in such an environment? How would she behave? How might you? How might others? If you can imagine this, then you would start to have some idea of what life is like for a chicken used for eggs, jailed together with other hens who are upset from the relentless confinement of a battery cage—the world's harshest prison cells.

The restriction of such cages is so severe, the AWBI considers their use a violation of the PCA Act, 1960, which as stated before requires that confined animals be permitted reasonable opportunity for movement, leading it to issue a circular to state governments in 2012 advising that battery cages be phased out by 2017[2]—but this hasn't stopped their use. These cages remain the norm in India, housing the vast majority of the country's chickens, hundreds of millions of birds each year.[3]

Their continued use is not just a matter of lack of law enforcement, but also a lack of industry will. In discussions about cage sizes and space allowances by a committee of the Bureau of Indian Standards (BIS), which works under the Ministry of Consumer Affairs, Food & Public Distribution, egg industry representatives have argued tooth and nail with veterinarian Dr Manilal Valliyate who was present as an AWBI delegate, against providing the birds even the slightest bit more room. Dr Valliyate is the ex-director of veterinary affairs for PETA India and the group's current chief executive officer and former co-opted member of the AWBI.

The industry representatives have even contended—despite ample documentation on the effects of battery-cage housing by animal protection groups, scientists and governments, not to mention the application of common sense—that more research must be done in the country in order to prove chickens are genuinely stressed by being unable to engage in natural behaviours in the limited space.[4] Let's examine this. Do birds really suffer in wire prisons with almost no room to move?

What a Hen Needs

In India, each bird in a battery cage is given about 300 to 400 square centimetres of usable space,[5] which is less than the size of an A4-size paper. Depending on the style of the system, each cage would contain up to ten hens,[6] all made to stand on wire.

On farms, cages are placed next to each other in rows and are stacked in tiers. The point is to pack as many birds as possible into the smallest amount of space so that just one farm can have lakhs of birds. These cages are routinely kept fully indoors in large warehouses. Gartech, a Pune-based manufacturer of cage systems, boasts its GE Ultima layer battery has a 'high stocking density, possible up to 8 tiers'.[7] That would be rows of cages full of hens stacked on top of one another, tier upon tier, in vast sheds.

The cackles of thousands of miserable birds all crowded together means they never enjoy a moment without maddening noise. As we know, chickens 'talk' with dozens of distinct calls meaning different things. While we may not understand them, they surely understand each other. How must these hens feel to be incessantly surrounded by the cries of other sad, desperate birds?

The space the chickens are allotted is so restricted, they cannot even fully spread their wings or engage in any of the most basic behaviours that are natural and important for them—walking around, dustbathing, perching and nesting are a far cry. Anyone who has ever seen a chicken in more natural surroundings knows looking for food by scratching on the ground is innate to them. When allowed, chickens do this for more than 50 per cent of their time.[8] Such attempts inside a cage would only cause discomfort or, worse, injury.

These behaviours are not merely *nice* for hens to engage in; they fulfil important needs and so are hardwired into how they function, even after generations of being forced to live in barren, restrictive jail cells with automated watering and feeding.

Building a nest, for example, allows hens to adequately nurture and care for their unborn chicks. In nature or if free in a backyard, a chicken would carefully find a secluded place, away from predators or other perceived danger, to build a nest before laying an egg. This behaviour is so important to hens that many go through the empty motions of building a nest in battery cages without having anything to build the nests with. Other hens in these cages, prior to laying eggs, attempt to escape or anxiously pace.

Chickens' feet are designed for wrapping around a branch while perching. Being able to perch, such as on a branch especially for rest and sleep, protects them from predators. Dustbathing helps keep their feathers healthy and removes parasites. Scratching at the ground for food, apart from being a foraging activity, keeps their claws worn down.

In addition to these, being able to walk around and discover their surroundings is a natural need as it engages their minds, just as walking around does ours.[9]

Chickens, like humans, also like variety. When allowed to, they eat insects but also love to eat a wide variety of plants. PETA India's rescue chickens, who now live at a wonderful farmhouse with other rescued birds, have considered berries and fruits a real treat. On commercial farms, they do not get to experience the basic joy of pleasurable taste and are fed a cheap, unnatural diet. This can contain grains, but also the processed remains of other animals as by-products.[10] Dr T. Kotaiah, managing director of poultry industry firm Indbro Research & Breeding Farms Pvt. Ltd, admits farmers are constantly on the lookout for cheaper feed.[11]

We can surmise, therefore, that hens kept in battery cages feel frustrated by not being able to move about and are depressed from being unable to engage in pleasurable and natural activities, distressed from being unable to protect themselves or their eggs, aggravated from being forced to live in a crowded and hostile environment and likely often unwell from cheap food. The lack of exercise, overcrowding and the build of the cage also means many hens experience chronic pain and various resulting health problems. Does this sound like suffering to you? Let's examine it some more.

Cracked Feet, Twisted Claws, Broken Bones

Pretty much everything in intensive housing systems for chickens is automatically controlled, including light, ventilation, water and food.[12] Automation helps make human involvement on such farms minimal, which means the farm can hire fewer staff, but automated systems often means more suffering for the birds. Even where the hens are kept in poorly designed cages and cannot reach food or water because they've gotten their heads, necks or other body parts caught in the wires, they are typically just left to die.[13]

Automated feeding, temperature and other functions on layer and broiler farms, as egg-laying hens and chickens used for meat are referred to respectively by the poultry industry, also mean all hell can easily break loose during a power failure. A short time ago, 7,000 chickens died in China from suffocation due to a power cut.[14] Earlier, locals upset by the pollution and stench coming from a farm in Andhra Pradesh deliberately cut off its power supply causing 7,00,000 chickens to die during a heat wave.[15]

Hens in battery cages are forced to stand and sit on sloped wire flooring. The sloping allows the eggs to roll away from the hens and into a collection groove.[16]

The wire also allows the urine and faeces to fall through, but it commonly lands on birds in the lower tiers. Underneath the lowest tier typically lies a massive heap of wet excrement. The ammonia from the bodily waste generated by the birds on such farms can cause them respiratory and eye problems.[17]

Being forced to live surrounded by wire damages birds' feathers and skin, but also causes tremendous problems for the animals' legs and feet, even in better designed cages. Dr Karen Davis, president of United Poultry Concerns (UPC) in the United States, describes, '[W]hen hens are forced to stand and sit on a wire mesh, their feet can become sore, cracked and deformed. The hen's claws, which are designed to scratch vigorously, and thus stay short and blunt, become long, thin, twisted and broken. They can curl around the wire floor and entrap the hen, causing her to starve to death inches from her food and water.'[18]

Various kinds of foot problems are common in chickens housed in battery cages including, unsurprisingly, open sores, swollen foot pads, lesions and fissures. It's easy to understand why when we think about what would happen to our own feet from the constant pressure of a wire floor.

As hens in these systems have zero opportunity for normal movement, exercise and natural vitamin D from the sun, their muscles and bones deteriorate. To make matters worse, hens bred for unnaturally high egg production are already prone to osteoporosis as calcium needed by the chickens is used by their bodies for egg shells.[19]

Around the world, today's egg-laying hens are forced to produce up to 250 eggs or more per year thanks to human manipulation of their bodies. The red junglefowl, who is thought to be the key ancestor of today's domesticated chickens, lays just a maximum of fifteen eggs each year.[20] When we compare, it's easy to see how extraordinarily unnatural and gruelling egg production is for today's commercially raised hens.

There are so many factors and events hens go through that can cause broken bones that it can be considered a miracle if a chicken makes it to the slaughterhouse without suffering at least a fracture. The bones of hens used for commercial egg production can be so brittle they often break in the cages themselves, such as during the laying period.[21]

Another opportunity for bone breakage is when they are roughly removed from their cages by workers for slaughter. Those hens whose feet have gnarled into the wire are not handled more gently. They are simply yanked so hard their toes snap. Then comes being thrown into trucks, jostled about and finally roughly unloaded. Sometimes hens are tied together upside down in a bunch on motorbike or bicycle handlebars and transported this way instead of in a truck, or they are weighed like this when they reach their destination. At slaughter, they are further manhandled and in so-called modern slaughterhouses, their feet are put into shackles by workers focused on speed, rather than care.

The consequences of poor bone health can be so serious: It causes spinal cord damage and paralysis in many birds. This condition is called 'cage layer fatigue' because it is a direct outcome of forcing these birds to live in cramped cages. The birds then die from being unable to access water and food. [22]

Parasites, Disease, Cannibalism, Starvation

Hens kept in filthy, overcrowded conditions are also susceptible to a whole host of infections and other diseases and parasites, including the quick-spreading bird flu, and so, in order to recover profits lost from sick and dying birds, as covered in Chapter III, workers pump them full of drugs.

One of the disease conditions common in hens used for commercial egg production is a prolapsed vent. This is where a portion of the hen's reproductive system remains hanging outside and visible after laying an egg. Such hens often become victims of being pecked at by other hens in that region, and even cannibalized. [23]

The terror and pain of being trapped with another individual pecking you bloody and slowly tearing away at your flesh is almost unimaginable. In a human setting, the closest comparison may be what it would likely be like to be stuck in a jail cell with a deranged, violent prisoner (box-cutter lady?) who is slowly stabbing you to death while prison guards turn a blind eye.

Caged hens also commonly suffer from fatty-liver syndrome thought to be linked to their inability to exercise. With this condition, the blood vessels in their livers can rupture causing the birds to bleed to death. [24]

Manipulating birds' bodies to produce an unnatural number of eggs is not enough for many farm owners, who exploit them in still other ways. Moulting is a natural process in chickens in which feathers are shed and renewed over time, and it can take a few months. It usually occurs about once a year, timed to help chickens get through winter. This is a period of rest and recuperation for the bird's body, particularly related to reproduction, as their egg production drops or stops altogether.

To maximize egg production from hens, and to speed up the time of moulting, many farmers artificially induce moulting by starving birds for days or weeks, which may include withholding water for a significant period of time. Other farmers may not starve the birds, but significantly restrict nutrients. Drugs may also be used. And specific times of artificial light and darkness are also often used to jolt birds' bodies into an induced moult.[25]

Forced moulting is hell on the animals' bodies. Dr Ian Duncan from the department of animal biosciences, University of Guelph, Canada says, 'The evidence that forced moulting reduces well-being is overwhelming. Mortality doubles in the first week of food deprivation, doubles again in the second week, and the behavioural evidence suggests that hens suffer enormously.'[26]

Laws on Paper, Fights in Court

In 2011, the AWBI issued a circular which acknowledged that 'starvation-forced moult regime is widely used in layer farms across the country'. It stated that this practice violates the PCA Act, 1960. It called on states and union territories to ensure forced moulting is discontinued.[27]

However, just as with their battery cage circular, there is no enforcement whatsoever of the AWBI circular against forced moulting. Indeed, Arun, whom you will remember from Chapter IV, documented the plight of chickens undergoing forced moulting at a Sakku Group's egg farm.[28] Sakku Group runs Venkatrama Poultries Ltd, which claims to be the largest egg producer in India.

In what seemed to be a response to the hue and cry raised by animal protection groups on the suffering of chickens in today's farming systems and the lack of enough rules to govern these modern systems, the Law Commission of India submitted its 269th report, entitled, 'Transportation and House-keeping of Egg-Laying Hens (Layers) and Broiler Chickens' for the government to consider.[29] The Commission suggests the animal husbandry department certifies farms that are 'cage-free' to encourage the industry to move away from battery cages, yet what is cage-free remains undefined. Merely moving the chickens out of cages would not amount to good welfare if they are still kept severely crowded, as has been seen in such systems abroad, and as can be observed on farms raising chickens for meat.

In August 2018, a petition filed by animal rights activist Gauri Maulekhi in the High Court of Uttarakhand against the cruelty of battery cages resulted in the bench directing the central government to frame the Prevention of Cruelty to Animals (Egg-Laying Hens) Rules and the Prevention of Cruelty to Animals (Broiler Chicken) based on the Law Commission's 269th report. The court also banned the usage of battery cages in its state but still allowed other cages. Specifically, it said, 'Sufficient space should be allowed for the housing of each egg-laying hen to permit the bird to spread its wings, stand up straight, turn around without touching another bird or the side of the cage. The bird must have access to nest box.'[30]

Shortly after, the Delhi High Court directed the environment ministry to set up a committee for the formation of guidelines on the breeding and transportation of chickens, taking into account the Law Commission's recommendations and the views of the industry and other stakeholders.[31]

Today, animal welfare falls under the remit of the agriculture ministry. Although the Law Commission's 269th report reads, 'The very idea of having this report is to put an end to the cruel practices of confining birds in battery cages,'[32] the Ministry of Agriculture and Farmers Welfare draft Prevention of Cruelty to Animals (Egg-Laying Hens) Rules 2019, which have yet to be passed does not recommend the elimination of battery cages. Rather, it suggests, 'Floor space per bird shall not be less than 550 square centimetre ...' While this space allowance is slightly more than what is provided to egg-laying chickens in India now, it is only the minimum amount of space hens were required to be given in European Union (EU) battery cages until such cages were banned there.[33]

'More' Space

In the EU, battery cages have just been replaced by different cages, referred to as 'enriched cages'. Right now, considering the space recommendation in the 2019 draft Egg-Laying Hens Rules, India does not appear on track to phase out battery cages. Even if it did, the industry would likely just switch to some other type of caging practice like in the EU. In fact, an alternate caging system modelled on the EU method with slightly different spacing requirements (minimum 750 sq. cm in the EU[34] versus minimum 900 sq. cm) is exactly what an earlier 2017 draft of the Prevention of Cruelty to Animals (Egg-Laying Hens) Rules recommended.

The phrase 'enriched cages' may sound nicer than 'battery cages', but the hens are still jailed in wire cages, and each is provided with about a postcard-sized area of more space per bird, still too little to allow them to fully stretch their wings. That's it! And with just a single nest box and limited areas for any other expression of natural behaviour in this confined space, the dominant hens can take over the best spots.[35] Numerous animal protection groups have condemned the so-called enriched cage system.

Just before the EU ban on battery cages, British animal protection charity Viva! described filming inside what they thought was likely the largest enriched cage facility in Britain at the time. The facility was owned by Noble Foods, and it had started using enriched cages before the official EU mandate came through. They reported, 'To say that cages stretch almost as far as the eye can see isn't much of an exaggeration. They also climb upwards tier after tier with multiple gangways running between the stacks of cages. Fifty per cent of hens in Britain are still caged and despite these supposedly higher welfare cages, the birds we saw were debeaked, as are most hens … The purpose is to deny birds the ability to damage each other when the frustration of their lives results in aggression. It doesn't work. Bored, desperate and perhaps driven insane, we saw the results of this violence, with one hen removed from her cage injured and frightened after the others had turned on her during their never-ending ordeal of confinement and frustration. For her there was temporary respite, but in this vast and sunless factory it is perhaps impossible to check on so many hens.'[36]

Another British animal protection group, Animal Aid, has also filmed enriched cage systems at Sunrise Eggs in Lincolnshire, England. The film can be viewed on the group's website. It described, 'Despite the claims of improved conditions, enriched cages provide only an additional 50 cm^2 of space per hen compared with traditional battery cages. This is smaller than the area of a beer mat. As you will see in our film, the only enrichment provided in these cages is a scratching area, which often consists of a small piece of AstroTurf [artificial grass surface] that soon becomes covered in excrement. There is also a "nest-box", which may simply be a screened-off area of the cage. There is no requirement to provide any form of bedding or comfort in the misleadingly named nest-box, or in any part of the cage.'[37]

Ammonia-Filled Sheds

Chickens used for meat, except for those used for breeding, are typically kept in sheds, but their manner of housing still causes terrible problems for the birds. And we are talking about an astronomical number of birds: an estimated one million chickens are killed for meat just every four hours in India.[38] In India, these sheds may be fully or partially enclosed, with wire mesh or chain-link fencing on some portions of the walls.

The sheds can contain hundreds or even thousands of birds. For example, the Indian National Bank for Agriculture and Rural Development (NABARD) provides an economic model for basic broiler farming with a unit size of 10,000 chickens,[39] but big players would be rearing many more.

In these extremely crowded conditions, each individual bird is hardly given any room to move. As per the BIS 'Code of Practice for Poultry Housing', the space guidance for 'light breed' birds is 700 sq. cm and for heavy breeds it is 900 sq. cm.[40] If provided the full 900 sq. cm space, the birds might just be able to stretch a wing. However, they still cannot flap their wings or engage in most other natural behaviours.[41]

Chickens find it impossible to establish a workable social structure in such large, crowded numbers, just as we would, and find it hard to even rest. Here, the more aggressive birds are able to reach food and water more easily than those who are timid, injured, sick or weak, but the frail ones cannot expect help or extra care from the farm staff. The birds often suffer injury from other birds climbing on top of them. Like in battery cages, frustrated chickens raised in sheds also often peck at each other and cannibalize their companions.[42] And like hens, in order to address the consequences of being housed in such frustrating conditions, they may be mutilated.

Sunstars Poultry, a company based in Coimbatore, boasts on its website, 'Sunstars Poultry hatcheries produce a majority of the broiler consumed in the developed world. It is a multibillion-dollar industry, with highly regimented production systems used to maximize bird size versus feed consumed. Birds are produced and maintained under high density, which makes production and harvesting more economical.' It goes on to unapologetically brag, 'Generally, large numbers are produced at one time, so the resulting birds are uniform in size and can be harvested at the same time. Once the eggs hatch and the chicks are a day [old], they are often vaccinated, beak-trimmed and/or toe-clipped (this involves the removal of half of the top beak and the clipping of the toe ends). After these procedures, they are moved to enclosed buildings to be raised until harvest.'[43]

Notice the use of the word 'harvest', despite Sunstars referring to chickens, and not crops. What they really mean is 'slaughter'.

'Clipping of the toe ends' plainly means a portion of the chickens' toes are amputated without painkillers or anaesthesia. This is done to stop the growth of claws. Chickens' combs (the often-red flesh on top of the bird's head) and wattles (the skin that hangs from head or neck of the bird) may also be cut off with scissors or shears. This is referred to as 'dubbing'.[44]

The greater the number of birds being reared to be killed in a shed, the more urine and faeces get collected. Chickens raised in sheds are made to live in their own combined waste. The ammonia from the waste can cause sores, burns and ulcers on the chickens' bodies, legs and feet. In such cases, even walking can become unbearable. The ammonia and dust arising from faeces, the birds' feathers, skin and so on often cause respiratory and eye problems too. The ammonia has also been linked with ascites, fluid accumulation in abdominal cavity, which often results in the birds' heart failure and death.[45]

Birds used as parents for broiler chickens are either raised similarly or in wire cages in India and their bodies are used for an abnormally high numbers of eggs. The Poultry Site, a news portal for the global poultry industry, describes, 'Most of the broiler breeders are in cages with artificial insemination. Best of the breeding flocks produce up to 200 hatching eggs and 160 chicks.'[46]

Artificial insemination is extremely traumatic for chickens. Arun describes what he saw at a farm, 'Artificial insemination in chickens is a very rough and cruel process. There are a few males who are kept in cages for this purpose. The anal areas of these birds are shaved by labourers. This is done to help the workers during the process of trying to squeeze out the semen from male birds. Workers do this manually. They go about opening each cage and pulling the legs of the terrified male birds and then they squeeze out the semen from their bodies into small, funnel-type glasses. They collect semen from around fifteen to twenty birds at a time. And then immediately, they inject this semen into female birds. Even the female birds are pulled out from their cages roughly and the semen is injected into them using a syringe. The same syringe is used over and over again for all the female birds. And they are then pushed roughly back into the cage. And then other bird is pulled out. Workers do this bare-handed.'[47]

Worldwide, more than 50 billion chickens are raised and killed for eggs and meat,[48] most of them in harsh detention in intensive housing systems. In contrast, the red junglefowl can be found roaming in the jungles of India and southeast Asia, free. Considering what their cousins endure, these wild birds do not know how good they have it, just as I once did not realize how good I have it, just as those people I watched through the windows of the police van living their lives did not realize how good they have it, free.

The red junglefowl are stunningly beautiful birds with the males, like peacocks, being even more gorgeous than the females. Their feathers are a striking mix of hues of red, brown, orange, white, green and black, which allows them to be hidden amongst the similarly coloured leaves of the jungle. The males have impressive bright red crowns on their heads, making them look regal, strong and proud.

You may say I've just described a common rooster. Well, yes, they are similar and we've all seen domesticated, colourful roosters. But if we try to view domesticated roosters through the same lens with which we view wild birds and not animals used for meat, you have to admit, aren't they lovely? Looking at these dazzling birds raises the question, what makes them nothing more than a sandwich, but peacocks deserving of our admiration?

7

MUTILATION AND MANIPULATION

By day nine, the broiler's legs can barely keep its oversized breast off the ground. By day 11, it is puffed up to double the size of its cousin. It looks like an obese nine-year-old standing on the legs of a five-year-old. By day 35 it looks more like a weightlifter on steroids and dwarfs the egg-laying hen.[1]

—Felicity Lawrence, special correspondent
for the Guardian *comparing chickens used for*
meat with those used for eggs

The book *Frankenstein* is about the brilliant student of science Victor Frankenstein who recreates and brings a dead body to life. Only, Victor could not predict what kind of creature this exercise would generate and had not made suitable provisions for dealing with this, well, 'monster'. The monster is rejected by human society and, confused, dejected and seeking revenge, goes on to kill numerous people.

Manipulation of nature has been the subject of numerous other fictional books, shows and films. More recently, the popular Netflix show *Stranger Things* featured a child born with telekinetic abilities after her mother was involved in a drug experiment. The child is made to live in a laboratory by a wicked scientist who works to harness her superpowers for his own gain.

In fiction, exploitation of others' bodies is usually portrayed as evil, or as having disastrous effects, and many may consider such things fantasy and nothing more. But while scientists have not yet managed to awaken the dead, other forms of manipulation, of animals' bodies, take place in real life. Take for instance what we do to certain dogs.

The *Washington Post* recently reported on a researcher's findings that a huge number of Americans believe that some dogs, like Dobermann pinschers, are born with stumpy tails and pointy ears.[2] I'm going to go ahead and guess this isn't just true for Americans, but what many people around the world think. But a Dobermann pinscher naturally has floppy ears and a long tail. Dobermann pinschers' trademark short tails and angled ears are, in fact, the results of body modifications they and numerous other breeds of dogs are commonly forced to endure to meet 'breed standards', fashion-led guidelines on how various breeds of dogs should physically appear, which are upheld by kennel clubs, dog shows and breeders.

Maiming used to be done because of myths (Romans thought tails spread rabies) or for practical reasons such as to prevent the ears of dogs who were used to guard farms from being caught in the jaws of predators. Now the mutilations are done to satisfy these arbitrary cosmetic preferences, or on dogs who are forced to fight each other in a pit for a depraved form of human 'entertainment'.

Dogs use their tails, to a degree, for balance and use the movements of their ears and tails to communicate with other dogs and their human guardians. Dogs are expressive animals, as anyone who has ever met one knows, and so it's hard for me to even imagine Mehboob without a tail! Having a tail to swish around seems as inherent to a dog as having a trunk to pick up grass is to elephants. Mehboob tells us he is feeling happy, alert, guilty or scared—everything with his ears and tail. And seeing his wagging tail and wiggling butt, expressions of happiness, brings me immense joy, making it difficult to comprehend how some rank fashion as more important than allowing dogs to be dogs.

Many veterinarians refuse to conduct the surgical removal of body parts dogs use, if it is not necessary to do so for their health. Yet, there are still plenty of veterinarians willing to perform unnecessary cosmetic surgeries just to make a quick buck.

Ear-cropping, or the cutting off of a portion of a dog's ears, even when performed by a veterinarian under general anaesthesia, causes post-surgery pain and trauma and can lead to complications from infected wounds. The cut-up ears are then taped and re-taped to try to form a pointy shape, causing the dogs further distress.[3] To make things worse, some breeders take matters into their own hands and use scissors or a blade to slice the dogs' ears without any anaesthesia or painkillers.[4]

Tail-docking is usually done on puppies without anaesthesia, even when done by veterinarians, with scissors or a scalpel. As veterinarian Dr Karen Becker describes, 'The cut goes through skin, cartilage, nerve endings and bone.'[5] As an alternative, breeders also often use something like a rubber band to cut off the blood supply of the tail so that it eventually falls off.

Tail-docking and ear-cropping for cosmetics is considered so cruel, it is now illegal in numerous countries,[6] including India under the Prevention of Cruelty to Animals (Dog Breeding and Marketing) Rules, 2017. Mutilation is also illegal under Section 11 of the PCA Act, 1960, while maiming violates Sections

428 and 429 of the Indian Penal Code. The laws against mutilation, however, get murky for animals used for food.

Chemicals, Hot Irons, Saws

Section 11 of the PCA Act, 1960, says, 'Nothing in this section shall apply to (a) the dehorning of cattle, or the castration or branding or nose-roping of any animal in the prescribed manner' and the law goes on to state, 'or ... the commission or omission of any act in the course of the destruction or the preparation for destruction of any animal as food for mankind unless such destruction or preparation was accompanied by the infliction of unnecessary pain or suffering'. However, 'the prescribed manner' for dehorning, castration and the other procedures mentioned is not described anywhere in law and what is considered 'unnecessary pain' is also unclear.

Just as dogs are born with tails and elephants have trunks because they need them, cattle have horns to act as a visual warning to other animals, to fight and for self-defence, to scratch an itch and beauty (it is believed female animals are attracted to males with the largest or strongest-looking horns or antlers[7]). It is thought there may also be a connection between horns and digestion in ruminant animals.[8]

The Bombay SPCA has a permanent resident rescued bull with the most majestic horns I have ever seen. This bull must weigh about 900 kilos, with much of that weight on his head. Female cows must consider him very sexy indeed. Yet, while more common abroad, cattle reared for dairy and used later for beef may have their horns gouged out or chopped off, or have the area from where their horns would grow burned or otherwise destroyed—all typically without painkillers.

Dehorning is done to control cattle more easily (though the process can make them nervous or even aggressive), save space on farms and avoid causing carcass bruising once the animals are killed.[9]

There is an 'anything goes' approach to how this is done and weapons used for horn removal or to stop horn growth—and they really are weapons as they inflict tremendous pain—include guillotines, fire-hot irons, bone saws, hand saws, sharp wires and caustic chemicals.[10]

Chemical disbudding (where horn buds of calves are destroyed before they grow into horns) involves holding a calf down and applying a chemical to burn off the horn buds—the chemical burns everything in its path, including, if applied sloppily, the calf's eyes and face.[11]

The horn buds may also be burnt off another way, such as with an iron heated up in fire. The searing iron is applied to the sides of the calf's head, often repeatedly, until the farmer is satisfied the bud has been completely damaged. The intense heat damages the tissue but also sometimes the underlying bone.[12] While fire is a common method, University of Tennessee, US, explains in 'Dehorning Calves' that the iron may also be made hot through 'household current, batteries or butane'.[13]

When tools such as sharp wires, saws or cutters are used to cut off the horns of grown cattle, the surrounding skin is deliberately caught in the cut to prevent horn regrowth, and the process leaves bloody, gaping wounds. Horn removal is, in fact, so brutal, it can lead to problems like sinusitis, haemorrhage, tissue necrosis, bone fracture and even death.[14] Video of dehorning and disbudding procedures can be found on PETA US' official YouTube page.

Concerns over the effects of dehorning or disbudding on cattle recently led one sensitive farmer in Switzerland, Armin Capaul, to encourage his country's government to provide a financial incentive to farmers who let horns be.[15] Swiss voters rejected the proposal, but only by a small margin. Capaul's efforts were widely covered by the press in Switzerland and abroad, and he was happy to have at least raised awareness of the animals' plight.

Clamps, Rings, Blades

Except for those bulls who may be used for sperm collection and breeding, male cattle are typically castrated too. Castration of a bull in India typically involves twisting his neck so hard that he falls to the ground, tying all four of his legs together and then using a Burdizzo castrator, a metal device with a large clamp, to crush the blood vessels, nerves and vas deferens connected to the testes, cutting off the blood supply and causing the testicles to atrophy. This is done without any painkillers or anaesthetics and there's no good reason to believe that this would be any more pleasant for a bull than it would a human man.

When Dr Manilal Valliyate, veterinarian, expert on large animals and current chief executive officer for PETA India, was just starting out in his career, he worked with the state of Kerala's animal husbandry department at its veterinary dispensary in Palakkad district. Farmers would come to the dispensary requesting castration of their bulls. A livestock inspector at the dispensary performed the procedure, and Dr Valliyate remains haunted by the castrations he watched. He told me, 'The very process of forcing the animal to fall on the ground with ropes, tying all their legs together so that they can't move, and them writhing in pain when the castration equipment crushed their spermatic cord—all this is still in front of me. Today, I'm working to make a difference, to prevent the horrifying pain the animals go through during such procedures.[16]'

Under Dr Valliyate's leadership, PETA India has been working to change how castrations are done. As a result of its efforts, the AWBI issued an advisory to the Veterinary Council of India and state animal husbandry departments expressing clearly that the common method of castration currently in practice qualifies as cruelty to animals under the PCA Act, 1960.[17] The AWBI called for bulls to be castrated under anaesthesia by a registered veterinarian. Later, the commissioner of the Department of Animal Husbandry, Dairying and Fisheries issued a circular to animal husbandry directors in all states and union territories stating that cattle must be given anaesthetics prior to castration.[18] Yet, the crude method remains common, and PETA India continues to work towards getting the use of anaesthetics accepted in practice, including by conducting trainings with government veterinarians.

Pigs and goats in India also suffer extraordinarily during castration. Dr Valliyate was shown how this is done to pigs as part of his veterinary studies. He describes, 'Without giving any anaesthetics, the piglets were held and lifted in the air, the surgeon simply putting an incision on the skin, pulling out the testicles and cutting the spermatic cord. The piglets were screaming in pain and unfortunately it hardly made any difference to the demonstrator and we, the students, were told that this is the most normal and practical way of doing the procedure. I still remember most of the students literally praying that this procedure was not assigned to them for their practical surgery examination.'[19]

On farms, castration of pigs and other animals is often done by farmworkers, not veterinarians. Pigs are commonly tied upside down to a pole and held in place while an incision is made with a blade, and then using their hands, the farmworker will force each testicle out of the incision, crudely twisting, yanking and slicing it out.[20] Whether done by a veterinarian or not, however, there is absolutely no gentleness afforded to the pigs in the process. Following this, something like turmeric may be applied to the wound, or not, and the gash is sewn up with a needle. The squealing pigs are then left in obvious colossal pain.

Goats are often castrated similarly. They are held down while an incision is made, and the testicles are roughly pulled out by farmworkers.[21] Alternatively, a rubber ring is fitted tightly around their testicles, causing them to gradually decay, or a Burdizzo clamp is used to destroy the spermatic cord as they cry out in pain.[22]

Sharp Sticks, Fire and Liquid Nitrogen

In India, a cow or buffalo without a rope threaded through the nasal septum is a rare sight. The rope is used to control the animal through pain and discomfort. If a bull, such as one used to carry a heavy load, moves in what the farmer considers the wrong direction, his nose rope is yanked to set him on the right path. Cows are often forced to walk along with their handlers who use the rope through their sensitive noses as a leash. During transport, attempts are made to hold cattle in place by having their nose ropes tied to the beams or sides of the vehicles. As the vehicle jostles about, their noses tear and rip.

Farmers insert the ropes by piercing the animals' noses with a sharp stick, or metal object that resembles the end of an ice pick.[23] To facilitate this, they tie an animal's head to a tree, log or pole. A rope is fastened to the end of the pointed object and tugged through the nose. During this procedure the cow or buffalo desperately tries to get away and yanks his or her head back in pain. The process is drawn-out and typically requires multiple attempts.

I occasionally join the Animal Rahat staff on scouting trips in the sugarcane belt of rural Maharashtra to look for animals in veterinary need. During these trips, we come across many farmers using bulls to haul carts of heavy sugarcane who fasten the nose ropes so tightly that they become deeply embedded in the animals' flesh and drip with blood. Animal Rahat's staff cut or at least loosen the ropes and provide medical care, and the group is working with local communities to encourage them to transition to the use of face halters and humane methods of handling and moving cattle instead of the use of nose ropes altogether.

Animals reared on farms for animal-derived foods, particularly cattle, may also be branded to create a marking indicating what farm the animal is from. Common painful methods of branding include heating a metal object in fire and pressing it against the animal's side, and freeze branding. For freeze branding, the iron is brought to a cold temperature of about 70 to 185 degrees below zero before applying it to the animal's skin. Dry ice, alcohol or liquid nitrogen may be used as a coolant.[24]

Dr Valliyate described watching branding performed during his veterinary education too. He said, 'We were taken to the cattle farm inside the veterinary college campus and briefed about the importance of identifying animals and recording their details. The professor demonstrated how the metal rod with numbers are dipped in liquid nitrogen and pressed against the skin of the hind quarter for some seconds. What surprised my classmates and me was, unlike the claim that freeze branding only causes the death of pigment-producing cells in the hair follicles, many animals showed signs of severe pain and distress, by lowering their back, moving forward and pressing their head on the wall and railings of the barn, and bellowed loudly. The very caution the professor and helper took during the procedure, avoiding contact with the numbering rod and the liquid nitrogen, was good enough to establish how painful the process would be for animals. I remember some of us asking the professor whether there was a better, humane way of identifying animals, and it was explained that both hot and freeze branding are convenient and economical for animal farmers, and hence are chosen over other identification methods. It was also explained that use of analgesics or anaesthetics prior to the procedure is neither practical nor economical.'[25]

Breeding for Unnatural Physical Traits

Animals' bodies are also manipulated to suit human fashions and other desires through selective breeding, at troubling consequences to the animals themselves. Dogs are thought to have originated from a wolf-like ancestor thousands of years ago.[26] But that may be hard to believe looking at today's toy poodle or Chihuahua. That's because dogs have, over the course of many years, been deliberately bred for certain physical or personality traits to form the breeds we have today. Simplified, that means if two dogs who have smaller than normal snouts are bred together, they are likely to have children with small snouts. Repeat this process over many generations, and the puppies will end up with difficulty breathing. In fact, if you think pugs look like they have trouble breathing, that's because they often do and can require surgery. They and other short-nosed and flat-faced dogs like bulldog, boxer and Pekinese and Shih Tzu are susceptible to upper airway problems.[27]

Over time, the physical traits considered stylish in dogs, like long backs, spotty coats, small body size and so on have become increasingly exaggerated. In order to achieve the exact abnormal look, dogs of specific breeds are often made to mate within a small gene pool (such as mother mating with son, sister mating with brother). Using two very closely related dogs to produce puppies is now prohibited under Indian law, but who's checking? Breeding for exaggerated physical traits and inbreeding makes pedigree dogs, as they are called, more susceptible to developing medical problems than mixed breeds and dogs who mate naturally from a large gene pool, like Indian strays.

The kinds of ailments various breeds of pedigree dogs more commonly face include cancer, kidney disease, joint ailments, hip dysplasia, heart defects, epilepsy and eye, skin and ear infections, and more.[28] Rocko, a pug who was made to live in a car by a family who didn't want him in the house and who was rescued by PETA India, had an ear and skin infection that required treatment, and has big bulging eyes. His ear infection, long left untreated before PETA India got him, was so aggressive, he kept his head tilted out of habit even after it was cured. Breeds with shallow eye-sockets, like Rocko's, like pugs, French bulldogs and Boston terriers can also suffer proptosis—a condition where the dog's eyeball pops out and hangs from the socket.

Certain breeds are prone to other bizarre ailments too. A BBC programme on the subject called *Pedigree Dogs Exposed* showed a King Charles spaniel suffering from syringomyelia. This is a condition in which fluid-filled cavities form in the spinal cord near the brain, and it develops when the dog's skull is too small to accommodate his or her own brain! The show also featured bulldogs who cannot mate or give birth without human help. For English bulldogs, the birth canal of the mother is often too small to accommodate the size of the bulldog pups.[29] As Universities Federation for Animal Welfare points out, this odd circumstance is 'caused by changes in body shape (of both puppy and mother) due to selection for particular features' and 'unless a caesarean section is carried out, the birth is likely to end in the painful death of the mother'.[30]

When the bodies of animals used for food are manipulated through selective breeding to suit the demands of the meat, egg or dairy industries, they too suffer—such as the osteoporosis-prone, modern egg-laying hens, or the mixing of large cattle breeds with smaller ones for increased milk production that leads to difficulty in some mother cows giving birth.

As explained earlier, chickens used commercially for meat nowadays are not the same as those used for eggs. You'll remember those used for eggs have been selectively bred to produce an unnatural quantity of eggs. Well, those used for meat have been selectively bred to produce an unnatural amount of flesh per bird in the shortest amount of time.

Globally, broiler chickens are perhaps the most genetically altered of all other animals used for food. These chickens have been selectively bred to grow so unnaturally large and top-heavy for big breast muscles and so fast that they can be killed between just six to eight weeks of age, yet these birds would not actually reach adulthood until they are about six months old. They are also commonly bred to require less food intake.[31]

This extreme manipulation has happened over a relatively short period of time. Just some decades ago, even at sixteen weeks, chickens would weigh less than what a modern chicken typically does today at six weeks of age.[32] Imagine, if humans were manipulated to grow to even larger than regular adult size while still babies over the course of just some generations. We would become big in size, but our insides—skeletons and organs—would struggle to keep up. That's what we have done to these birds.

This abnormal growth is, therefore, unsurprisingly tough on the chickens' hearts, other organs and young bones, and results in severe and painful health problems. It leads to the death of many birds, but the regular loss is considered worth it by many farmers who simply want to get the most meat out of the least birds in the fastest amount of time.

Chickens Too Big for Their Hearts

Esperanza was a hen who was raised for meat in the US. She was found in a forest preserve presumably after falling off a truck on its way to a slaughterhouse. She could hardly walk and was suffering from a wing injury, suspected to be from a farmworker roughly grabbing her and shoving her into a crate for transport. Esperanza ended up with caring people from the American animal protection group Free from Harm, who provided her with veterinary care. She became fond of her rescuers and allowed them to stroke her as she purred. This sensitive chicken was set to go to a sanctuary in Chicago where she would have had eighteen other chicken friends, but before she could go, she began trembling and hyperventilating. Her rescuers had seen these ailments in other broiler chickens they had rescued—she was having a heart attack. After spending her final moments in the arms of one of her rescuers, she died.[33]

Esperanza is far from being the only chicken to have had leg problems. We humans generally have access to doctors, medicine and ice compresses, and yet a bout of mild foot tendonitis, inflamed tendons from too much pressure on my foot from workouts at the gym, made it difficult for me to walk for weeks. Compare that to the pain that would be suffered by heavy broiler chickens like Esperanza whose growth is so freakish, they become too big for their own legs to handle: Their leg bones often become bent or warped, their tendons frequently rupture, their tissues tear, and many suffer the dislocation of joints, bone fractures and diseases.[34]

Tibial dyschondroplasia is common in chickens reared to be heavy for meat. It is when cartilage does not develop as it should to allow the formation of healthy bone. Symptoms include swelling in joints and lameness. Bacterial chondronecrosis, which results from an infection and causes bone corrosion, is a reason for lameness in these chickens too, while spondylolisthesis effects their spine and causes the pinching of the spinal cord.[35, 36]

As a result of their many problems, broiler chickens often have trouble standing, or walking like Esperanza did, and are frequently left to use their breasts or their wings for support. Many walk abnormally, and some who are so bad off that they cannot walk at all and opt to crawl or use their wings to propel themselves laboriously forward. Chickens with spondylolisthesis may be seen sitting with their legs splayed forward or even walking backwards.[37] Animals who are severely lame regularly dehydrate or starve.[38]

Continued sitting or lying in their combined waste in the sheds due to inactivity, their body structure, overcrowding, disease or an inability to move in a normal manner results in painful burns, blisters on their bodies and dermatitis on their foot-pads.[39] The dirty litter also leads to other skin problems.

Studies have shown many broiler chickens are in chronic pain in the weeks before they are killed. These birds can usually be found sitting or resting. When given a choice, such chickens have preferred feed with painkillers, and when given painkillers, their activity level has improved, showing that the pain they are in is enough to have a debilitating effect.[40]

Like Esperanza, chickens reared for meat commonly suffer from various forms of heart failure. Ascites is one such condition, mentioned before in relation to the ammonia inhalation, that is thought to contribute to it. It results from these chickens' hearts and lungs failing to process oxygen appropriately in their bodies.[41] For chickens suffering from ascites, a side of the heart swells, leading to increased pressure on the liver and fluid accumulation in the abdominal cavity. As the Poultry Site describes, signs of this condition include 'poor development, progressive weakness and abdominal distension, recumbency and sudden deaths'.[42] The birds may also suffer shortness of breath and turn blue.

Another heart condition that effects broilers is sudden death syndrome (SDS). SDS is precisely what it sounds like: suddenly, the bird just dies. As Compassion in World Farming (CIWF) describes in a report about the welfare of broiler chickens, the birds suddenly start to flap their wings, lose their balance, sometimes cry out and then fall on their backs or sides and die, usually all within a minute.'[43]

You might think that the loss of birds from heart ailments should motivate farmers to do something to reduce this issue. However, heart problems indicate rapid bird growth, and one chicken farmer once proudly wrote, 'Aside from the stupendous rate of growth … the sign of a good meat flock is the number of birds dying from heart attacks.'[44]

Broiler chickens also commonly suffer from respiratory disorders, disease of the liver and spleen, and have weak immune systems overall, putting them at further risk of illness.[45]

And since broiler chickens are just babies at the age they are typically slaughtered, they are not old enough yet to reproduce. Therefore, those broiler chickens used as parents are permitted to become adults, but since their bodies may literally collapse if they are given as much food as the broilers killed early on are, farmers leave them deliberately hungry. This results in the parent birds taking five to six months to reach a weight like what other broilers do at six weeks.[46]

Genetically Manipulated to Be a Meat, Egg or Dairy Machine

Genetic manipulation is often misleadingly referred to as 'genetic improvement' by the meat, egg and dairy industries, but the improvement refers to the volume or amount of product produced, such as milk, and not the animals' welfare. On a web page about 'genetic improvement' the Indian National Dairy Development Board (NDDB) explains, 'To make dairying profitable, productivity (milk production per animal) needs to be increased.' It goes on to explain the best way to do this is 'by improving genetic potential for milk production in future generation of animals by using animals with high genetic potential for milk production as parents.'[47] That cattle who are made to produce unnatural quantities of milk often suffer lameness and other health issues does not feature on NDDB's page.

India is seeking to expand its pork meat industry. An article in GlobalMeatNews.com on this topic explained how senior government officials from Punjab visited pig-breeding farms in the UK. It explained that the team was interested in pig genetics and breeding techniques.[48] Meanwhile, the Tripura Animal Resource Development Department says on its website, 'Among the various livestock species, piggery is the most potential source for meat production and pigs are more efficient feed converters after the broiler.'[49]

Abroad, in countries where the pork industry is heavily developed, pigs are commonly bred to grow quickly with less food (called, as you will recall, feed efficiency in the industry), similar to broilers, and for lean, muscular meat. This selective breeding has led to conditions associated with a recessive gene that all fall under the term porcine stress syndrome (PSS). Unfortunately for the pigs who are already forced to live in stressful environments, those who suffer from PSS are exceedingly predisposed to stress. These pigs may, perhaps like any panicked individuals, have difficulty breathing, suffer heart attacks or die among experiencing other symptoms of the condition.[50] The condition is so common, Farm Sanctuary has issued a document warning pig rescuers that pigs with PSS require extra-special care as they can even die when given anaesthesia for minor or necessary surgical procedures.[51]

In its report, 'Modern Breeding Technologies and the Welfare of Farm Animals', CIWF explains selective breeding has led to similar problems to those effecting broiler chickens. These pigs suffer painful joint and leg, heart and lung ailments.[52]

Genetic manipulation in pigs is also thought to be likely linked to the abnormal behaviour of tail-biting in some pigs, though the frustration from the extremely restricted housing conditions in which pigs, especially abroad, are typically kept is also thought to have a major effect.[53] Tail-biting is when one pig bites the tail of another, but it can extend to biting other body parts. As the UK National Animal Disease Information Service explains, 'In the growing pig this can take the form of tail, ear, flank, stifle or even vulval or penis biting.'[54]

Pigs are extremely good mothers, but in an intensive farming environment they are not allowed to be. Here, as mentioned before, with their abnormally large sizes and restricted space, piglets often get inadvertently crushed. Selective breeding for pigs to have larger than normal litters makes matters worse as it can result in babies who are too small when born and so more susceptible to crushing.

Weaker babies may not be able to access food if they have stronger siblings and can suffer from a huge number of health problems as a result. Because of these conditions, a high piglet mortality rate is considered fairly normal.[55]

And though pigs are selectively bred to be 'feed efficient', they suffer when not provided food that is natural to them. This can lead to acidity and other issues, including gastric ulcers, haemorrhage, stomach bleeding and death. Stress and poor housing conditions are thought to exacerbate these concerns.[56]

In India, cattle are not specifically bred for meat. They are either supplied by the dairy industry, or are those cattle who were previously used for work. However, with India's place as a leading beef exporter, and its willingness to manipulate cattle for milk production, perhaps we will also see India breed cattle to be 'meatier' one day.

Where cattle are selectively bred this way, they too suffer leg and other health ailments. CIWF's report on breeding technologies describes, 'The detrimental impact that selective breeding can have on animal health is vividly illustrated by the selection of Belgian Blue cattle for double muscling. This leads to larger, heavier muscles particularly in the hind quarters and is also associated with a shrinking of the pelvic dimensions. As a result, cows often carry calves which are too large for natural birth, that is through the pelvic canal. This leads to 'the frequent or inevitable use of caesarean section' with some cows undergoing a succession of caesareans during their lifetime.' Repeated caesareans itself can cause other problems.[57]

Victims of Frankenscience

Animals used for food are also increasingly being genetically engineered. This is not the same as selective breeding. Instead, it's when genetic material from one animal is transferred to another, or when genes of animals are added to, removed or manipulated. Cloned animals are also considered genetically engineered. There are different types of cloning, but most people would have heard of reproductive cloning where attempts are made to create an animal with the same nuclear DNA as another animal, or rather one that is genetically identical to him or her.

Dr Julia Baines who works as a science policy advisor for PETA UK warns, 'Whether it involves mice, sheep, dogs or monkeys, cloning is a form of Frankenscience that serves only to increase animals' suffering. Females' eggs are harvested in surgical procedures, and they're then implanted with cloned embryos. They continue to suffer long after this. Cloned animals are often heavier than their naturally conceived counterparts, which means that their births are even more painful for their mothers. Mortality rates among young cloned animals are extremely high, during both pregnancy and infancy— Dolly was the sole surviving adult from 277 attempts. In fact, 90 per cent of cloning attempts fail.[58] Dolly the sheep became famous for being the first mammal effectively cloned from an adult cell in 1996.

The manipulation of animals this way takes place for a variety of questionable reasons, including research on xenotransplantation: The idea is that eventually cells or other parts of animals, including entire organs, can be put into humans (like using a pig heart in place of a human heart in a human body). Not only does the human body reject animal parts (it often even rejects organs from other human donors![59]), but there is a risk of disease transference from animals to humans. Animals used for food are also genetically engineered for increased 'productivity'.

A paper that appears in *Canadian Veterinary Journal*, 'Genetic engineering of animals: Ethical issues, including welfare concerns', describes genetically altered transgenic pigs and sheep for higher growth hormone levels, or rather, to grow bigger and faster than nature intends. It further mentions pigs who have been genetically engineered for higher levels of omega-3, other animals who have been altered in efforts to make them disease-resistant, and more who have been modified in an effort to address the environmental impact of the raising of animals for food.[60]

Of course, a person doesn't need to eat a genetically engineered pig to have omega-3 in their diet. Walnuts, kidney beans, black beans, edamame, flaxseeds and squash are all plant-based sources of omega-3s.[61] And issues like disease and pollution can be best addressed with increasing public adoption of plant-based foods.

Like Dr Baines, the *Canadian Veterinary Journal* paper cautions ethical problems with genetic engineering, including the invasiveness of the techniques, such as surgical procedures and the killing of animals to allow for the process and who are not needed for further use. It explains large numbers of animals are also required for genetic engineering since many of the embryos used do not survive.

There is also the issue of the unpredictability of the outcome of the experiments (remember the monster of Frankenstein?) and the inevitable welfare consequences to the animals who are engineered for certain traits just as there are with selective breeding. The paper says, 'For example, many of the early transgenic livestock studies produced animals with a range of unexpected side effects, including lameness, susceptibility to stress, and reduced fertility.' Meanwhile, Dr Baines warns, 'Cloned animals are often heavier than their naturally conceived counterparts, which means that their births are even more painful for their mothers.'

All of this said, animal protection advocates are sometimes left to consider how manipulation can be used for good—to reduce suffering. For instance, cattle can be selectively bred to be born without horns to protect them from the trauma of dehorning. And because of the sheer number of cattle raised for dairy or stray dogs and cats on the roads, to prevent more baby animals from being harmed or killed, castration and sterilization (though with anaesthesia) is necessary.

So, where should we draw the line? What manipulation should be allowed, and at what point do we say it's gone too far?

It is common to hear animal milk-drinkers share the myth that cows produce far more milk than their babies need: This is not true, not naturally. Without human interference, animals are born producing the right amount of eggs their bodies can handle, the appropriate amount of milk for their own offspring, are able to mate and give birth without human assistance, and are equipped with the tools they need, such as horns, to survive in their own natural environment.

Animal protection campaigners would, therefore, answer that question this way: Unless there is a sound veterinary reason for why a procedure is required to improve the welfare, not the so-called productivity, of the animal or animals it effects, animals' bodies are not ours to manipulate.

8

WORKED TO DEATH

*The animals of the world exist for their own reasons. They were not
made for humans any more than black people were made for white,
or women created for men.* [1]

—Alice Walker, American author, women's
rights and civil rights activist

Roushya and Houshya have been through a lot together. They
spent over a decade of their lives hitched to the same awkwardly
built cart, hauling tons of sugarcane from the fields to the factory
over and over all day long during the months-long sugarcane season
each year, and working in other crop fields the remainder of the
time. No matter how exhausted they were, how uncomfortable or in
pain, how hungry or thirsty, when it was time to lug the sugarcane,
usually loaded far beyond the legal limit, they had to move. Not
obeying or going fast enough would mean another beating, hard
yank of their nose ropes, or worse. Like this, in fear of and enduring
punishment, they would end up travelling long distances each day

in the scorching sun, without a drop of water, on uneven, potholed roads. They suffered from swollen limbs, torn muscles and raw, open friction wounds from the cart that never fully healed while they were made to work. They were forced to trudge ahead, even as they frothed at their mouths in thirst.

Animal Rahat rescued Roushya, Houshya and other bulls from this hard life of servitude by providing several farmers mini-tractors in exchange for them and eight other overworked bulls. These bulls now live at Animal Rahat's sanctuary in Sangli.

Imagine how it must have felt for these old gentlemen to have the weight of the carts that they had hauled for just about all of their lives permanently lifted from their backs and necks, the nose ropes that were used to punish them removed, their wounds tended to and allowed to heal, be provided with water aplenty, and finally be allowed to rest. Considering their history together, and this new chance to live out their remaining years at the same sanctuary in peace, it's no wonder that Roushya and Houshya remain paired up as best friends.

Roushya and Houshya are both eighteen years old, an advanced age in bull years. At dawn every day, Houshya paws Roushya with his hoof, and the two long-time friends go for a stroll around the sanctuary grounds together, just like two human grandfathers who get together every morning for a walk in the neighbourhood park.

Roushya's caretakers report he is jolly—that he enjoys rain so much, he starts jumping like a young bull when it drizzles. And despite his love for Houshya, or in all likelihood because of it, Roushya nudges himself forward to be groomed by his caretakers first. You see, Houshya is still somewhat apprehensive of being touched by people. Perhaps Roushya senses this and is being kind, trying to put Houshya at ease when he pushes himself ahead. Perhaps he is saying, 'See! I'm doing it. You can too. It's okay!'

Roushya has a particular fondness for one of his caretakers, Navnath Hajare. When Navnath grooms him with a brush, Roushya becomes quiet and still, as if in a trance. And likewise, when Roushya grooms Houshya every day with long, sweeping licks, Houshya stands calm.

Roushya is a giant. He towers over most people. I met Roushya during a visit to Animal Rahat and became a little startled when he, a huge bull, started walking towards me with his head and horns lowered, as if, I thought, to charge. A caretaker noticing my unease was quick to inform me that Roushya simply wants to be scratched between the horns. I was happy to oblige.

Roushya wasn't always friendly. When he first arrived at the sanctuary, he used to balk at the sight of humans, but gradually, through the love, care and patience of Animal Rahat's caretakers, he learnt to trust and even enjoy the company of people, including those like me he had just met. Houshya, however, is not so quick to forgive and forget his former abuse by the two-legged and fur-less.

When they are not being groomed or walking about, Roushya and Houshya can be found whiling away the time together in the shade.

Most of the animals at Animal Rahat's sanctuary, which is called Home for Retired Bullocks, are bulls who have been rescued or retired from lives of hard labour. In fact, perhaps because these bulls have been used to being in pairs—hitched to another on a cart—most of them find a bull who becomes their best friend here. Thereafter they groom each other, eat together, wander together and sleep next to each other—all quietly, like pals who have gotten to know each other so well that the silence is comfortable and nothing needs to be said.

In addition to running the sanctuary, Animal Rahat also encourages farmers to care for old bulls instead of sending them to slaughter after a lifetime of work and provides assistance to help farmers do so.

Bulls Pushed Beyond Their Physical Limits

There are 60 million cattle, according to estimates,[2] oxen and buffaloes, used for work in India. While the dairy industry is a primary supplier to the beef industry, cattle used for work also commonly end up slaughtered, either after they are maimed, which is common, or when they weaken with age and become unfit to work. Or else, like cows from the dairy industry, some end up abandoned on the roads or are housed in overcrowded *gaushalas* or municipal cattle pounds. The latter is more likely in states with laws prohibiting cow and bull slaughter.

Perhaps because cattle are commonly thought to be extraordinarily strong, and because most people are simply unaware of cruel practices routinely used to control them—many are surprised to learn just how much suffering these animals endure.

Of course, even strong animals have a physical limit, and cattle used for work are pushed far beyond it what with the basic protective laws in India usually ignored. The sugar factories in Maharashtra are under pressure by Animal Rahat to use tractors instead of bulls or, if they refuse, to at least ensure the law on weight limits is obeyed, yet many companies continue to pay for the sugarcane by weight. That means the more sugarcane the farmers bring on their bullock carts, the more they earn. This setup has terrible consequences for the bulls who are forced to haul the heavy loads.

The enormous weights they are made to pull, combined with a lack of sufficient water and adequate nutrition, means bulls commonly collapse from exhaustion or sustain injuries. Cattle may not scream when in pain, but, of course, this doesn't mean they don't feel it. If you think about it, in nature, loud cries would only attract the attention of a hungry lion looking for easy prey, and so, it makes sense that bulls are not built to express pain the way we do. This quality may protect them from lions but not humans—in our world, their seeming stoicism results in their being pushed to work often to injury or even death.

Bulls do, however, communicate how they are feeling in other ways. They wince, try to lick their wounds and show reluctance in getting up or moving ahead when they are hurt. Sadly, this kind of refusal, as Roushya and Houshya knew too well, often results in a blow with a stick or, ironically, a leather whip made of some other poor cow or bull. The stick used to smack and prod bulls is often studded with nails. Other times, the punishment for refusing to move forward can be even worse, with the animals' tailbones twisted and broken (which is comparable to the pain of broken fingers). Of course, if the injury is bad enough, even if they are beaten or treated violently, bulls will simply be unable to move. So, like this, those bad off enough are cumbersomely dragged on to a tempo, causing even more pain, and taken to be killed or simply left where they are to eventually starve and die.

This happens to other animals used for work too. During a recent scouting trip for animals in veterinary need with Animal Rahat staff, on a small stretch of road by a brick kiln, we found four seriously injured, collapsed and abandoned donkeys. Most brick kilns in the area use donkeys to haul bricks. One of the donkeys appeared to have suffered having his two front legs run over by a car! He wasn't screaming, as donkeys too, like bulls, wouldn't (though they may bray in distress), but there's no doubt he was in immense pain.

Sick and Tired

Not being provided the right diet or enough of it, or water, isn't just a matter of bulls experiencing weakness, hunger and thirst—it can lead to other serious gastric and health problems too, and it does. Cattle fed inadequately, like many used for work are, commonly suffer from painful conditions like indigestion and bloating, as well as diarrhoea and dehydration. They may refuse to eat because of the pain, further exacerbating problems especially if made to haul loads, and vomit. They can have difficulty breathing, or the rumen, which is a part of their stomach, can become inflamed. They can develop an irregular body temperature, an abnormal gait and their eyesight can be impaired. They can also suffer from liver abscesses, become recumbent or die.[3]

While Indian breeds of cattle are more tolerant of the hot Indian climate than foreign breeds, heat stress is a serious issue, including for cattle on dairy farms, and remains a risk for all cattle, especially buffaloes who are designed to spend huge amounts of time cooling off in water, when they are forced to work in the sun.[4] Cattle suffering from heat stroke may drool, foam at the mouth, breath with their mouths open, tremble, lose balance and become agitated.[5] The condition, if the situation is not addressed, can be fatal.

Yoke gall is a painful condition caused by the friction of the cart yoke constantly rubbing on the cattle's necks. It results in inflammation and swelling. It can become infected and form into a giant, pus-filled sack. Veterinarian Dr Sudheesh S. Nair, assistant professor at the Kerala Veterinary and Animal Sciences University (KVASU), describes on his blog that this agonizing condition does not stop work. He writes, 'The cruel treatment devised by the animal handlers [was] putting more load to make the pus pocket "flat". I had witnessed a cardiac arrest in [a] bullock due to overload.'[6] Sometimes this area of the neck on the animals becomes cancerous. The pain of having to bear the tremendous weight of a cart on an area of the body that is already raw, tender or diseased is unbearable to even imagine.

This problem is worsened manifold when two animals of different sizes are hitched to a cart together, as they commonly are, or when different species of animals are, like a bull and a pony. In such cases, the uneven distribution means one animal ends up bearing the brunt of the load.

The stress on the legs and feet of animals used for work is also considerable and routinely causes inflammation of the joints, tendons and ligaments; lameness or other often irreversible damage.

Dr Manilal Valliyate explains that when the cattle lose function in a joint, more stress is placed on the other joints, tendons and ligaments. As a result, even the healthy parts of the legs are subjected to wear and tear, often ultimately leading to all of the legs becoming affected. He warns that forcing cattle to spend much of their lives on pavement, like the bulls used to lug sugarcane are—when they are really meant to walk on grass—is inherently cruel as it puts even more pressure on the animals' bodies.[7]

Animal Rahat's veterinarians say pneumonia and respiratory disorders are also common in the cattle used for work. Stress, exhaustion, poor nutrition, dehydration, car exhaust fumes, being kept and sold at crowded markets, a lack of shelter from weather extremes, and poor and unhygienic housing conditions are all factors that can contribute to bulls being susceptible to these ailments. Cattle with pneumonia may suffer difficulty breathing, fever, muscle and joint soreness, diarrhoea, coughing, a poor appetite and other problems. The condition can cause permanent health damage or death.[8]

Depressed Bulls

Poor or absent animal husbandry techniques also contribute to distress for the cattle. For example, a failure to notice or address problems with teeth can mean the bull faces difficulty eating or simply cannot eat, while shoeing of cattle in India typically involves the twisting of their necks until they lose balance and fall to the hard ground, then tying their feet together, so that a usually untrained man can fasten metal shoes to their soles with nails and a hammer. This ordeal is, as you can imagine, horrifying for the cattle. They lie pinned to the ground with their eyes open wide in fear. Sometimes the procedure doesn't go right, and a nail becomes embedded in the soft flesh of the bull's foot. Animal Rahat is trying to influence communities to at least perform shoeing on soft ground and by suitably trained individuals.

Animal Rahat regularly seizes various kinds of crude, homemade tools used to whip, restrain and control cattle used for work. They include razor-sharp barbed wire spirals or metal rods with protruding nails. These devices are often kept on the sides of the animals' heads or bodies to keep them in line. So horrifying they are just to view, Animal Rahat and PETA India joined together to display them outside the Indian Ministry of Environment, Forests and Climate Change in an appeal for stronger legislation to protect animals.

Nose-ropes, which are often made with cutting nylon, are also torture devices used to control cattle. As earlier explained, bullock-cart drivers often tie the ropes so tightly that they embed deep into the skin of the animals' nostrils.

Various myths and rural practices used to sell animals at higher prices impact the animals' welfare too. Farmers often get the horns of their cattle sheared to make them appear younger. This causes the inner sensitive layer of the horn to get exposed to direct sunlight. Farmers then routinely paint the horns, using harmful, carcinogenic paints containing lead. These practices make the animals vulnerable to horn and eye cancer.[9]

Veterinarian Dr Naresh Upreti, chief operating officer of Animal Rahat, visited a cattle market in Vellore, Tamil Nadu. He described a type of force-feeding practice to make the bulls appear fuller and healthier: 'We observed that most of the bullock owners were forcefully drenching their animals using diluted rice bran so that the rumen gets a fuller appearance and hence the physical appearance of the animal could fetch them better price for the animal in the market. In the process of forceful drenching, sometimes the liquid gets in to the respiratory tract and the animal coughs up forcefully. To do this the animal was first tied with the nose rope tightly around a tree branch or the head of the animal was held tightly by yanking the nose rope, and then a plastic pipe, closed from one end, was used for forcefully drenching the water mixed with rice bran.[10']

The toll this life of hardship takes on the animals isn't just physical. Cattle used for work can often be found standing dully with their heads lowered. Dr Valliyate explains cattle too get sad and this is a sign of depression.[11] This behaviour can also indicate helplessness, extreme exhaustion, hunger or physical pain, sickness or disease. Depression in bulls should come as no surprise, especially considering even when not made to work, they are not free. Not only are they not allowed to move around, they are often not even free to lie down, or to be comfortable. Instead, they may be kept tied to a post, usually by a short rope, and commonly by both sides of their face, severely restricting movement.

In contrast, the cattle residents at Animal Rahat's sanctuary—particularly those who have been there long enough to recognize their hard days of working in the fields are behind them—stand tall, are active, appear proud and majestic and have a large area in which they can roam.

Tortuous Events

To make matters even worse for animals used for work, in addition to working in the fields and being made to drag heavy loads, bulls are commonly used for fairs and other functions, and for events such as races, fights—and *jallikattu*.

Every year, bulls, horses and ponies are made to transport families and their hefty luggage for hundreds of kilometres on a gruelling multi-day journey from Maharashtra to Karnataka for the Chinchali Fair. The animals struggle—commonly suffering from thirst, dehydration, injury and exhaustion. Animal Rahat has been working to transition these families to bus transport instead of animal-pulled carts to spare the animals this arduous journey.

During races, which are especially popular in some states like Maharashtra and Punjab, as documented by PETA India, to force the bulls to run at breakneck speed, participants twist and bite the animals' tails, beat them with their bare hands and jab them with sticks that are often nail-tipped.[12] In Tamil Nadu, the group also documented bulls used for racing being electroshocked with crude, homemade devices.[13] Bulls of uneven size are sometimes paired together on a cart, making the race even more difficult and, quite frankly, putting into question these racers' common sense. When a bull collapses, participants force him to stand by shouting at him, yanking him by the nose and inflicting other pain. The yanking of ropes leaves the bulls' nostrils dripping with blood.

In Karnataka, male buffaloes are used for racing in events called *kambala*. These buffaloes are also subjected to verbal abuse and physical force—including shouting, hitting with hands, slapping on the face, violent pulling of nose ropes, rough handling, tail pulling and so on. Many buffaloes froth at the mouth, salivate and breath heavily during the race. And as if being yanked around by one nose rope wasn't bad enough, inspectors found that in some cases, two or three ropes were inserted through the same hole in the buffaloes' sensitive nasal septums.[14]

In Goa, a type of bullfight takes place. During these events, two bulls are incited to attack one another. As one Goa tourism website, goatrip.co.in, says, 'Bloodshed is not uncommon ...[15]'

For *jallikattu*, which is conducted in certain parts of Tamil Nadu, bulls used may also work fields or be raised and trained specifically to take part.[16] During this event, men form a mob to pounce on lone bulls to 'tame' them while surrounded by a huge screaming crowd. As PETA India has documented,[17] the bulls become so frightened by the mob that they slip, fall, run into barriers and traffic—and even

jump off cliffs or down wells in their desperate attempts to escape—
frequently leading to broken bones or death. At least one terrified
bull was reported to have died from cardiac arrest during a recent
jallikatttu event.[18] Numerous human participants and spectators
have died at *jallikattu* events too after getting in the way of panicked,
fleeing bulls.[19]

As can be seen in the documentation, *jallikattu* participants
purposely disorient the bulls, including often by forcing them to
consume alcohol. And because the bulls would rather run away from
the mob than towards it, handlers twist and bite the bulls' tails; stab
and jab them with sickles, spears, knives and sticks; yank their nose
ropes; and punch them behind-the-scenes in a holding area called
the *vadi vasal* to force them ahead.

There is no doubt every bull feels terrorized when pushed to take
part in these spectacles, as both races and *jallikattu* exploit bulls'
natural nervousness as prey animals by deliberately placing them in
a situation in which they have to run to try to avoid danger. And like
for cattle used for work, when debilitating injuries occur, whether
during training or at these events, the animals are abandoned or
killed.

The use of bulls in such performances is considered so cruel it
was banned by the Indian environment ministry in 2011, but these
events continued to happen. In 2014, the Supreme Court of India
ruled in favour of arguments made by the AWBI and PETA India
and confirmed a ban on the use of bulls in performances. The
court acknowledged causing animals unnecessary suffering and the
infliction of pain common during such events as a violation of the
PCA Act, 1960.

Yet, there has been intense pressure on the government from
those who would like to see these events continue, often because of
gambling or other vested monetary interests. The money that can be
made from holding or even watching these spectacles is significant.

The same Goa tourism site, mentioned earlier, admits on bullfighting, 'Betting is common in such games. Often large sums are involved. Small scuffles and commotions are quite common during the bull fights, especially if there is an unexpected defeat.' And according to a pro-*jallikattu* website run by a major promoter, it can cost anywhere between ₹15 to 40 lakhs to put on just a single *jallikattu* event.[20]

Presumably, largely because of the level of money involved, my part in working with PETA India towards a ban on *jallikattu* and similar events resulted in death and rape threats against me, and I was burned in effigy.[21] However, now, to appease those applying pressure in favour of these events, some of them, like *jallikattu*, have either been allowed to take place under various newly passed laws by certain state governments, or such attempts are being made. Other colleagues at PETA India had also received so many threats they were hard to keep count, but the group perseveres and continues to campaign for an end to the use of bulls as unwilling participants in such events. PETA India is now challenging legalization efforts in the Supreme Court.

Changing Minds, Changing Times

While some of the suffering inflicted on bulls, such as when they are used for performances, is just plain cruelty, bulls used for work are typically controlled with violence simply because that's just the way they have been handled for generations, and because farmers fear their own bulls. When asked why they hit bulls, use nose ropes and so on, farmers typically explain they believe the bulls may otherwise harm them. They do not always appear to recognize the vicious cycle that the bulls, if they do become aggressive, are likely just reacting to the abuse they suffer or trying to defend themselves from it.

And so, Animal Rahat's veterinary and other staff are working with rural communities in Maharashtra to help them transition away from this old mindset, to understand the psychology of bulls, appreciate that animals feel physical and emotional pain, recognize when the bulls require veterinary care and why seeking that care is important, to empower them with the ability to administer first-aid, and to—through teaching practices like grooming—build a stronger, positive bond between the farmers and their animals.

Gentle and pleasurable touch is important to cows and buffaloes, as it is to humans, and farmers spending time grooming cattle with brushes relaxes them as it mimics how cattle groom one another (like Roushya licking Houshya). Over time, the relationship between the farmer and the bull becomes more trusting and cooperative.

But though farmers in the communities Animal Rahat operates are increasingly open to changing practices, old habits die hard. Change is slow, and usually communities will only agree to making one or two amendments at a time, rather than overhaul how they treat their bulls in general—that too, after months, even years, of effort. For example, some villages in the areas where Animal Rahat operates have agreed to stop shearing and painting the horns of their cattle, while others have agreed to stop tying them by both sides of their faces when resting, and yet others have promised to go easy on nose ropes (though it's usually not hard to find at least some animals with nose ropes even in these villages) and so on. Of course, pain and suffering is inherent in forcing animals to carry even the legally permissible industrial loads.

That's why Animal Rahat is also working to transition farmers and industries away from the use of animals altogether for the most gruelling work. Started in 2011, Animal Rahat's Tractor Project works by offering subsidized and reduced-cost tractors to replace bulls through tractor manufacturers and by working with sugarcane factories.

To get the project off the ground, Animal Rahat helped purchase the first five tractors which were used by workers at Sangli's Kranti Sugar Factory in 2011, allowing Roushya, Houshya and others to be rescued. Since then, the programme has expanded across Maharashtra, and the number of tractors has grown to more than 5,000, sparing thousands of bulls from the most punishing work during sugarcane season. Bulls continue to work other crop fields, which is still physically difficult, but there they are used to haul lighter loads. Or, if necessary, Animal Rahat guides the farmers on the animals' retirement.

Establishing tractors as an effective alternative to the use of animals has turned out to be a win-win situation. The tractors are much more efficient than animals and so both farmers and factories can increase their productivity and output. Farmers who switch to using tractors also avert the risk of losing their livelihood as a result of an animals' illness or injury, and the tractors can continue to be put to use outside of the sugarcane season.

Animal Rahat is now expanding its work to replace the use of animals with tractors in the brick kiln industry too. I had the wonderful opportunity to tag along with Animal Rahat to visit a community that was previously using donkeys to haul bricks. With Animal Rahat's help, they were provided a couple of tractors, allowing over twenty donkeys to be rescued. The community has already been so uplifted with the additional work they are able to do with only a couple of tractors that they welcomed me and the Animal Rahat staff with enormous fanfare.

The rescued donkeys are now living at the wonderful IPAN sanctuary in the Nilgiris where nobody will ever put a load on their backs again, and where they can do all the things donkeys like to do. I had the pleasure of visiting these donkeys too, and they seemed to know that they are in safe hands there. Many came forward to greet me, and after I distributed carrots, they were reluctant to let me go. Some even tried to gently tug at my clothes with their teeth to say they want more.

Many farmers prefer the use of tractors over animals for other reasons too, and that is status. They like the way they look on a shiny new tractor, much in the same way a person with a new sports car wants to be seen around town, and a man with a tractor is apparently considered better marriage material than a man with a bull in the farming communities. What's more, I was informed by Dr Upreti that the farmers using bulls looked down on the community using donkeys, considering themselves to be of higher rank. Suddenly, with tractors coming in, members of both groups stand equally tall.

Not everyone is a fan of the Tractor Project or initiatives to help bulls, though Roushya, Houshya and many other residents of Animal Rahat's Home for Retired Bulls sanctuary certainly are. Some argue that tractors cause pollution, others say with less use of bulls for work or performances they will be sold to slaughter, not realizing, perhaps, that these same bulls already often end up at the butcher and discounting their quality of life when they are forced to haul industrial loads or to run for their lives in cruel games.

Some, especially *jallikattu* apologists, even claim native breeds of cattle may disappear altogether if not used by them, but this is just fearmongering to rally support of their blood sport. These individuals have no qualms loading the bulls they profess to want to preserve on to trucks for slaughter when they are no longer deemed of use.[22] And the truth is, breeds in India have long been changing due to the dairy industry's preferences and a variety of other factors much before any ban on *jallikattu* came into place. Most people also recognize cruelty and conservation are not the same.

Regarding tractor pollution, Food and Agricultural Organization (FAO) figures show the rearing of cattle and other animals for food (how many animals used for work are ultimately used) are responsible for more greenhouse gas emissions that cause climate change than the exhaust from all forms of transportation combined.[23] How the rearing of these animals contribute to environmental problems is covered in detail in Chapter XII of this book.

For those still reluctant to support tractors to give bulls and other animals a break, I quote author Matthew Scully who wrote in *Dominion: The Power of Man, the Suffering of Animals, and the Call to Mercy*, 'When you start with a necessary evil, and then over time the necessity passes away, what's left?'[24]

9

THE FINAL JOURNEY

Animals are not goods. They are beings. [1]

—*Reineke Hameleers, director of Eurogroup for Animals*

Should a person be sent to prison for up to ten years for giving pigs water on a hot day? As unbelievable as it may sound, this is the question that was deliberated by a Canadian court. The case lasted for two years, and some months in, it looked like Anita Krajnc, the caring woman who fed water to thirsty, desperate pigs through the slats of a truck headed for a slaughterhouse there in 2015, even after the driver told her to stop, would face at least some jail time or a hefty fine of 5,000 Canadian dollars or both.[2]

The contention was that under Canadian law (and Indian law too, really), pigs are nothing but property, and so, Anita was said to have meddled with the farmer's 'property', and it was suggested she could have fed the pigs something to harm them. Of course, the pigs were not harmed—not by Anita anyway, but later by the butcher, yes—as they made it to the slaughterhouse. The judge ultimately noted that this wasn't the first time someone kind had given water to pigs destined for slaughter and that such acts never stopped the slaughterhouse from accepting the animals to kill, thus showing nobody really believed anyone was trying to poison the pigs. The case against Anita was finally dismissed resulting in thunderous applause by her supporters in the courtroom.

It's not just in Canada. Pigs, cows and other animals around the world are treated like mere goods, as if they are inanimate objects, and hauled, often extremely long distances in heatwaves and freezing temperatures to meet local demand for meat. This shows a failure to set up enough systems to move frozen meat instead of living beings, or as is often the case in India, efforts to circumvent certain state anti-slaughter laws.

In 1999, after Ingrid Newkirk, who grew up in Delhi and went on to found PETA affiliates worldwide, heard from concerned citizens that Indian cattle used for meat and leather need help, a small group of animal welfare experts set out to conduct an in-depth study[3] and to document their plight. Investigations of animal markets, transport routes and slaughterhouses that have been managed since then, and other evidence, shows their findings remain relevant today.

The investigators discovered countless cows and bulls are smuggled huge distances into Kerala from various states through neighbouring Tamil Nadu to avoid state laws against killing them. They learnt these animals go through cattle markets in Tamil Nadu, along with buffaloes, as a break point from where they are purchased to be killed. The group decided to start at Pollachi market, a major trading point for cattle in Tamil Nadu, and follow transporters from there headed to Kerala.

Times have changed but awareness about animal rights activism amongst animal transporters was limited in India back then, and so the investigating team was allowed to observe and tag along without too much difficulty. The team included a veterinarian who administered painkillers and other basic aid to as many animals as possible. Among other things, the powerful footage they gathered resulted in millions of people around the world considering that leather is dead skin and thinking about, mostly for the first time, how its production is not kind.

Marched Towards Death

The investigators documented cattle destined for slaughter at Pollachi market broken, bruised or dead from rough transport in the searing heat or from careless unloading. Cattle with broken bones, those who had already died or were dying were found strewn across the market. The market did not have its own facility for veterinary care, and so injured animals were simply left by transporters to die if not purchased for slaughter.

In contrast, cattle at the market considered to have a higher monetary value, like those deemed desirable for dairies, were reported to be in a satisfactory physical shape showing that where there is a will, gentler transport is possible. Their time at the market was far from pleasant though. Mother animals who arrived with their calves in tow faced the trauma of forceful separation the moment there was a buyer.

Indeed, the investigators came across a pair of panicked buffalo calves tied together with rope threaded through their noses. The calves were trying to run away, likely to search for their moms who had been sold, while a handler was attempting to control them through heavy blows. One of the team members, unable to stand the abuse, decided to buy the calves. Of course, their mothers would have never learnt what became of their children, but they were sent to live out the rest of their lives at the IPAN sanctuary.

From this market, while buffaloes were more commonly loaded on to trucks, to avoid notice of cows and bulls being smuggled across the border, large numbers of them were marched on foot towards

Kerala as if they were being walked innocuously, simply from one farm to another. For this, four, five, or even more cattle were tied together by nose ropes and forced forward by handlers wielding sticks.

As some cattle were sick or old while others healthy or young, because some were tall and others short, the animals moved at a different pace, resulting in pulling, immense pressure on their nostrils and rope burns. Cattle moving slowly or veering in the wrong direction frustrated the handlers who smacked them on their backs, sides and faces. The pain caused the animals to jerk their heads, leaving many of their noses bloody and ripped.

The marched cattle were not provided a single drop of water, and because they were considered animals who would soon be killed, were also not fed. Hungry, thirsty, exhausted and often injured or in pain, some simply collapsed. Handlers forced them up by breaking their tailbones or smeared chili seeds or tobacco into their eyes and pulled them up by their nose ropes. Members of the investigating team used water to flush out the animals' burning eyes.

Trucked Like Goods

Just before the Kerala border, the marched cattle were packed tight on to goods trucks—the kind of trucks used to carry anything from vegetables to machinery, not built for animal transport—with only the aid of a makeshift dirt mound—to cross the border under the cover of nightfall. The animals, confused, their eyes wide with fear, balked and initially refused to climb on to the truck. When we consider what the inside of a truck looks like to them—a dark, scary, enclosure from which there is no escape—we can understand their reluctance. The handlers forced them up by repeatedly twisting and snapping their tailbones, beating them with sticks and bare hands, and yanking them by their nose ropes.

The trucks had a tarpaulin cover for a roof and were also fully covered on the sides with wooden slats in order to hide the shipment of cattle from the public as best as possible. In the vehicles, as an attempt to hold the cattle in place, the handlers tied the crammed animals together and secured their noses to ropes stretched across the tops of the vehicles or to their sides. State border guards were bribed to allow the trucks to pass. The trucks then careened at breakneck speed on windy, potholed roads, toward their destination.

While the slats allowed for a little ventilation it was not enough. The overcrowded cattle baked in the heat, and some suffocated to death. The ropes loosened up or ripped, and many cattle fell on top of one another, inadvertently gouged and blinded each other with their horns, and live cattle ended up trapped under the dead.

When the backs of the vehicles were opened up for unloading, handlers climbed in, twisted the necks of the cattle still alive to turn them towards the opening, and yanked them outward to be unloaded. This happened in the early morning hours when it was still dark, making it difficult for the animals who survived to see. Without a proper ramp and in darkness, the cattle were pushed from the trucks, sometimes on to makeshift dirt mounds, other times just the ground, or were pulled off with ropes. Several cattle suffered broken horns, legs, ribs or pelvises as a result.

The investigators found cruel transport was not unique to cattle being transported to Kerala. At Mumbai's municipal Deonar slaughterhouse, a member of the team managed to film bulls and buffaloes arriving for slaughter already dead or with bloody eyes, other wounds, broken bones, and those who were dying being left out under the blazing sun for long hours. As stated before, the slaughterhouse was so used to getting animals in bad shape that it had numerous trolleys available to move them from place to place. I and others observed the same horrors during subsequent visits.

Rules Considered Made to Be Broken

The Transport of Animals Rules, 1978, require that animals be deemed fit for travel by a veterinarian prior to transport. They further mandate that veterinary first-aid equipment be brought along, animals be provided with food and water, adequate ventilation be ensured, padding material be used in vehicles, that goods vehicles when used be specially fitted to transport animals such as with anti-slipping material, and that goods vehicles only be allowed to carry six cattle at a time. But the investigating team discovered all of these rules were blatantly ignored.

The findings documented on this death trail led to PETA India being founded to help cows and other animals in need. PETA India notified government authorities of the investigation's findings and requested them to take steps that would see the country's laws on animal handling and transport enforced. PETA affiliates also encouraged India's large and growing leather industry, through the Indian Council for Leather Exports (CLE), to make welfare improvements in its supply chain.

With no initial signs of any steps towards improvements being made by either authorities or industry whatsoever, and to respect consumers' right to know what kind of cruelty they are likely supporting if they buy leather, the footage shot by the team was publicly shared. The investigating team had filmed slaughter processes too, but it was their documentation of transport that horrified the world the most. The video footage can still be found on PETA India's official YouTube page.

The resulting global public outrage led to about forty major international retailers including Adidas, Gucci, Gap, Liz Claiborne, Kenneth Cole and others to hold off on buying leather from India,[4] demanding that the treatment of animals used to produce it be at least in line with the country's own animal protection laws. This was hugely significant as it was the first time major retailers had ever taken any kind of stand on leather, but PETA affiliates have since been helping them see—backed with material from other investigations from around the world—that no animal, whether Indian, American or reared anywhere else, voluntarily gives up her skin. Today, retailers are increasingly using innovative plant-based leather (such as Hugo Boss's use of pineapple fabric for vegan shoes[5]) and other non-animal materials instead.

Finally, in June of 2000, having understood the animals' plight, the then prime minister of India, the late Atal Bihari Vajpayee, sent a letter to state governments across the country. He wrote, 'Steps need to be initiated for enforcing existing laws and associating with non-governmental organizations to achieve the objective of more humane treatment to animals.' He added, 'Our inability to protect our animals against the greed of unscrupulous traders in their mindless pursuit of wealth has led to this terrible situation.'[6] PETA India's staff were overjoyed upon hearing this news. They thought this to be the first step towards achieving some relief for the cattle who suffer so immensely for the meat and leather trades.

At the same time, the late Murasoli Maran, who was commerce minister then, had urged states to set up committees to ensure animal protection laws are enforced. He pledged, 'There would be surprise inspections of places where cattle are sold and loaded into trucks.'[7] PETA India considered this promising too.

Public Relations More Than Action

Soon after, under the pressure of major retailers putting a hold on their business with Indian leather exporters, the CLE decided to show it is taking some action. It started a pilot project to improve conditions at Pollachi market and at a municipal slaughterhouse in Coimbatore. The project was supported by a few German retailers and PETA affiliates who had hope the endeavour would reduce suffering. PETA India offered support by arranging the help of Miriam Parker, an internationally renowned and globally experienced agriculture scientist, to work with the CLE in developing a plan to train transporters and slaughterhouse personnel in animal handling. The idea was that the project would then be rolled out to markets and slaughterhouses nationwide. Parker developed a set of basic best practices that all parties considered simple improvements reasonable to expect within the Indian system.

Ramps and a water trough were built at Pollachi market and some limited infrastructural progress was made there and at the Coimbatore municipal slaughterhouse, but the local government provided just basic support, and the roll-out never really got going despite repeated promises by the CLE. Through its inaction, the CLE also made clear it was not even willing to take steps to ensure the skins it obtains come from only licensed (and not unlicensed and illegal) slaughterhouses. The project ultimately began to seem more a public relations tool for the CLE to win back and maintain customers, and an avenue for the German retailers to continue supporting the Indian leather trade, instead of a genuine effort to bring about meaningful, country-wide change in how Indian animals used for leather are treated.

In fact, the CLE saw it so much as a public relations exercise, that it had hired Arup Kavan, the then managing partner (south), of Ogilvy & Mather public relations firm based out of Chennai to deal with the pilot project rather than, say, a veterinarian, or any professional more suited to addressing issues regarding animal handling, transport or slaughter. (If you read this book's Introduction, you will remember Ogilvy & Mather had briefly hired a filmmaker, Soum, to shoot visits to the pilot project sites, leading Soum to become vegetarian overnight.)

I met Arup many times. I noticed he always ate vegetarian and seemed genuinely moved by the animals' plight. He was also incredibly competent and hardworking but could only take matters as far as what any support given to him by the leather industry and local governments would allow. And so, as per his requirement to his client, Arup produced voluminous reports describing the work being done at the pilot project locations and other project sites under consideration for the CLE's information, as minimal as it was, which the CLE then used to create the illusion of major progress to calm buyers. And while the level of support by local authorities appeared to play a factor in the inadequate progress, let's not forget the CLE operates under the aegis of the Indian Ministry of Commerce and Industry and both the then commerce minister and prime minister had publicly expressed a desire for conditions for animals to get better. This indicates if there was a determined enough desire by the CLE for law enforcement and other improvements along the leather supply chain, considerable progress, including more pressure on local authorities if needed, could have been made.

After much deliberation, PETA affiliates pulled their support of the sluggish project they had long backed through which the public understood that progress was not satisfactory, and that leather being produced in India (and all around the world) remains inhumane.

More Rules to Be Broken

Around the same time as all of this, in response to the growing public awareness of and objection to cruel animal transport, the Transport of Animals on Foot Rules, 2001 were passed. They require, among other things, that the owners of the animals make food and watering arrangements when transporting animals by foot; diseased, blind, emaciated, lame, fatigued or mother animals who have recently given birth not be made to walk; veterinary first-aid be provided; sticks not be used to beat them; chillies or other substances not be smeared into their eyes; ropes when used be cushioned; animals not be tied tightly together with short ropes; no more than two animals be tied together; only animals of similar size and strength be put together; and that a fitness certificate from a veterinarian be obtained and carried.

Some years later, the Transport of Animals (Amendment) Rules, 2009, were passed, which provided more guidance on space requirements for cattle, sheep, goats, pigs, and horses when transported by road or rail.

More recently, the Central Motor Vehicles (Eleventh Amendment) Rules, 2015, were issued that require vehicles used to transport animals be in accordance with relevant standards developed by the BIS for the transportation of various species of animals. The rules also require that permanent partitions be put into the body of the vehicles to allow each animal a separate space.

The requirements of the standard that applies to cattle, sheep, goats and other farmed animals include that the means of transport should be designed and maintained so to ensure the safety of animals. It is further stated that the vehicle should be appropriate for the species of animals it carries, allow for safe loading and unloading, and have non-slip floors.

PETA India used the findings of the investigating team and the documentation obtained through other investigations to become part of a case in the Supreme Court, to address the disregard for laws pertaining to animal transport and slaughter in India. The case lasted for over a decade, and while the court ordered each state and union territory to form a committee for the implementation of animal transport and slaughter laws and to crack down on illegal slaughterhouses—and though Maran had urged states to set up committees way back in 2000—the state-level groups, when they exist, are either ineffective or do not focus on this issue. And so cruel transport and unlicensed slaughterhouses remain rampant throughout the country.

For example, in 2014, a Right to Information Act request revealed the Maharashtra state animal welfare board—whose primary function was to, in part, ensure implementation of laws regarding animal transport and slaughter—hadn't met for the previous eleven years. It was found then that the last meeting of the board before 2014 was held in October 2002.[8]

Finally, in May 2017, the government passed the Prevention of Cruelty to Animals (Regulation of Livestock Markets) Rules, 2017, stating, among other things, that cattle including bulls, cows, buffaloes and calves as well as camels must not be brought to livestock markets to be sold for slaughter (the law still allowed for them to be transported from farm to slaughter). The law seemed to be a recognition that animals destined for slaughter via markets suffer especially egregious neglect and abuse, but it was met with massive opposition by those involved in the beef trade and certain state governments. By July, the Supreme Court had suspended this law,[9] and in April 2018, it was announced that the central government has amended the law in a fresh draft with the plan to allow livestock markets to be used to sell animals to kill as usual.[10]

Cruel Business as Usual

Over the years, news reports about animal transport and investigations by animal rights groups reveal a continued disregard for animal transport and slaughter laws. Cattle today face the same problems they did twenty years ago.

Dr Naresh Upreti of Animal Rahat recently visited the Pollachi market. During his visit, the market had around 3,500 animals available for sale. He estimated about 70–80 per cent of them were being sold for slaughter.[11]

Dr Upreti observed the water trough and ramps put in by the CLE were still there, but the water was contaminated and not fit for consumption. Food was not provided to the animals. He saw calves crying for their mothers from whom they had been separated. Most of the animals at the market were tied in place so tightly with their nose ropes they could hardly move, and many of them were left for hours under the scorching sun with no shade.

He noted that animals going for slaughter included calves and adult cows who were young as well as old. Despite the ramps, reluctant animals were pushed, pulled by their nose ropes and yanked, and their tails were twisted to force them on to the trucks. About forty cattle—if you only counted the adults—were packed tightly on to regular goods trucks, tied by their nose ropes to the tops and sides, just like in 1999. Calves were mostly tied to the inner sides of the vehicles.

An article in *DNA* notes that the Central Motor Vehicles (Eleventh Amendment) Rules, 2015, still exist only on paper. It described that there is a total lack of awareness about the rules amongst the police.[12]

There is also a lack of appropriate vehicles. Cattle continue to be transported overcrowded in regular goods trucks. Raids on such vehicles take place all over the country, with the resulting news stories confirming that these animals are transported in exactly the same way they were decades ago.

A recent article in the *Indian Express* described ninety-six bulls being transported, allegedly for slaughter in Gujarat, in two trucks. A member of the police force was quoted as saying, 'Four among the fifty-two bovines being transported—their legs were tied and they were crammed on either side of a horizontal partition—had died.'[13] Another one reported twenty-two dead cows found on a truck in Mathura,[14] while a third gave news of residents of a village in Hisar district, Haryana, catching a truck overloaded with cattle and finding thirty-one buffaloes dead in the truck.[15] The *Times of India* recently reported that in Nagpur, 'Over a 100 cattle, which were being transported illegally in the region have died of suffocation in the last one week.'[16]

And then in August 2019, a PETA India investigator visited the market adjacent to Mumbai's Deonar slaughterhouse and documented dozens of animals dead and dying from transport strewn across its grounds and the slaughterhouse's unloading area—just as had been observed years before. He also recorded sickening scenes of bodies of dead buffaloes being moved through the market premises by a bulldozer; a shed rammed full of the corpses of buffaloes, goats, and sheep; and piles of dead animals' bodies in bins. One transporter told him, 'We get hundreds of goats here. It's a continuous three to four days' journey. We still take a break for tea and snacks. But the animals are in the truck for three days. Sometimes one dies, and others climb over him, causing more deaths due to stampede.' [17] The video of the investigator's findings can be viewed on PETA India's YouTube page.

Sometimes, when religious fanaticism or communal sentiments have driven action rather than animal welfare, violence against transporters or those accused of eating or stocking beef has erupted in India, tragically leading to critical injuries and even deaths. Police have also been attacked.[18] This brutal force ultimately causes both humans and animals to suffer as it results in many citizens viewing even sincere enforcement of animal transport laws as illegitimate.

Violence against cattle transporters and the police has also been carried out by the cattle transporters themselves. Many cattle are smuggled across the border into Bangladesh to be killed in a trade so lucrative, many consider it worth defending at any cost. The *International Business Times* reports, 'Along the largely porous boundary between Bangladesh and the Indian state of West Bengal, cattle-raids and cattle-smuggling, often conducted by criminal gangs, raise hundreds of millions of dollars annually in illicit profits.'[19]

The article describes what police believe was conflict between two rival groups of cattle smugglers, resulting in four men being burnt to death along with a cow. It reports, '... even when soldiers from India's Border Security Force (BSF) seize stolen cattle, they are often attacked or even killed by mobs of people led by the smugglers themselves' and goes on to state 'Himal [magazine] suggested that border patrol officers in both India and Bangladesh profit from the illegal smuggling by taking bribes to guarantee safe passage for the cattle in order to supplement their otherwise meagre salaries. Customs officials and politicians in India also feed at this gravy train. Media reports have implied that some of the people who are wounded or killed along this lawless border were targeted for assassination by border guards themselves if they felt their bribe payments were insufficient.'

Deaths in Trucks, Deaths at Sea

While sheep and goats are transported in a variety of ways, including in the boots of cars and in auto-rickshaws, tied on to the backs of bicycles, stuffed inside sacks on the backs of horses, and forced ahead on foot by farmers who beat them with sticks, many, such as those who end up at the Deonar slaughterhouse, are transported in double-decker fashion on trucks.

No matter the type of vehicle though, sheep and goats are commonly loaded and unloaded in markets and slaughterhouses across India without the help of ramps, or with just make-shift dirt mounds. Instead of gently lifting each animal on to the truck, transporters often pull them up or throw them by their fur, ears or limbs. Just think about how it would feel to be roughly lifted solely by your hair or ears, or by just one arm or leg, even if it for just a short moment, and we can understand why when this happens to them, they cry out in pain.

And as admitted by the transporter at the Deonar slaughterhouse, sheep and goats are also packed on to trucks so tightly they often die. A few years ago, the *Times of India* reported that an SPCA based in Chennai stopped a truck carrying more than 200 sheep on two decks, with at least twenty of them dying during transport. The animals had travelled all the way from Rajasthan to be killed in Chennai. Sadly, a mob arrived and drove away the seized truck and the animals could not be helped.

The same article reports, 'Chennai consumes about 60,000 sheep every month, and most of the supplies come from other states. Heads of cattle for slaughter are regularly procured from Rajasthan, Maharashtra, Andhra Pradesh and Karnataka, as sheep population in mofussil areas in Tamil Nadu are enough to meet local demands only. Animal husbandry authorities said that while transporting from a far-off place, about 10 to 15 per cent of animals are prone to die. Unless dead animals are accounted for and removed, they might be sold to unsuspecting consumers as fresh meat.'[20]

Sheep and goats are also often transported by sea or air to the Middle East from India, live. They are transported to be used for sacrifice, or just to meet the local demand for meat. By September of 2016, about 12,000 sheep and goats had been transported to Sharjah that year via cargo flights from Ozar airport near Nashik.[21,22] While mortality during transport by sea is high, air transport is a frightening and bewildering experience for animals too, and problems can occur.

For instance, also in 2016, 121 sheep from Ireland died of suffocation on a flight to Singapore due to apparent heat stress or suffocation.[23] They would have been used for Hari Raya Haji celebrations.

Sea transport is widely recognized as exceedingly hard on the animals and the industry regards a certain level of mortality as normal. Many cattle and sheep are transported by ship to the Middle East from Australia. Animal protection group Animal Australia has conducted numerous investigations of this industry. On their website BanLiveExport.com they describe stocking densities routinely so high the animals cannot even lie down normally together; hard abrasive floors which can lead to injury, wounds and lameness; wounds becoming infected from faeces; wet faeces that can cover cattle in their own waste, putting them at greater risk of heat stress; animals dying of heat stress; ammonia from the animals' waste and the general miserable conditions resulting in animals refusing to eat, eye infections, salmonellosis, pneumonia and more; filthy food and water troughs contaminated with faeces; fatigue but an inability to properly rest; and death.[24]

There are regularly reports of hundreds or even thousands of animals dying while being transported by sea. As Roland Briefrel, a campaigner against the trade in live exports notes, 'In the ten years from 2001 to 2011, 12,049 cattle were reported dead onboard ships, and at least 454,374 sheep died on the ships in that decade.'[25] Heat stress alone leads to mass deaths. Animals Australia describes an incident, 'In 2013, more than 4,000 Australian sheep died on board the *Bader III* as temperatures in the Gulf soared—turning the ship they were travelling on into a floating oven.'[26] In November 2019, nearly 15,000 sheep drowned in the Black Sea when *Queen Hind*, a ship that was bound for Saudi Arabia from Romania, capsized. The crew and only thirty-two sheep were rescued.[27]

Pigs are also transported by regular goods tempos or trucks in India, or with their legs bound and on the backs of motorbikes or bicycles, in auto-rickshaws and the like. Like cattle, sheep and goats, they may be transported long distances on goods vehicles. One such truck with forty pigs crammed inside caught by the Punjab police had travelled all the way from Rajasthan.[28] Inside them, pigs may be kept with their legs bound or secured with a netting or ropes.

While it may be harder for the general public to see through slats inside trucks carrying larger animals—chickens being transported, such as to 'wet markets'—shops where they are killed live for customers—in cage contraptions on trucks are commonly seen throughout India. For these animals, transport starts at the farm where they were raised for meat or eggs.

Arun observed the process of gathering broiler chickens at a farm linked to Venkateshwara Hatcheries Group. He saw chickens there lifted by their wings or legs and thrown into cages for transport as they clamoured to get away. The process is violent especially because it is fast: workers feel pressured to finish the task quickly. One worker claimed they have just an hour and a half to ready 2,000 birds for transport. A worker also claimed that out of 2,000 birds, fifty to hundred chickens die en route, with more dying when the weather is hot. The procedure was also documented on a farm associated with Sugana Foods where the chickens are also similarly handled.

The removal of egg-laying hens from cages is even more brutal as quickly taking birds out of cages means they are yanked out, even if their toes have gnarled into the wire, and even if it means breaking their bones. A video taken at a Sakku Group farm shows even young children engaging in this process.[29]

At destination, chickens are once again violently handled. They are pulled from trucks by their legs or wings and tied together in a bunch by their legs to be weighed. They then await slaughter, broken, bruised, traumatized, hungry, thirsty and in pain.

FAO recognizes that not only in India, but around the world, 'Transport of livestock is undoubtedly the most stressful and injurious stage in the chain of operations between farm and slaughterhouse and contributes significantly to poor animal welfare and loss of production.'[30]

FAO also points out other common outcomes of animal transport are heart failure, especially in pigs; sunburn, also in pigs; digestive disorder of bloat in ruminant animals, especially when they are restrictively tied; fighting between incompatible and frustrated animals, and more.

To try to minimize mortality and other problems for animals in transport, the World Organisation for Animal Health (OIE), of which India is a member, has developed basic guidelines for animal transport that it encourages its members to follow. The guidelines cover determining fitness to travel, what the competencies should be of handlers and transporters, emergency response procedures, space allowances and so on.

But for now, in India, with a lack of suitable vehicles and effective enforcement, untrained transporters with their callous view that animals for slaughter require no further investment or care and are just goods to be taken from one place to the other, someone's 'property', the OIE guidelines, just like Indian animal transport laws, remain just words on paper.

10

SLAUGHTER

Auschwitz begins wherever someone looks at a slaughterhouse and thinks: they're only animals.[1]

—*German philosopher Theodor W. Adorno*

It is not easy to gain entry into a slaughterhouse. Butchers are aware there is disgust and public objection to what goes on inside them. However, undercover investigations that have been successful over the years due to a combination of wit and luck, as well as the released findings of official visits, are among the ways we can have a detailed understanding of Indian slaughterhouse operations.

The first slaughterhouse I ever visited, two decades ago, was the now approximately 150-year-old one operated by the Kolkata municipality in the Tangra area of the city, where many leather tanneries were based. West Bengal is one of the handful of Indian states where cow slaughter is allowed. It was also the first slaughterhouse visited by Arup Kavan, and others sent by the CLE to accompany Miriam Parker, veterinarian John Gripper and me on a site visit that day. The CLE had facilitated this trip, and later others, as they considered location options for their pilot project. It was also to allow Miriam and John to make broad recommendations for animal welfare improvements that could be applicable to slaughterhouses across India. I know it was the first time the CLE representatives personally witnessed the butchery of cattle their business is built on, because they could not hide the horror on their faces. I could barely hide it on mine.

Before the sights and sounds of this slaughterhouse hits you, it's the stench penetrating the air—the rancid reek of decades' worth of animals having urinated and defecated in fear, of entrails and internal organs being pulled out of their bodies, of decomposing flesh, a lack of adequate water and washing facilities, of death—that lets you know you're close. It took all my might not to vomit before I even entered the slaughterhouse gate. Should a place producing food ever result in that kind of visceral reaction?

The slaughterhouse was accessible from the road, but the butchers were not used to having visitors there. A large, intimidating crowd formed around us the moment we entered, asking who we were, why we were there. The municipal authorities knew to expect us even if they hadn't passed the information on to those working there. The CLE representatives managed to pacify their concerns enough for them to allow us to stay. Nevertheless, a small suspicious group followed us throughout.

The place was noisy, filthy and chaotic, with dozens of men shouting at and yanking cows and buffaloes by nose ropes towards the slaughter floor. Young boys were also present as helpers. The slaughter halls were just two very long buildings next to each other with a shared drainage gully. Each building had about ten or so stands where the cattle were killed by a team of four or five butchers. Considering the hours of operation, it was estimated that around 300 cattle were killed per day there back then,[2] and the slaughterhouse has the same capacity today.

The Calf Who Didn't Want to Die

One young bull fought hard to stay alive. He was surrounded by a group of men, some pushing him, others pulling him, his eyes wide with fear as he battled to stand his ground to avoid being forced through the door arches on to the slaughter floor. Though just a calf, he understood he was in grave trouble, as he could see the cut apart bodies of others who were killed before him. He thrashed and bellowed, but the men pushed and pulled him harder, until he finally stumbled into the slaughter hall.

What must he have been thinking—there, all alone, amongst predators and dead bodies, and without his mother or anyone he trusted to help him? Was he crying in the hope that his mother would hear?

In the slaughter hall, some of the men twisted the calf's neck, and he fell to the ground with a thud. There, with what looked like a dulled kitchen knife, they sawed at his throat. He looked at me through the crowd in his last moments as he gasped, making a haunting, guttural sound. And then, after enough blood gushed from his neck on to the floor, he was gone.

Bigger cattle were generally cast to the ground with ropes. With so many different butcher teams working, their methods somewhat varied, but it generally involved twisting the animal's head until they fall, or using a rope to tie the front and back legs together and then yanking the rope so that the animal loses his footing and slams to the ground, or a combination of both—thwack, thwack, thwack.

All of the animals were killed in full view of one another, but slaughter methods differed, with some animals being cut with small, dull knives, others with larger and more efficient knives, and several animals being stabbed in the chest after their throats were slit. The dismembering and skinning of cattle began on the floor, which was awash with blood, guts, urine and faeces and then the bodies were hoisted on to a wooden spreader bar to complete the dressing process.

There was no evidence of a post-mortem examination of the carcasses by a veterinarian, no sign of any meat being rejected for human consumption, and no effort made towards cleanliness or hygiene to avoid the sale of carcasses contaminated by faecal matter and other waste making it to markets.

The guts, hides and larger waste products were collected and moved out to an open yard at the side of the building, and otherwise the blood and waste were being washed with plain water directly into the drains.

After returning to my hotel, I sobbed. I had never seen anything like that before. I made a mental promise that day to the calf who lost his life that I would spend the rest of mine fighting for animals to help spare others suffering like he did in his short, painful existence.

Today, the Tangra slaughterhouse is still in use,[3] though what was referred to as a 'fully automated abattoir' costing ₹25 crore had been opened by the Kolkata Municipal Corporation in 2012, but reportedly shut its doors in 2017 due to financial difficulties and litigation over the tender process for operating the facility.[4]

Perhaps it will open its doors again—so-called modern slaughterhouses are now cropping up in India, and private export-level ones also exist. However, 'modern' does not equal kind and most municipal slaughterhouses where cattle, pigs, sheep and goats are killed are still simply barren concrete rooms without suitable machinery or waste management systems. In them, butchers often work barefoot and without gloves or any sort of protective gear.

Who Feeds Tamil Nadu?

In 2005, an investigator from PETA India found a clever way to visit fourteen slaughterhouses in Tamil Nadu where cattle, sheep or goats were killed. The investigation covered municipal facilities, as well as some illegal, un-registered ones, and focused on cities with varied human populations in order to obtain a fair understanding of conditions of slaughterhouses throughout the state.[5]

The investigation showed, sadly, despite Prime Minister Vajpayee's call to state governments for the enforcement of animal protection laws and Commerce Minster Maran's assurances for surprise inspections of animal transport five years' prior, no improvements in the treatment of animals used for meat and leather had taken place. Today, there is still no suitable enforcement mechanism of animal transport and slaughter laws in force, and the modern facility that was finally built in Chennai in 2011 at the cost of an astonishing ₹48 crores is not in use because butchers' concerns were apparently not adequately taken into account at the planning stage. They argued later it was equipped with machinery that they worried may put them out of jobs.[6] And so, it would be safe to surmise, more than a decade on, conditions at slaughterhouses throughout the state are essentially the same.

Tamil Nadu was chosen for PETA India's study because of its dominant presence in the Indian leather industry. The state is said to be responsible for 70 per cent of India's leather tanning capacity and 38 per cent of leather footwear and components.[7]

According to Parker, at a minimum, slaughterhouses should have suitable unloading facilities, secure pens, adequate shade and shelter, facilities to provide water and feed, and a layout which minimizes the handling of animals. Within the slaughterhouse, there should be a layout that allows individual animals to be carefully cast and slaughtered as quickly as possible, with no animal being killed in sight of another, and with animals being fully bled before their bodies are further handled.[8] There should also be active management, and veterinarians must be working and present and workers suitably trained. And under the Prevention of Cruelty to Animals (Slaughter House) Rules, 2001, 'Every slaughterhouse as soon as possible shall provide a separate space for stunning of animals prior to slaughter, bleeding and dressing of the carcasses.'

PETA India's detailed report on its investigation explains most of the slaughterhouses observed in Tamil Nadu had either no ramps, ramps that were there but not in use, ramps that were inaccessible to vehicles or ramps that could be dangerous to use. None of the animals arrived at the slaughterhouses with any health certificates stating they were fit to travel, and the animals arriving in vehicles came in goods trucks, rickshaws, bicycles and cars—not those built specifically to carry animals.

Despite the typically overcrowded manner in which animals arrived at the slaughterhouses, and inadequate unloading facilities which put the animals at risk of broken bones and other injuries, there was no veterinary care or emergency slaughter arrangements available at any of the slaughterhouses to put animals quickly out of their pain. Instead, the investigator learnt, such animals were simply left to languish, sometimes for days.

Shelter and shade were either limited or non-existent at all of the facilities, and animals were commonly kept tied by short ropes in awkward, painful positions. Virtually none of the slaughterhouses observed provided adequate food and water supply for the animals too.

The investigator saw animals in every place being yanked, pulled, beaten, dragged and pushed. He also saw handlers twisting and breaking cattle's tailbones. Sheep and goats in particular, because they are lightweight, were violently manhandled with ease, lifted, dragged and tossed around by their fur or limbs.

There were no veterinary inspections being done of animals prior to slaughter to address their health or to ensure the carcasses of ill and diseased animals do not make it to the market, and as sick animals were not identified, they were also not separated from those who were healthy, nor were they provided any veterinary relief.

The animals were not stunned in any of the slaughterhouses visited and were slaughtered in full view of each other. Stunning is the process of using a machine to make animals hopefully unconscious, subdued and immobile, such as through striking through the animal's forehead with a captive bolt pistol. And though stunning may itself sound horrible, the idea behind it is to ensure animals are unaware of the knife going across their throats. Stunning also helps keep animals in place, making the slaughter process easier, and the stab to the throat more precise.

On stunning, former president of the British Veterinary Association, Gudrun Ravetz, has said, 'Our view is that all animals should be stunned before slaughter, based on peer-reviewed evidence that indicates an unacceptable time lapse between slaughter and the onset of permanent insensibility when animals are not stunned. A number of notable bodies including the [UK] Farm Animal Welfare Committee and the EU Food Safety Authority all agree that there is a high probability that the cutting of sensitive tissues at the neck will trigger a significant pain response in a conscious animal.'[9] In other words, when an aware animal's throat is slit, it likely hurts badly and hurts essentially until she dies.

The investigator also observed persons not employed by the municipalities often working at the slaughterhouses, including children. He reported that there was no authority from the relevant municipality or any management present at any of the facilities during his visits. He further said there were no active veterinarians at any of the slaughterhouses even when they were present, and no records maintained to share about any matter relevant to animal welfare.

A Buffalo's Spine May Break but We'd Rather Have Tea

At the Chennai municipal slaughterhouse, the investigator found one buffalo with a snapped spine, an injury that appeared to be from transport. Though the unloading of animals began at 4 a.m. and slaughter started at 6 a.m., the veterinarians first arrived at the slaughterhouse too late to deal with the situation, at 7.15 a.m. The injury may have been due to the fact that though the facility had unloading ramps, only one was in use. Two were inaccessible to the vehicles, and the unused ramps were used by workers to rest and one even featured a small tea shop!

It is against Indian law to slaughter very young animals, but calves were a common sight. At the Ooty municipal slaughterhouse, the investigator witnessed animals arriving to the slaughterhouse dead and injured. One dead calf was observed lying next to a vehicle that was unloaded, and two seriously injured calves were stretched out inside the floor of the same vehicle. One calf who appeared to die from strangulation by the rope with which he was tied was kept with live animals in the penning area. An animal handler informed the investigator that some animals had arrived five days prior, but there was no trace of food or water.

At the Tiruchirappalli municipal slaughterhouse, the investigator noticed all of the sheep had bloated stomachs. Upon enquiring about this, he was told that each animal was force-fed large amounts of water as it was thought this would increase the weight of the animals and make the cleaning of the innards easier after slaughter. The investigator noted that most of the animals had such bloated stomachs, it appeared difficult for them to normally move.

Some of the practices observed were especially inefficient or particularly cruel. For instance, at the Coonoor municipal slaughterhouse, during slaughter, handlers would cast and push about five sheep together in a row so tightly that only the first and last sheep would be restrained by hand. A butcher would then slit the throats of all of the animals together in a row. No care was taken whatsoever to ensure accurate individual cuts, and when the handlers restraining them would let them go, the sheep's bodies would writhe about wildly as they gradually lost consciousness over varied amounts of time depending on the depth of their cut.

Cattle were cast to the floor in ways similar to in Kolkata, causing pain and distress. In Ooty, some cattle were made to lay on their sides with their legs tied together for up to ten harrowing minutes before butchers got around to slitting their throats. Knives used at the various facilities were often not sharp, and time to death sometimes prolonged. As a result, dismembering and even skinning commenced prior to death for some animals.

The floors of the slaughterhouses in Tamil Nadu, like in Kolkata, were awash with urine, faeces, blood and the insides of dead animals. Skins and hides were left on the slaughter floors throughout the day while inedible body parts were eventually dumped in a corner, attracting stray dogs, rodents, crows, insects and other scavenging animals. Even for animals who were slaughtered on the floor and then hoisted for dressing, the carcasses were typically placed back on the filthy floor in a heap prior to being taken to market. Carcasses were commonly swathed with flies.

The investigator reported on the putrid stench emanating from these facilities, just as it has in every slaughterhouse I have ever visited. He described floors in all the facilities studied being extremely slippery from the blood and waste, and a lack of supply of running water. Wash basins and knife sterilizers were non-existent. Workers typically did not wear shoes, and sometimes not even shirts.

Like in Kolkata, there was no post-mortem veterinary check of any of the carcasses to determine the meat's suitability, nor was any carcass ever rejected by anyone for human consumption. The health mark, when applied on carcasses, was done so by the butchers themselves instead of authorized inspectors. The carcasses were then moved to market in dirty gunnysacks, or directly placed in or on grimy vehicles not suited for carcass transport.

The investigator also found where municipal facilities did not meet the public demand for meat, unlicensed facilities filled the gap. For example, in Thanjavur, there was no licensed municipal slaughterhouse in use for cattle, yet there was a huge beef market right next to the slaughterhouse indicating illegal slaughter someplace nearby. That said, there is no difference, in terms of welfare, in how animals are handled at the municipal versus unlicensed facilities in the state.

Slaughter by Hammer

The practice of force-feeding animals large volumes of water was also observed during a visit Miriam, John, Arup and I made to the slaughterhouse in Bengaluru on Tannery Road shortly after we visited the Tangra facility. Disturbingly, we watched several bulls in a crumbling blood-drenched and offal-covered slaughter hall gag on and spew out water; cry out; gasp; lift their heads, flail about or attempt to stand despite having their feet tied and their throats slit thanks to shallow cuts, tremble and gradually lose consciousness.

A report prepared by Miriam and John about what they witnessed reads as follows (keep in mind, westerners refer to both cows and bulls as cows), 'First the animal's head was held back, and cows were made to drink around one litre of water. Unable to swallow comfortably in this position, this was clearly quite distressing. Once the head was pulled back the muller cut the animal across the throat severing just the jugular veins ... When we questioned this method we were told that it was the intention to cut in this fashion so as not to sever the windpipe. We monitored a number of animals and signs of death, i.e. loss of rhythmic breathing and fixed dilated pupil took on average two and a half minutes to achieve.'[10] It is unclear why these butchers wanted to keep the windpipe intact, but their decision to do so meant the animals died slowly. Following the visit, Miriam began advising relevant authorities in Bengaluru and elsewhere to at least ensure deep cuts.

The offering of water in this case, and perhaps even at Tiruchirappalli may be at least partially because it is customary under halal slaughter practices to offer water to the animals prior to slaughter. This is intended to be a kindness, but in Bengaluru and at Tiruchirappalli they have turned it into a cruelty.

It's been more than seventeen years since the Karnataka High Court ordered closing all slaughterhouses inside Bengaluru within six months.[11] It is said that a modern mechanized slaughterhouse is being set up in the Harohalli industrial area. However, Harohalli residents are objecting to this, citing environmental and health concerns.[12] Understandable—who would want a slaughterhouse in their backyard?

More recently, in 2013, a video was circulated on the internet showing how pigs, cows and other cattle are killed in Kerala.[13] The video starts with a screaming pig laying on his or her side in a decrepit slaughterhouse, while a butcher reins multiple blows on the animal's head with a hammer as the pig's body convulses. Three blows, of what was likely more blows can be seen in the video. The video then pans out to another section of the slaughterhouse, where a skinny cow or bull is blindfolded and then struck on the head with a hammer so hard that the animal falls. The dazed animal then gets back up, and the blindfold falls off. At this time, the video pans to a third animal, another cow or bull, this one not blindfolded, who is hit at least four times on the head with a hammer. Then, the video again focuses on the animal who was blindfolded, and this time she or he is struck about three more times and falls down once again. Even after the animal was down on the ground, the blows continue. The video pans back to the other cow or bull who was hit at least four times, and this time the animal is restrained by a worker's foot.

A knife is then sawed into the animal's throat, back and forth, back and forth.

None of this process is quick or uniform, as sometimes the blows seem to happen immediately after the other, other times the butchers wait a bit between blows. The hammering seems to be used as an alternative to stunning, but it does not cause the animals to immediately, if ever, lose consciousness. It is nothing but a hideous, unnecessary and egregiously cruel step in the slaughter process.

In response to this video and pressure on the Kerala government to do something to stop this abuse, an order was issued by the principal secretary, Department of Animal Husbandry, in late 2013, asking local government bodies to ensure the use of a captive bolt pistol in every slaughterhouse within six months from the date of the order and to initiate penal action against anyone found violating it. Almost eight months later, the *Hindu* reported, 'Cattle slaughtered in abattoirs across the state continue to have a torturous end as a government order directing local bodies to introduce captive bolt pistol to end the barbaric practice of repeated hammering on the head of animals has been let to fall between the cracks.' The same article said, 'Animal Husbandry Department sources said the introduction of the captive bolt pistol would have to wait till modern slaughterhouses were set up.'[14]

The same order had also called for the use of the 'deep-cut method', or rather a deep enough cut to the neck to sever the carotid arteries, in the meantime. As M.P. Praveen, a journalist with the *Hindu* observed, 'This direction is equally important considering that butchers at most slaughterhouses hack at animals' throats with dull, rusted blades inflicting much pain to the animal besides raising questions of hygiene about the meat.'[15]

For now, such directions and plans essentially exist on paper in Kerala. Like in Bengaluru, modernization has yet to actually materialize and there has been no word of mass corrective training of Kerala's butchers, government inspections of the slaughterhouses or raids to collect hammers, or cruelty cases brought against errant slaughterers. It can be assumed it is a cruel business as usual at the Kerala slaughter facilities, five years on from when that video of hammering was released.

Modern, but Not Kind

So-called modern slaughterhouses also come fraught with problems: They are usually only modern by way of infrastructure, but cruelty remains inherent in how they function.

Deonar slaughterhouse in Mumbai, run by the municipality, is considered a modern slaughterhouse. Despite its efforts to keep prying eyes out, I have managed to visit it several times, including along with Miriam, John, Arup and members of the CLE. As previously mentioned, it has also been investigated by a member of the team that followed the death trail described in the last chapter and later PETA India. It exists within a massive high-walled compound surrounded by barbed wire. Having been on the inside of the wall, it's easy to see why they try to keep the public out.

Walking grounds where hundreds of living beings lose their lives daily is eerie to say the least. As the slaughterhouse workers went about their routine, I couldn't help but think—this is among the last breaths this bull will take, this is the last time he will feel the sun on his skin, or as I stroke his face, mine may be the only kind touch he ever received. During visits, as I passed animals in the unloading area, in the sheds, or in line for slaughter, I found myself looking into the cattle's pure-black eyes and trying to burn the animals' faces or traits into my mind so that someone will have known they existed, as if that somehow makes things slightly better. Of course, it does not. There was the bull with the tremendously huge horns, the brave sheep who head-butted the transporter, the buffalo with the beautiful long eyelashes, and so on—all of them now dead.

An investigator's account of Deonar reads, 'By the time of our tour at 10 a.m., there were already more than a dozen downed cattle. Four had broken feet or legs and could not stand. One bull kept trying to rise to his feet but could not put his right front leg down. He struggled, moving in circles as he tried to get that foot on the ground, until he collapsed under the heat of the sun. This same bull also had a broken horn, nearly half-gone, oozing blood. The slaughterhouse veterinarian providing the tour noted that the bull's foot was broken and that the broken horn was quite painful, but made no effort to provide any sort of pain relief to the animal.'[16]

In a subsequent visit by a colleague and me, thirty-one dead and severely injured cattle could be counted strewn on the grounds or propped up on trolleys. Here too there was no emergency slaughter system to quickly put animals out of their misery, nor any medical efforts made by the veterinarians to provide relief to the animals who needed it. At the time of my latest visit, cattle were slaughtered in front of each other without stunning, and cast by having their front and back legs separately tied together and pulled to the ground where all of their legs were then tied. Many animals waiting for their turn urinated in fear. The cuts to the animals varied, with some losing consciousness quicker than others.

Sheep were led into a raceway with a concrete floor and walled sides to be killed, but they too had their throats slit without stunning. Because of the line speed, the butchers were unable to ensure the knife was kept sharpened.

Pigs are killed at Deonar too. They are kept waiting in a lairage, and when I visited with Miriam and others, the physical conditions of the pigs were found to be deplorable with some dead or downed pigs unable to move. The pigs were stunned prior to slaughter using a current via large circular padded tongs applied to the sides of their heads. The then slaughterhouse manager, Dr V.N. Vishnupurikar, was unable to give any details about the voltage used.[17]

Most pigs in India, however, are not as 'lucky' as these hapless pigs who end up at Deonar. Most are killed crudely, with their legs tightly bound, and stabbed with a knife to the heart as they scream out in pain.

In late 2016, an inspection of the modern Ghazipur slaughterhouse—which is said to be one of India's largest run by a municipal corporation and which is used for domestic and export purposes—was led by Satya Sharma, former mayor of the East Delhi Municipal Corporation (EDMC), in the presence of an additional commissioner of the EDMC and the director of veterinary services of the EDMC, both of whom also supervise the functioning of the slaughterhouse. Also present were animal welfare experts of the Delhi Slaughterhouse Monitoring Committee, appointed by the Supreme Court of India, including representatives from PETA India and People for Animals. The slaughterhouse functions under the supervision of the EDMC and is leased to Allana, an exporter of processed foods, including meat.[18]

This is a strange relationship because the Prevention of Cruelty to Animals (Slaughter House) Rules, 2001 state, 'The municipal or other local authority specified by the Central Government for this purpose shall, having regard to the capacity of the slaughter house and the requirement of the local population of the area in which a slaughter house is situated, determine the maximum number of animals that may be slaughtered in a day.' In other words, a municipal slaughterhouse is supposed to cater to local, domestic demands for meat in their area and determine the number of animals it kills accordingly, not export.

Agricultural and Processed Food Products Export Development Authority (APEDA) records show Deonar too engages in export.[19]

Inspectors visiting the Ghazipur slaughterhouse noted that no feed was offered to animals in the lairage or waiting area; water troughs were dirty and empty and that some were inaccessible to animals; buffaloes, most of whom originate in the dairy industry, were held in crowded conditions; veterinary examinations prior to slaughter were not being done even on sick animals; weak, sick and debilitated animals were found in the lairage; sheep were handled roughly, hit with sticks, and thrown from one pen to another; and that the passageway for sheep was extremely crowded.

However, perhaps even more shocking was their finding that electric shocks with a live wire were administered to force buffaloes to move towards the slaughter hall. The animals were not stunned before their throats were cut and they were hoisted upside down on hooks. The animals were videotaped kicking and struggling, even as they were being bled out.

Backyard Slaughter

Chickens in India are usually killed in meat shops where a buyer chooses the bird he or she wants to eat. It's easy for any member of the public to observe how this is done. There is no stunning involved and the chicken is held down for a knife to go across the throat. Care is often not taken to ensure a deep cut for quicker time to death. These chickens are then commonly thrown into a drum as they writhe about until they die. However, since chickens are small and easier to handle than large animals, when in a hurry, dismembering routinely begins prior to loss of consciousness. In another method, called the *jhatka* style of killing, the head is chopped off altogether. Or a chicken's neck is forced across a static blunt blade.

At so-called modern slaughterhouses, chickens are shackled and hung upside down by their feet on a conveyor belt system. They then have their throats slit either manually or automatically. At facilities where they are stunned, their heads may pass through an electric bath prior to the cut.

Stunning, while generally considered less cruel and recommended by veterinary experts, does not guarantee a less painful death, and certainly not when stunning is misinterpreted to mean a hammer to the head! In systems used around the world, chickens often move their heads and miss the bath or even miss having their throats cut properly at modern slaughterhouses. As the conveyor belt system immerses them in scalding-hot water to remove their feathers, many are scalded to death in the feather-removal tanks. When slaughterers are under pressure to work at high speed, animals of any species can miss being stunned properly, and inappropriate stunning can cause serious injury.

In India, animals are not commonly stunned for two reasons: one, lack of infrastructure, adequate management and equipment maintenance in slaughterhouses; and two, the view of some that meat from animals who are stunned cannot be considered halal.

Those who hold this view say that Muslims are not permitted to eat meat of an animal who has died prior to the slitting of the throat. However, as methods of stunning can be chosen that do not kill the animal, a position against stunning is not a view uniformly held by all Muslims.

There is a great deal of debate on which method of slaughter is humane: halal, *jhatka*, the use of stunning or some other. I'm sure that if animals could speak in a language we could understand, they would say 'none'.

11

FISH USED FOR FOOD

Now I can look at you in peace; I don't eat you anymore.[1]

—*Writer Franz Kafka while admiring a fish*

One summer, when I was around eight, my parents took me to a carnival where they distributed live goldfish in plastic bags to children as prizes. I won first place in a game and was handed five goldfish in a big transparent bag. I remember my father being unhappy about this, but to avoid me throwing a tantrum, he agreed to let me keep them. We rushed home and I excitedly waited for my mother to empty and clean out a large glass jar that she otherwise used for storing lentils and the like. My dad then filled the jar with tap water, and I dumped the fish inside.

There it was, their new home: Five beautiful goldfish crowded in a barren jar, with nothing to engage their minds and no oxygen filter, where they would swim endless circles until they died. I didn't know any better than to provide them this pathetic abode back then, but apparently neither did my parents, nor do many people.

I loved them, named each of them and would stare at them for much of the day (for as long as they lasted). The goldfish were kept in my bedroom and I fed them flakes that my father picked up from a pet supply store. My dad told me not to feed them too often, but I didn't understand what that meant. And so, I kept putting food in their 'tank', every couple hours or so, because I didn't want them to go hungry. The jar would thus become dirty quickly, from food and the animals' waste, leading my father to periodically clean it by dumping out part of its water in the kitchen sink and replacing it with clean tap water.

Once, during this process, a fish fell out of the jar straight down the kitchen drain. I screamed, and my father luckily managed to grab hold of the squirming fish and pull the panicked little creature back up. Other times, even after he started closing off the drain prior to cleaning the jar, a couple of fish would sometimes fall in the basin and he would pick them up and put them back in their glass 'home'.

My favourite of the fish, Fishy (hey, I never claimed to be creative), who was orange and white, died after just a matter of days, but only after putting up a good fight—gasping desperately for breath until his demise. This was traumatizing for me to watch and I cried and cried. My parents let me say my goodbyes and then flushed Fishy down the toilet. Soon after, over a short period of time, the others died too one by one. I remember starting to realize when they were soon going to go, as they would begin to swim in weird ways or lay at the bottom of the jar. When I would see this, I would panic and feed them even more. Each death resulted in more mourning. I'm sure my father wished he had never let me take the goldfish home.

When I reflect back to that time, I think, my, how we tortured those poor fish! They were probably born on a crowded goldfish breeding farm, pulled out of the water in nets, put into plastic bags, jostled about, kept sitting in the sun waiting to be some child's prize, and then I took five home to torment them some more by putting them in a jar of untreated tap water that was likely chlorinated and burned their gills, and where they struggled to get enough oxygen, while a terrifying monster, me, gawked at and overfed them. Every now and then, another monster, my father, would come and partially empty their home while some fell out into an atmosphere in which they could not breathe, smack on to a hard platform, and then they were handled by the monster's fingers and put back in the jar in which they were barely alive.

Undoubtedly, many other fish handed to kids at fairs have suffered far worse. Many are tossed into garbage bins while still in bags to starve to death or flushed down toilets live as soon as the parents realize their kids are bored of them, or the fish are left entirely to the children to care for. As most people would not have an oxygen filter or tank at home, countless fish would be put into tiny barren jars or bowls in untreated tapwater. Fish would also more likely be distributed alone than in a group. I was an over-feeder, another kid would be an under-feeder and so on. And yet, to this day, many carnivals and fairs around the world continue to give away animals like goldfish and betta fish to children as if they are mere toys.

Thankfully, this doesn't happen in the city of Berkeley, California, anymore because as of 2017, giving away fish at festivals there is banned. High-schooler and former intern for a city council member, Simone Stevens, proposed the idea for a bill to protect fish from being given away this way. She cited worries about vendors keeping fish in awful conditions, improper care and transportation, unwanted fish being thrown away and high mortality rates.[2]

Rome has also banned the distribution of fish as fair prizes and bans the keeping of goldfish in the typical round bleak bowls people commonly think of as goldfish bowls. Among the concerns raised about housing fish like this were insufficient oxygen for the fish and poor water quality.[3] Paul R. Bowser, PhD, professor emeritus of aquatic animal medicine at Cornell University, told the website Dodo, 'Think of it this way. The goldfish is living in its own metabolic wastes.[4]'

In Switzerland, it is illegal to keep goldfish on their own because they, like humans, are a social species and can become depressed and listless in solitary confinement.[5] Which reminds me, how did the social goldfish I kept in a jar feel as they watched their jar mates fight for breath, get ill and die? How did the last one left standing, or rather swimming, feel? I shudder to think.

But if how goldfish feel should matter, what about fish and other water dwelling animals used for food?

More Fish Eaten Than All the Humans Who Ever Lived

Today, we are annihilating aquatic creatures in almost unimaginable numbers to satisfy the highest demand for these animals' flesh than there has ever been. Per person, worldwide, fish consumption is more than double what it used to be in the 1960s.[6]

Official FAO figures were used to do some math by FishCount.org.uk and it estimates between 0.97 and 2.7 trillion were caught annually from 1999 to 2007. For farmed fish, it calculates between 51 and 167 billion fish were killed around the world in 2017. The site further estimates 21–40 billion crayfish, crabs and lobsters and 150–380 billion shrimps and prawns were killed on farms that same year.[7]

The Population Reference Bureau estimates some more than 108 billion members of our own species have ever existed on planet Earth in all of humanity's history.[8] That means, using the figures calculated by FishCount.org.uk, up to twenty-five times more fish may be caught per year from rivers and seas than the number of people who have ever lived. Additionally, we have been farming over five times the number of sea animals each year than humans have ever existed.

How many distinct sea animals are killed was computed by FishCount.co.uk considering their species' average weights, as

FAO figures do not count fish or other sea creatures separately, but how much tonnage of their flesh is produced. You can read more on exactly how the figures of unique animals were derived on this website. But they are not just a mass of meat—like Fishy, they are individuals who desired to live and valued their own lives.

Today, while many fish being sold live in Indian markets continue to be caught from their natural homes, we are also consuming much more factory farmed fish. Malcolm Beveridge of the FAO's aquaculture division recently told *Quartz*, 'For the first time in human history, most of our aquatic food now comes from farming rather than fishing.'

And India is one of the biggest fish-killing nations. A short while ago, former Indian Ministry of Agriculture and Farmers' Welfare Union Minister, Radha Mohan Singh, issued a press release announcing excitedly, 'India becomes second largest fish producing country in the world[10].'

If how many individual lives are involved factored into how seriously we considered how our actions impact animals' welfare, the treatment of marine animals used for food is a matter that would be examined with utmost care. The rearing of fish is the fastest growing segment of factory farming.[11] And yet, as Lewis Bollard, programme officer for farm animal welfare for Open Philanthropy Project, expresses in an article, fish are 'the forgotten farm animal'.

He writes, 'When we think of farm animals, we likely don't think of carp. But this family of freshwater fish—which includes the three most populous farmed fish species in the world: crucian carp, silver carp, and catla—is likely the most numerous farmed vertebrate animal in the world, with an estimated 25–95 billion farmed every year.' He also points out compared to chickens used for meat, who are killed at about five to eight weeks, 'carp are farmed for 12–14 months' meaning, they are forced to endure farm conditions for a longer period of time.[12]

This is now changing, but many of us have been justifying the mass massacre of aquatic animals by way of suffocation, mutilation and worse by refuting the notions, especially for certain species, that they can experience much or any pain, or that they are smart. They appear so different from us, almost like alien creatures from another planet, so perhaps it's easier to dismiss them even more than we do animals on land.

But if we really think about it, we may recognize that this view is flawed. Like land animals, the animals who live in our waterways have to be sensitive enough to avoid danger, clever enough to traverse their complex environments, and equipped with unique abilities to survive in their extraordinary part of the world.

Yet, some people deny fish are animals altogether, forgetting lessons taught in elementary biology classes, referring to themselves as 'vegetarian' even if they consume fish flesh. This is so common that the ridiculous description of fish as 'swimming vegetables' is well known. And so, because of the common human denial of fish capabilities, and since we kill so many more sea animals than land species, I have spent a significant portion of this chapter covering how scientists are finding that as different as they seem from us and other land animals, they aren't actually so dissimilar when it comes to feeling pain.

In court, we are supposed to be considered innocent until proven guilty but when animals used for food are judged by humans, many of whom have vested interests in consuming or selling their body parts, they are usually not given the benefit of the doubt. Instead, such animals have commonly been considered not being able to suffer or think at least until proven, through numerous, often cruel experiments, that they can. This is not a fair trial. To study whether fish feel pain, scientists deliberately inflict pain.

Fish Caused Pain to Prove They Feel Pain

In one experiment, acetic acid was injected into the lips of rainbow trout, which resulted in the fish breathing rapidly, rocking in much the same way distressed humans and other mammals rock from intense pain, and robustly rubbing their lips on surfaces in their tank. To check that the fish were indeed feeling pain, some fish were injected with both acid and a painkiller, while others were not inflicted with pain, so that their behaviour could be compared.[13]

In other research, scientists dropped brightly coloured toy blocks into the tanks of rainbow trout knowing that these fish usually avoid anything that could be hazardous. When scientists injected the fish with acetic acid, they were often too preoccupied, apparently with pain, to bother avoiding the perceived danger. In comparison, fish injected with both acid and a painkiller behaved as they normally would, avoiding the blocks.[14] This is somewhat like how a charred person charging out of a burning building might be too distracted by their suffering to realize they are running towards a car.

In another study, zebrafish were given a choice between two aquariums: one completely devoid of any enrichment, the other more interesting with things like plants and a way to see other fish. In normal circumstances, the fish unsurprisingly preferred the more engaging aquarium. However, when the fish were injected with acid, and the barren aquarium contained pain medication, the fish changed their choice to the empty, but medicating, aquarium. In another similar test, the fish were injected with a painkiller directly instead of via the uninteresting aquarium's water. In those cases, the fish chose the more stimulating aquarium.[15]

None of this should be unexpected because biologically, fish are equipped with a nervous system and pain receptors and the anatomical tools to experience and respond to pain. In her book *Do Fish Feel Pain?*, the late Dr Victoria Braithwaite, former professor of fisheries and biology at Penn State University in the US, says, 'there is as much evidence that fish feel pain and suffer as there is for birds and mammals ...[16]'

Meanwhile, in a paper published in the journal *Animal Cognition,* entitled, 'Fish intelligence, sentience and ethics', Dr Culum Brown, who specializes in the study of fish, states, 'A review of the evidence for pain perception strongly suggests that fish experience pain in a manner similar to the rest of the vertebrates.[17]'

In the same paper, which involved a review of nearly 200 other research papers on fish, Brown argues the science shows fish are also brainy. I have covered some of their cognitive abilities in the first chapter of this book, but additionally, fish have traits such as learning fast, manipulating others by tricking or reconciling with them, and some fish use tools, something that we once thought only humans and chimpanzees can do, but now know more species can.

Yet, intelligent fish who have the capacity to suffer are slain in painful ways, including by being pulled into an atmosphere in which they cannot breathe, which would be akin to killing land animals through drowning, and are often impaled, crushed, sliced into parts, cut open and even gutted live. We can see much of this easily in a casual stroll through Indian fish markets.

The Crayfish Who Escaped

Crustaceans—like crabs, prawns, lobsters—and other sea animals also demonstrate that they feel pain. Yet, crustaceans are commonly subjected to procedures most would consider unacceptable for land animals—such as being boiled, torn apart, bound and kept for long periods on ice, or skewered—all while alive.

Recently a crayfish opened hearts and minds around the world. A video that went viral shows the animal precariously standing outside the edge of a boiling pot of soup with one claw still drooping in the bubbling liquid, being cooked. In an effort to live, the crayfish can be seen detaching that claw before making a run for it out of the pot. The clip first appeared on Weibo, a Chinese social media site, and users clamoured for the crayfish to be spared. Jiuke, who uploaded the video, claims he let the crayfish live.[18]

In another video, also from China, four crabs can be seen cooking in a pot of water, live. One climbs out of the pot and turns off the cooker![19] The crab would not have known how the cooker works, of course, and must have turned it off accidentally, but one would hope the animal's strong will to exist resulted in a compassionate decision by the cook to let them all live.

Robert Elwood, a scientist from Queen's University in Belfast, UK, was asked by a seafood chef whether crustaceans feel pain. This led Elwood to scientifically explore the question. Elwood first studied how prawns react to painful stimuli. He expected to see mere reflex responses, involuntary actions, like when we humans instinctively zap our hands away from something hot, rather than acts that look more like tending to the pain (like how we might run a burn under water or rub an aching arm).

Instead, when he applied acetic acid on the antennae of prawns, they began trying to soothe the antennae with their legs with intricate and persistent strokes. When a painkiller was applied before the acid, their attempts to address the discomfort decreased.[20]

When Elwood administered an electric shock to a particular part of a hermit crab, or when brown crabs had a claw pulled off, these animals would massage the hurt area, even if it meant getting into an uncomfortable position to reach the site of the wound. Elwood says such behaviour is complex, not merely reflexive.[21]

In another study, he and a colleague observed the reaction of shore crabs to light electrical shocks. Dozens of crabs were held in a bright space and then given a choice between two dark hiding places. Once their preference was known, crabs in one shelter were given an electric shock. When the same crabs returned to the same dark space, they were shocked again. By the time this was repeated once more, most crabs who had been previously shocked avoided the hiding spot where they had this experience.[22]

In yet another test, a type of crabs were offered a couple varieties of shells to choose to live in, one of which the animals would prefer. Once inside the shells of choice, they were shocked. The shocked crabs were then more likely to move to another shell when given the chance.[23] I mean, who wouldn't?

Lobsters, like crayfish and crabs, are often boiled alive to be cooked. The late writer David Foster Wallace described in an article titled 'Consider the Lobster' published by *Gourmet* magazine, 'If you're tilting it from a container into the steaming kettle, the lobster will sometimes try to cling to the container's sides or even to hook its claws over the kettle's rim like a person trying to keep from going over the edge of a roof. And worse is when the lobster's fully immersed. Even if you cover the kettle and turn away, you can usually hear the cover rattling and clanking as the lobster tries to push it off. Or the creature's claws scraping the sides of the kettle as it thrashes around. The lobster, in other words, behaves very much as you or I would behave if we were plunged into boiling water (with the obvious exception of screaming). [24]'

Inky the Octopus's Great Escape

And what about cephalopods—like squids, cuttlefish and octopuses, who face horrors such as being bashed, stabbed, cut into with knives or scissors or, especially in certain parts of Asia, eaten and grilled alive? Well scientists are studying them too.

When asked by *Vice* whether an octopus feels pain, Dr Jennifer Mather, a professor of psychology at the University of Lethbridge in Canada, said, 'It's probable that the octopus's reaction to pain is similar to a vertebrate. They can anticipate a painful, difficult, stressful situation—they can remember it. There is absolutely no doubt that they feel pain.[25']

Apart from their ability to feel physical hurt, thanks in part to publicized clever antics of octopuses like Inky, who was an inmate at New Zealand's National Aquarium and who executed a daring escape by sliding out of a small opening at the top of his tank and sliding down a drainpipe into the freedom of the sea, scientists and the general public are now recognizing octopuses as remarkably clever.[26]

In fact, scientists have known octopuses are wily creatures for a long time. In the 1950s, three octopuses were taught to use a lever for food. Two behaved while handling the task, but a third one, Charles, shot water at anyone who came near, destroyed the lever, and tried to pull down the light that was above their enclosure.[27] He made clear how he felt about being part of the test.

Other aquariums that keep octopuses have also described their attempts to escape, climb into other tanks for midnight snack raids, damage bright lights that bother them and other mischievous antics. Otto, an octopus at a German aquarium, was so upset by a light shining into his tank that he would climb to the edge of his enclosure and spurt water at it to turn it off. As it took aquarium staff some time to figure out what was causing the light to fail, as soon as it would be fixed, Otto would be at it again.[28]

Mather has been observing octopuses for decades. She talks about how octopuses use information from their environment to change behaviour and make choices. For instance, a type of octopus in the Pacific Ocean has been seen taking two parts of a split coconut to use as a shell, showing that the octopus is anticipating what tools will be needed in the future and planning for that—in other words, demonstrating intelligence.

In various tests, she has also observed octopuses playing, or rather, showing that, like my dog Mehboob or cats Tim and Mil, they need to engage their minds. In one such test, she and her colleague deliberately created a boring environment for octopuses and provided them a small bottle. A couple of the octopuses repeatedly began spraying water at it, so that it would bounce.[29] Octopuses have also shown they can solve puzzles, steer their way through mazes and perform other amazing feats.[30]

Cuttlefish and squid have not been studied as extensively as octopuses, but they have also been observed to demonstrate smarts. Divers describe cuttlefish as incredibly curious, emerging from behind rocks to check them out. Kohei Okamoto at the University of the Ryukyus, Japan noticed pharaoh cuttlefish in his laboratory doing something quite bizarre—copying hermit crabs by positioning their tentacles in a certain way and changing colour! Okamoto conducted tests and found they did this when small fish were around, and also when they were put in a new, bigger tank. It was theorized the cuttlefish were trying to trick the little fish into thinking there were no predators around as hermit crabs do not eat them, and in a larger tank, trying to fool any predators that they are a species they would not normally eat.[31] And Humboldt squid communicate with each other through coded language by changing colour at different speeds.[32]

Regarding squid and cuttlefish feeling pain, cephalopods have nerve cell endings, nociceptors, which exist to transmit information about pain to the central nervous system. In squid, though, nociceptors activate almost throughout their body, not only where they are injured, which means their whole body may ache where wounded.[33] This is thought to be because the squid's body is such that the animal cannot tend to any wounds and so it does not make biological sense for the pain to be focused.

Catching Everyone in the Path at Sea

Where marine animals ranging from fish, to crustaceans to cephalopods and more continue to be wild caught, there are many different ways. In India, boats and vessels used to capture them span from those which are small and simple to mechanized and motorized boats. Mechanized vessels used by Indian fishers include trawlers, gillnetters, bagnetters, seiners, liners and dolnetters[34]—all of these represent vehicles equipped for different types of fishing methods. The several common methods of wild fish capture described in this chapter are among those used not only in India, but on a global scale, to catch huge quantities of fish.

Wild fish populations around the world have been on a major decline for many years bringing the situation to crisis point: As per a FAO figure, over 70 per cent of the world's fish species are either fully exploited or depleted.[35] In 2006, scientists warned that the effects of fishing at the rates that we do it and climate change can result in a total collapse of the species of fish caught to be eaten by 2048, colossally disrupting biodiversity and ecosystems.[36]

This situation has contributed to fishing methods being used to squeeze capture of as many fish as possible from the sea to meet consumer demand. One such hideously destructive method of catching fish, used by India and much of the world but banned in Sri Lanka,[37] is called bottom trawling.

Weighted bottom trawl nets can be as large as a sports field and as they scrape along the ocean floor, they indiscriminately destroy and capture everything in their path.[38] It would be like someone using a giant heavy net to lug up everything on the road you live on, crushing and hauling up buildings, cars, crows, pigeons, cats and humans just to catch the stray dogs.

Bottom trawling devastates fragile coral reefs, can leave major ruts in the seabed kilometres long, and catches numerous non-target fish and other animals, including those who are endangered, all referred to as 'bycatch', along the way.

Worldwide commercial fisheries—not only from bottom trawling—are said to reject 40 per cent of the total marine catch! Nearly half of what they catch! An estimated 50 million sharks are caught as bycatch every year.[39] And each year throughout the 1990s, 650,000 whales, dolphins and seals lost their lives around the world due to bycatch[40]. Of course, not every individual is properly counted or recorded so the real figures of animals who are caught accidentally are likely even worse.

And what does being dragged from the far depths of the ocean in nets do to fish? They suffer excruciating decompression as brought to the surface and many are crushed under the weight of others or against debris. Thus, as the catch is dragged in, fish can be seen with the eyes popped out of their heads and their insides coming out from their mouths. Their swim bladders rupture, their bodies become bloodied, bruised and torn.[41] They suffer as we would if the situation was reversed and someone grabbed us and everything around us in a net and pulled us into the bottom of the sea.

Another popular commercial fishing method, particularly for certain fish like tuna, is longlining. People are eating so much tuna, so much more than the oceans can healthily provide, that vessels are constantly on the move to catch those remaining.[42]

This method uses what can be thousands of baited hooks hanging from a single line which may be 50–100 kilometres long that is set and hauled behind a boat. Depending on the target fish, longlines can be used near the surface or the seabed. Animals who are attracted to the free meal the system offers include numerous non-target species such as birds, sea turtles, sharks, seals and others.[43] Fish and other animals caught on hooks suffer for prolonged periods of time, until the line is hauled up. Some animals get away but suffer serious injuries, others drown or bleed slowly to death.

Once large fish like swordfish and yellowfin tuna are pulled towards the boat, fishers often dig pickaxe-like large hooks into the animals' bodies, whether it's their sides or even eyes, any part that the hook can sink into, to haul in the heavy animals.[44]

Gillnets are commonly used in India by small-scale fishers due to the generally low level of investment required and simple structure, but they are also used around the world.[45] They are long sheets of netting that can be set at various depths. Some may be only dozens of metres long, while others kilometres. The net hole sizes vary depending on the target fish, but many non-target animals also get caught in the net.

Fish have trouble detecting the netting, and unless they are small enough to pass through the holes, they get stuck. Struggling only allows the netting to seize them by their gills or fins even more, and as the net constricts around their wriggling bodies, many would have difficulty breathing, and face bleeding and cuts. Fish trapped in netting also become easy prey for other animals. Trapped fish may suffer for days until the boat comes to collect the net. If they haven't already bled to death, fish face the effects of decompression if hauled up from significant depths, are ripped from the net by fishers and either suffocate to death or are cut open while struggling to breathe.[46]

TRAFFIC, the wildlife trade monitoring network, condemn gillnets as terribly damaging. They warn, 'Particularly problematic is when the nets are lost or abandoned and carry on "ghost fishing" for years. One gillnet confiscated by the authorities in Australia in 2009 contained twenty-nine tonnes of Antarctic Toothfish, plus a significant bycatch of skates.[47]'

Purse seine fishing is another method, and though they are banned in certain areas to help increase the fish population, they are often still in use. After a ban by Maharashtra, over seventy boats were seen near Mumbai using the banned nets.[48]

This method works in a drawstring fashion: A large circular panel of netted bag, which can be up to a kilometre long or even more when several nets are attached together, is placed around fish and then pulled up. The idea is often to catch single species of fish that shoal together. But, of course, it doesn't always work that way as different types of fish often shoal together—target and non-target species.[49]

Officials in Maharashtra worry purse seine fishing may be causing the deaths of whales, dolphins and porpoises. Marine biologist and former chief scientist, Central Marine Fisheries Research Institute (CMFRI), Vinay Deshmukh, was quoted by *Hindustan Times* as saying, "While catching a lot of fish at one go, larger mammals like dolphins and porpoises are entangled within these nets in their search for small fish, which makes for a major portion of their food. This happens because of the sheer expanse of the nets. They need air to breathe, and so these mammals come closer to the surface intermittently. When they get caught in the nets, they suffocate and sometimes drown. Overtime, they wash ashore with the flow of the tide.[50]'

Of course, target fish are also as much capable of feeling pain and desiring to live as non-target animals are, and whichever way the fish are caught and hauled up on to boats and ships, they face horrors: suffocation, being cut into or gutted live, tossed on to ice or thrown in freezing water, or even frozen alive while suffocating.

Molluscs like clams, scallops, oysters, mussels and others are also often caught in the wild. These animals are filter feeders, which means they remove food particles from water and help keep it clean. They play an essential role in keeping the water they live in healthy and a suitable environment for other animals to live. In the Gulf of Mexico, it is thanks to these filter feeders that sunlight can even reach deep areas, allowing plants and coral to grow and sustain life.[51] These animals are often pulled up by a method called dredging, which uses large metal baskets that have projections that act as rakes to dig into the seabed. This system causes considerable damage to the seafloor, disrupts and harms bottom-dwelling species.[52]

Factory-Farmed Fish Fed on Human Waste

Many people mistakenly think fish farming, aquaculture or aquafarming, as this form of factory farming of fish in cages, barren concrete tanks or other enclosures, either within natural waters, ponds or inland is often called, does not contribute to emptying the oceans of fish. However, using FishCount.co.uk calculations from a few years ago, out of those fish caught in the wild, an estimated number of fish, over ten times the number of humans there has ever been on earth, are turned into fishmeal (to feed the farmed fish) and fish oil every year.

A paper recently published in the *International Journal of Current Microbiology and Applied Sciences* describes India as the second largest country in the world for aquafarming.[53] India's freshwater fish farming largely includes the rearing of carp species, catfishes, freshwater prawns, pangasius, and tilapia while its brackishwater fish farming is focused on rearing types of shrimp.[54]

Water-dwelling animals who are factory farmed face consequences similar to chickens reared this way: bleak and barren surroundings, stress, severe overcrowding, aggression of enclosure mates for reasons such as competing for food, injury from jostling against other fish or from their enclosure, an inability to express natural behaviours, disease, rampant antibiotic, vaccine use and more. They also face cruel transport and slaughter.

In October 2018, Italian animal protection group Essere Animali released the findings of an investigation into some of the largest farms rearing sea bream, sea bass and trout there supplying the country's largest retailers with fish to sell.[55] Their footage shows fish's bodies being manipulated for more reproduction through the use of artificial light; fish being held out of water to have their eggs or sperm pressed out of them for artificial insemination; animals being hauled up from overcrowded enclosures where they spent up to eighteen months in nets, crushing and injuring those at the bottom; and the fish being dumped into containers filled with slush and ice. An hour later, these fish can be seen still gasping for breath. The footage also shows fish being tied with string forced through their gills and around their tails or having labels put on them with machines while they are still alive, and others shot through a tube into vehicle containers, or killed with blows to their heads with iron rods. The investigation also found workers carelessly handle fish, allowing many to fall to the ground during various procedures, to suffocate to death. Similarly, in India, apathetic or ill-trained workers and inexperience also add to the woes the fish face.

Former Union Minister Maneka Gandhi described her concerns about fish farms, which are encouraged by the government's Blue Revolution scheme, in *Firstpost*. She wrote, 'There are no vets, no training systems to the villages that change their community ponds to privately managed fish farms. The villager, who is given the pond, is never educated about the anatomy of the fish, what it feeds on in the wild and what it can digest, its diseases, sanitation of the pond, maximum stocking numbers, etc. All that is desired from him is that he grows the maximum number of fish and the largest ones quickly. The result is that fish growers feed the animals poorly (many of them feed them human faeces only) and rely on unnatural methods, such as chemically formulated feeds, antifungals, agrochemicals and antibiotics. Formalin and malachite green are chemicals used as disinfectants in the ponds. They are known to be toxic, but no one has banned them in India.[56']

Find the part about human faeces hard to believe? This practice is not a secret. Dr Partha Prathim Chakrabarti, principal scientist at the Central Institute of Freshwater Aquaculture told the *Guardian* newspaper that most of the traders using the east Kolkata wetlands are small-time businesspeople who produce 10,000 tons of fish meat from animals fed on wastewater, that is sewage, human waste. This system also isn't new—the ponds where fish are living off human faeces have been feeding city residents for at least three generations. Those rearing fish in other Indian cities like Nagpur, Chennai and Bhopal also often use human waste.[57]

Gandhi also describes in her article, fish in India are kept in miserable conditions in severely crowded, filthy tanks. When I was a child, my jar of five goldfish would get filthy so quickly that my father had to clean the jar every few days. Imagine what the situation is then on farms housing hundreds, thousands or even tens of thousands of fish. These fish have nothing to do but swim in maddening, meaningless endless circles—that is, if they have the space—in their own waste.

Following personal visits to places where fish used for food in India are reared and handled, PETA India put out an investigative report on what the fish face. In the section on Indian fish farms, PETA India wrote, 'According to investigators, the ponds in some government fish farms were kept in such an unhygienic condition that they were no better than drainage water, and many fish who were forced to live in dirty water contracted skin diseases. Fish were infested with parasites and suffered from other illnesses. Fish became stressed as handlers carelessly transferred them from ponds to plastic bags that lacked adequate water and oxygen. Fin rot is common in farmed fish because they are generally kept in extremely crowded spaces and the water in their tanks lacks oxygen and is of a poor quality. When left undiagnosed, the disease can spread to other fish.'

It should come as no surprise that fish kept in such conditions are susceptible to illness and disease. The industry's answer? The same as what it is in chickens and other factory farmed animals: vaccines and drugs. Antibiotics are administered to fish either through the water, orally or via injections.[58]

Andhra Pradesh is a shrimp-exporting state but too much antibiotic residue in shrimp effects exports to places like the

European Union and the United States. The Coastal Aquaculture Authority banned twenty antibiotics or pharmacologically active substances and listed out maximum permissible residuals allowed, but raids conducted in 2017 on aquaculture industries had shown banned substances still being sold all over the state.[59] In 2018, the National Fisheries Development Board (NFDB) and other agencies still felt the need to announce their plan to launch a campaign to educate aquaculture farmers on antibiotic overdose.[60]

That said, fish sold in the US are not antibiotic free either. One study that looked at twenty-seven fish from eleven different countries sold at an American supermarket found residues of five antibiotics, including those used to treat humans.[61] Antibiotics in human food contribute to antibiotics failing or working poorly in us when there is a need to fight illness. The antibiotics might also be effecting the fish badly—it is thought one antibiotic might be leading to spinal deformities in rainbow trout if it's fed to them while they are growing.[62]

As far as vaccines are concerned, which are administered to fish through injections, orally or through the water—a recent University of Waterloo, Canada, study concluded that vaccines used by commercial fish farmers are not suitably preventing fish from disease.[63] At the same time, there are side effects of vaccines to consider, particularly when fish are injected, such as growth retardation, vertebral column deformities and the development of scar tissue.[64]

In India, vaccines and drugs certainly do not seem to always keep fish alive. In his article Lewis Bollard wrote about the Indian farms he visited: '[M]ortality rates above 50% in common carp farms suggest that many fish are in poor health, and likely experience poor welfare.'[65]

Parasites, like sea lice, are another major issue in fish farming. In 2017, it was reported that salmon louse plagued nearly half of Scotland's salmon farms. In the previous year, the louse epidemic had caused so much damage that tremendous numbers of farmed fish were killed and millions suffered in other ways. Lice on fish farms is said to be growing worldwide with companies spending over the equivalent of ₹ 9,171 crores every year to try to tackle the problem.[66] The lice can cause itching, skin irritation, ulcerations or other more serious problems like starvation, stunted growth, secondary infections and death in fish.[67]

Is it any wonder then that salmon seriously get the blues? A study published in *Royal Society Open Science* found that on salmon farms, some fish float listlessly at the surface of their enclosures.[68] These depressed fish commonly die from their situation and so to say they have committed suicide wouldn't be terribly far-fetched.

Where fish are kept in caged systems within natural water or ponds, they can suffer from imbalances where algal blooms result in reduced oxygen in the water, causing them to die or at least be extremely stressed. Fish kept in cages in open water also have no defence from jellyfish or predators. Some jellyfish can even blind fish with their stings. The blinded fish then smash into and scrape against their enclosure and suffer injuries and infection.

Then there are other health problems, especially in certain species of fish such as skeletal deformities and blindness. For instance, cataract and the blindness that follows is a common problem in factory farmed Atlantic salmon. These animals also commonly suffer deformities and heart problems, such as being born with an upside-down heart or underdeveloped chambers. These fish are, therefore, susceptible to heart failure during stressful procedures. Farmed fish can also suffer malformations of the spine or head.[69]

Environmentally, crowded fish, like pigs and other land animals who are kept on factory farms, produce tremendous amounts of collected waste. Their waste and uneaten food can pollute natural waters and smother wild fish and plants. Diseases and parasites common to farmed fish raised in pens can affect fish in natural waters. Chemicals and antibiotics used in farmed fish or on the farm can also impact wild animals, humans and the environment.[70]

Knowing all of this now, I realize that it is not only the five goldfish I brought home when I was eight whose torture I have contributed to, but of all the fish I have ever had on my plate, and the other animals who may have been accidentally killed when those fish were caught.

12

THE UNSUSTAINABILITY OF EATING ANIMALS

Raising animals can take a big toll on the environment. You have to feed the animal far more calories than you extract when you eat it. It's especially problematic as we convert large swaths of land from crops that feed people to crops that feed cows and pigs. Plus clearing forests to make more farmland contributes to climate change, as do the greenhouse gases produced by all those animals. The richer the world gets, the more meat it eats; the more meat it eats, the bigger the threat to the planet. How do we square this circle?[1]

—Bill Gates, founder of Microsoft, and investor in the
development of plant foods that taste like meat

On 2 November 2018, tigress Avni, mother of two cubs, was controversially shot dead. Asghar Ali, who comes from a family with a history of recreational hunting, was part of the Maharashtra government mission and pulled the trigger. The state claimed the killing was an act of self-defence[2] after tracking Avni on suspicion of eating humans—an accusation that had been challenged by various experts.[3] Her death followed a major Let Avni Live campaign supported by countless members of the public, animal protection groups, celebrities[4] and some politicians like Priya Dutt.[5] It followed street protests, online appeals, efforts in the Supreme Court and a call to the president of India to grant her a pardon[6]—none of which ultimately worked. But are those who joined efforts to save Avni unwittingly engaging in behaviours that threaten the survival of other tigers like her?

Thanks in part to high-profile efforts by NDTV and Aircel's Save Our Tigers initiative, the public is generally sensitive to the position of tigers as an endangered species in dire need of protection. However, it's not only tigers who are in trouble but almost every other wild animal species with whom we share our planet—including polar bears and frogs, orangutans and snow leopards, koalas and sea turtles—and their biggest threat isn't shooters. And when these animals are in danger, so are we.

'You Eat a Chicken, You Kill an Amazonian Parrot'

Scientists say we are on the verge of the greatest mass extinction there has been since the time of dinosaurs, the largest in 65 million years, that 75 per cent of Earth's remaining species could disappear within the next couple of centuries.[7] However, this time, humans' actions, not a natural phenomenon, have brought our planet and its inhabitants to crisis level.

Already, plant and animal species are going extinct at an almost unimaginable rate of somewhere between 1,000 and 10,000 times greater than the natural extinction rate,[8] or rather the rate of extinctions that would happen without human interference, and this speed is accelerating. Alarmingly, within the past fifty years alone, humanity has killed off 60 per cent of animals across vertebrate populations on average.[9] With losses come more losses, since species depend on each other for survival. The consequences of a mass annihilation of flora and fauna are irreparable, as it takes millions, even tens of millions of years,[10] for the recovery of ecological systems.

The good news is, we still have time to reverse this catastrophic trend, although it seems there is not much time. Anthony Barnosky, executive director of the Jasper Ridge Biological Preserve at Stanford University, thinks we have at best twenty years to stop this mass extinction from becoming inescapable.[11]

So how is this destruction being caused, and how can we, as tiger protection initiatives suggest we must do, preserve our natural resources and animals' natural homes? Many speak of things like the burning of fossil fuels and plastic waste in our oceans as contributing factors towards species extinction. And they absolutely are, but as the eye-opening documentary *Cowspiracy: The Sustainability Secret*, which follows filmmaker Kip Andersen as he discovers facts about the environmental destructiveness of raising animals for food reveals, the rearing of animals for meat, milk and eggs is a leading cause of species extinction. This is because animal agriculture is also a leading contributor to the greenhouse gasses (GHG) that cause climate change, the foremost cause of dead zones in our oceans and habitat destruction, as well as the major reason behind other environmental calamities.

A study about how animal product consumption is considered the world's biggest cause of habitat loss and a key threat to plant and animal species appeared in *Science of the Total Environment*.[12] The researchers considered countries that are expected to expand factory farming outfits and calculated the possible land use and locations for animals reared for food and the crops to feed them. Much of the largest transition from forest to land for raising animals for food is expected in fifteen countries that are the rich in plant and animal life.

A *Science* article that covered the study quoted Gidon Eshel, a geophysicist at Bard College in New York who studies the ecological effects of the foods we eat, as remarking, 'Now we can say, only slightly fancifully: You eat a steak, you kill a lemur in Madagascar. You eat a chicken, you kill an Amazonian parrot.[13]'

Farmer Suicides and Water Wars

Climate change impacts wild animals who suffer from alterations in availability of food and water resources, but it affects us too.

India is already suffering from the effects of a changing climate like shifting rainfall patterns, droughts, melting glaciers and rising sea levels.[14] This means problems such as extreme weather like heat waves, cyclones and floods; a drop in crop production; a resurgence of several vector and water-borne diseases such as malaria, cholera and dengue fever; and an increased risk to food, energy and water resources. These climate-related problems affect the poorest of us the most.

On 10 January 2017, the Tamil Nadu state government declared a drought. The declaration came rather late, as it was after 144 farmers had committed suicide due to the damage and losses they faced. Some 106 farmers killed themselves in just a single month. The drought was linked to unusual weather: It was said the retreating northeast monsoon was the worst ever in the last 140 years. S. Panneerselvam, professor and head, Agro Climate Research Centre, Tamil Nadu Agriculture University, Coimbatore, called it, 'an unprecedented situation'.[15]

Later, in the summer of 2019, Tamil Nadu, and particularly Chennai, was in the grips of a water crisis following years of insufficient rainfall and a heat wave that exacerbated the issue. By late June of that year, all four major reservoirs in the city had essentially become bone-dry, their reserves plummeting to a seventy-year low.[16] City residents clamoured for water, either paying for it to be trucked in or standing in long queues with buckets as state water trucks made the rounds.[17]

Meanwhile, a 2019 report by NITI Ayog, an Indian government think tank, warns Chennai and twenty other major Indian cities including Delhi, Bengaluru and Hyderabad will run out of groundwater by 2020. This is expected to affect about 100 million people.[18]

Indeed, India is among the at 'extreme risk' countries where the economic impact of climate change will be most keenly felt in just a few years from now, according to research released by the British risk consultancy firm Verisk Maplecroft.[19] A 2013 report by the World Bank revealed the annual cost of environmental degradation in India already amounted to about Rs 3.75 trillion which is equivalent to about 5.7 per cent of the gross domestic product (GDP) at that time.[20] More recently, the World Bank warned climate change is expected to cost India 2.8 per cent of its GDP and worsen living standards of almost half its citizens by 2050 if nothing changes.[21]

The situation is so perilous that the United Nations (UN) has warned that climate change increases the risk of war among India, Pakistan, Bangladesh and China over limited resources.[22] It also raises the risk of conflict within India.

During the summer 2019 Tamil Nadu water crisis, a twenty-eight-year-old woman in Chennai,[23] and thirty-three-year-old man in Trichy were both murdered over water disputes.[24]

There have been protests, including demonstrations which turned violent, over Cauvery river use between Karnataka and Tamil Nadu—a row that has been going on for over hundred years. With climate change, however, as water in the Cauvery is supported by rainfall, this conflict is likely to get worse.[25] The Cauvery already fails to have the volume it needs to meet the requirements of the states that rely on it.

No Free Lunch: The Eco Cost of Consuming Trillions of Animals

Despite the simultaneous growing interest in plant-based foods, global meat production and consumption are increasing at extraordinary rates. In the four decades before 2011, worldwide meat production tripled, with 20 per cent of the increase happening in just the ten years before.[26]

The 77 billion cattle, goats, sheep, pigs and other land animals we farm to eat every year do not just exist: These animals are bred in unnaturally high numbers only to be used and killed and the majority of these animals face being reared in intensive farms. To meet the now unprecedented global demand for animal-derived foods, the numbers of animals bred also keep rising. A few years ago, a Compassion in World Farming (CIWF) report stated the number of land animals produced each year for meat, eggs and dairy is estimated to double by 2050.[27] When you bring aquatic animals into the mix, the number of animals killed each year can rise up to trillions. Trillions!

To put these figures into perspective, the total human population of the world currently stands at 7.6 billion. While this is a substantial figure, we already breed more than ten times this number of land animals for the meat, egg and dairy industries in just one year and as per one calculation, more than 6 million farmed animals are killed for food around the world every hour.[28]

The population of humans who consume animal-derived foods is also growing exponentially. A report released in 2010 by the UN Environment Programme's International Panel of Sustainable Resource Management points out that as the global population swells towards an anticipated 9.1 billion people by 2050, diets based on meat, eggs and dairy will be unsustainable. The report further stated that a global shift towards vegan eating is necessary to protect the world from hunger and the worst impacts of climate change.[29]

Professor at the University of Manitoba, Vaclav Smil has studied how this shift toward animal agriculture in human society has changed the makeup of the inhabitants of this planet. He reveals today, more than 95 per cent of the biomass of land-based vertebrate animals are humans and the animals we breed to eat and have domesticated. Ten thousand years ago, this stood at just 0.1 per cent, with the rest of the 99 per cent as wild animals.[30] Talk about changing the ecological landscape of the globe.

Think about it: to accommodate and rear so many animals bred for meat, eggs and dairy, farmers need to provide crops and water for the animals, land and water to grow the crops, farms to keep the animals, and so on. In contrast, humans eating plants directly instead of channelling them through animals, is far more efficient and kinder on the planet.

Animals Reared for Food First in Line for Water, Crops and Land

While India has over 190 million hungry people[31] and 163 million without access to safe water,[32] a study published by *National Academy of Sciences* reveals animal agriculture uses a staggering one third of the world's fresh water resources, as well as one third of the world's global cropland as feed for animals.[33]

While usage of water to produce various foods would vary by country and systems, figures publicized by Water Footprint Network help us appreciate the water needed for animal-derived foods massively trumps that of plants. As per its figures, it takes 15,415 litres of water to produce one kilogram of meat from bovine animals; 8,763 litres to produce that same amount of sheep or goat meat; 5,988 litres to produce that amount of meat from pigs; and 4,325 litres to produce that same portion of meat from chickens. It takes 3,265 litres of water to produce a kilogram worth of eggs, and 1,020 litres to produce that equivalent amount of milk. In contrast, it takes 962 litres of water to produce one kilogram of fruit and 322 litres to produce that amount of vegetables.[34]

It's not just mass use of water that's a problem: A report by Brighter Green,[35] a public policy action tank, warns animal waste and run-off from pesticides and fertilizers used for crops to feed animals spoil India's waterways. The report cautions, 'These organic and inorganic pollutants contribute to the contamination of an estimated 70 per cent of India's surface water and an increasing percentage of its groundwater...' It states the production of meat resulted in 3.18 million tons of wastewater a little over a decade ago. At that time, it amounted to nearly hundred times more wastewater generation as compared to India's sugar industry and 150 times that of the manufacture of fertilizer.

Consider also that according to FAO, 'almost 50 per cent of the grains produced in the world are fed to livestock'.[36] In India, as per Brighter Green, about half of the maize consumed each year is used for animals reared for food, not humans directly, while chicken feed is 95 per cent maize and soy. India is also a major exporter of maize and soy meal used to feed animals reared for food abroad.

Dr Eric Holt-Giménez, executive director of Food First/Institute for Food and Development Policy, explains the world already grows enough food to feed 10 billion people,[37] more than there are on the planet, but because of various factors, including that much of the world's grain is used to feed animals for human consumption, this food does not always reach those humans who need it the most.

What's more, the International Livestock Research Institute reveals facilities linked to raising animals for food occupy 45 per cent, or nearly half, of the global surface area.[38] It's no wonder then that much of this space is former forest land.

Healthy Rainforest, or New Leather Shoes?

As per the World Bank, the primary cause of deforestation in this rainforest is the rearing of cattle. Greenpeace shares the same in its report 'Slaughtering the Amazon' which states, 'According to the Brazilian government: 'Cattle are responsible for about 80% of all deforestation in the Amazon region. In recent years, on average one hectare of Amazon rainforest has been lost to cattle ranchers every 18 seconds. The cattle sector in the Brazilian Amazon is responsible for 14% of the world's annual deforestation. This makes it the world's largest driver of deforestation ...[39]'

To make matters worse, the Amazon burnt—fires devastated the rainforest and the animals in it. But it would be more accurate to say it was being burnt. The majority of the fires were thanks to loggers and ranchers who deliberately set fires to clear land for cattle reared for beef and leather.[40] As a result, brands like Vans, Timberland, and H&M vowed to suspend or stop selling Brazilian leather, but buying leather from somewhere else would just contribute to other animal welfare and environmental problems there.[41]

India has suffered from massive deforestation to raise animals used for food and leather and the crops to feed them. The Brighter Green report explains, 'Deforestation to clear land for pasture, fodder extraction, expanding agricultural cultivation of crops in forests and on grazing lands, and the widespread use of pesticides and fertilizers to grow crops like maize and soybeans are all contributing to rising rates of soil erosion, salinization, alkalization, pollution, and desertification in India. Hunger for land for both crops and livestock is also a primary cause of biodiversity loss.' Sorry, tigers.

Forests are essential for life, including human life. The Amazon produces about 20 per cent of the world's oxygen.[42] Forests also protect us against climate change by storing carbon. And so, the destruction of forests isn't just a sad situation for the plant and animal species whose home it has been. It puts the whole planet at risk. Scientists credit tropical deforestation for about 20 per cent of global greenhouse gas emissions.[43]

Forests also play an important role in rainfall. In fact, forests can create much of their own rainfall through transpiration—a process in which plants absorb water and then water evaporates from the plants. Without forests, there is less rain but without rain, we risk forests. Douglas Sheil of the Center for International Forestry Research (CIFOR) and an ecologist with the Norwegian University of Life Sciences warns deforestation can exacerbate irregular rainfall. In a blog, a writer for CIFOR points to research that shows we may have been grossly underestimating just how vital a role forests play in rainfall: 'Vegetation may contribute as much as 90 per cent of the moisture in the atmosphere derived from land surfaces—far more than earlier estimates.[44]'

Animal Agriculture: More Greenhouse Gas Emissions Than Transport

FAO figures put GHG emissions from animals reared for food at somewhere between 14.5 to 18 per cent of all human-caused emissions[45], more than that caused by transportation. That is more than all of the cars, trucks, ships, planes and other vehicles in the world combined.[46]

Vehicles produce a number of gasses, but primarily carbon dioxide, while methane is produced in the digestive system of ruminant (cows, buffaloes, sheep, goats, camels) animals. This gas is then released through these animals' flatulence, when they belch or through their manure. Animals reared for food emit more than one third of the world's methane emissions.[47] Methane is said to be seventy-two times more harmful than carbon dioxide over a twenty-year period.[48]

India is the world's fourth largest emitter of greenhouse gasses, only behind China, the United States and the European Union. India's rank as a top emitter is not an accident: Not only does it compete with Brazil (the fifth largest emitter) for being the largest beef exporter on the planet, it is often ranked as having the highest population of cattle, goat, buffalo and sheep in the world, second to China, in methane production.[49]

Author of a 2018 Indian Institute of Technology Delhi and the Deenbandhu Chhotu Ram University of Science and Technology study on India's methane emissions from animals reared for food,

Shilpi Kumari warns India is on track to raise surface temperatures at the rate of 14 per cent of the total contribution of the world livestock sector over a twenty-year period. She told SciDev.net, 'The impact on climate change is global in result, so the negative impact due to livestock emission is not restricted to India.[50]'

A paper published a few years ago, 'Greenhouse gas emissions from Indian livestock', that appeared in the journal *Climatic Change*[51] showed cattle used for dairy contribute to 60 per cent of India's methane emissions. The chicken meat and egg industries are also key contributors. The same paper explains in 2003, 86.1 per cent of the total emissions of nitrous oxide, also a greenhouse gas, from Indian animals reared for food that year was from the chicken meat and egg industries.

A case study conducted for the FAO, entitled, 'Livestock in the changing landscape in India; its environmental, social and health consequences and responses', says this of chicken-based industries: 'Air pollution results as the nitrogen in manure is converted to ammonia (almost 85 per cent of the feed nitrogen is unutilized and excreted through manure). Soil toxicity occurs when there is a build-up of nitrogen and phosphorous in the soil deposited through manure over a period of time.[52]' Raising animals for food is the cause of more than two thirds of global ammonia emissions—a key factor in the cause of acid rain.[53]

Exploding Pig Shit

The amount of waste the rearing of animals used for meat, eggs and dairy produces is almost unimaginable. Just one dairy farm with 2,500 cattle can produce the waste equivalent to a city of 4,11,000 people.[54] In their book, *The Sustainability Secret, Rethinking Our Diet to Transform the World*, the creators of *Cowspiracy* explain that enough waste is produced from farmed animals in the US alone in just one year to cover San Francisco, New York City, Tokyo, Paris, New Delhi, Berlin, Hong Kong, London, Rio De Janeiro, Delaware, Bali, Costa Rica and Denmark combined.[55] What a load of crap, literally, aye?

A 2010 paper published in the *Journal of Water and Health* warned that factory farms in the US were producing more than forty times the amount of waste than that processed by humans in US wastewater treatment plants, but that unlike human waste, 'no treatment is required of waste from animal agriculture.[56]' There, even now, such waste remains essentially untreated.[57]

Putrid manure from American farms is often stored in large outdoor basins, pools, known as lagoons, which release dangerous gases like ammonia and hydrogen sulphide into the air.[58] These lagoons often leak or overflow with significant rain or bad weather.

There are over 3,000 pig farm lagoons in North Carolina. When Hurricane Florence pounded this state at the end of 2018, flood waters mixed with numerous lagoons, contributing pig faeces to the pollutants left on its streets. Pig waste matter can contain up to twenty times more nitrogen than the contents of human sewage.[59]

If you think that's bad, consider that in the US, there have been bizarre reports of exploding pig shit. An article appeared in *Mother Jones* about this disturbing phenomenon, stating, '[I]n about 2009, in the pits that capture manure under factory-scale hog farms, a grey, bubbly substance began appearing at the surface of the faecal soup. The problem is menacing: As manure breaks down, it emits toxic gases like hydrogen sulphide and flammable ones like methane, and trapping these noxious fumes under a layer of foam can lead to sudden, disastrous releases and even explosions. According to a 2012 report from the University of Minnesota, by September 2011, the foam had 'caused about a half-dozen explosions in the upper Midwest ... one explosion destroyed a barn on a farm in northern Iowa, killing 1,500 pigs and severely burning the worker involved'.[60]

Farm Waste and Ocean Dead Zones

Waste from animals reared for food is also killing life in our rivers and seas by resulting in dead zones, areas where a lack of enough oxygen means no marine life. While things like vehicle emissions and human sewage contribute, nitrogen and phosphorous from animal manure from intensive farms are the main offenders.[61]

Nitrogen and phosphorus are considered nutrients but too much of them cause algae to grow so fast that it limits oxygen in water and results in air pollution, leading to illness and fish deaths. These algae growths are called algal blooms. The US Environmental Protection Agency (EPA) warns, 'Some algal blooms are harmful to humans because they produce elevated toxins and bacterial growth that can make people sick if they come into contact with polluted water, consume tainted fish or shellfish, or drink contaminated water.[62]' In North Carolina, numerous mass fish deaths were reported as pig waste entered waterways after Hurricane Florence.[63]

Animal waste has contributed to a humongous dead zone in the Gulf of Mexico, which is soon set to expand to over 17,145 square kilometres, an area stifled that is larger than the size of Nagaland. There are more than 500 dead zones in oceans around the globe.[64]

Indian waterways are also affected by animal and slaughterhouse waste. A Jammu and Kashmir State Pollution Control Board report cautions, 'The wastes from slaughterhouses and packaging houses are similar chemically to domestic sewage but are considerably more concentrated. They are almost wholly organic, chiefly having dissolved and suspended material. The principal deleterious effect of these wastes on streams and water courses is their deoxygenation.[65]'

Contaminated Drinking Water

The EPA warns in a policy data document that manure from farm animals is a primary source of nitrogen and phosphorus to surface and groundwater too.

It explains, 'Nutrient pollution in ground water—which millions of people in the United States use as their drinking water source—can be harmful, even at low levels. Infants are vulnerable to a nitrogen-based compound called nitrates in drinking water. Excess nitrogen in the atmosphere can produce pollutants such as ammonia and ozone, which can impair our ability to breathe, limit visibility and alter plant growth. When excess nitrogen comes back to earth from the atmosphere, it can harm the health of forests, soils and waterways.[66] Nutrient pollution would pose the same risks for people in India and elsewhere around the world.

World Bank statistics show 85 per cent of drinking water supplies in India are dependent on groundwater.[67] With the majority of slaughterhouses in India operating without any effluent treatment facility, the problem of untreated slaughterhouse waste ending up in waterways and effecting groundwater in India is a regular target of criticism by environmentalists and other members of the public.

As one of many examples of this, during a high court case regarding pollution caused by Kaloor slaughterhouse in Kerala, the Kerala State Pollution Control Board filed that, 'It is true that there is no proper waste water treatment plant or solid waste disposal plant in the slaughterhouse. It is true that the untreated wastewater along with a large quantity of solid waste, including cow dung, flesh and other objectionable waste, is being disposed to the Thevara Perandoor Canal from the slaughterhouse. The functioning of the slaughterhouse is creating untold miseries and nuisance to inhabitants and is also causing pollution of the TP Canal and affecting aquatic organisms.[68] The court was also told the discharge of untreated effluents and stagnant water is allowing mosquitoes to breed putting humans at risk of mosquito-borne illnesses.

An Aligarh Muslim University study looked at two slaughterhouses in Aligarh and 460 households living around them. It asked these households what it's like to live near these facilities and found, 'Nearly 74 per cent reported of incidence of flies/insects and mosquitoes in high number spreading infection; 98 per cent reported of horrible odour from slaughterhouse; 78 per cent reported of choking drains containing water with blood and debris; 58 per cent reported of drinking water contamination; 79 per cent reported of pungent odour from burning of fats and bones.[69]'

It Doesn't Have to Be This Way

Studies comparing the impact of plant-based diets with those which are meat-based put how unpleasant factory farms and slaughterhouses are into perspective.

A 2014 University of Oxford study that considered the differences in the environmental effects of diets in the UK found that people who eat meat are responsible for twice as many dietary GHG emissions as vegans.[70] In 2016, this same university described a study by Oxford Martin School researchers that took into account the environmental and health consequences of eating animal-based foods on its website. Considering different dietary scenarios for 2050, the researchers found vegetarian diets could spare 7.3 million deaths while vegan diets could spare 8.1 million. The university explains, 'The study projects that by 2050, food-related greenhouse gas emissions could account for half of the emissions the world can afford if global warming is to be limited to less than 2°C. Adopting global dietary guidelines would cut food-related emissions by 29%, vegetarian diets by 63% and vegan diets by 70% ...'[71]

The study also put a monetary value on the benefits of transitioning towards eating plant-based foods. The university states, 'The researchers also modelled the economic benefits of dietary change and found they could save $700–$1,000 billion (US) per year on healthcare, unpaid informal care and lost working days. The economic value that society places on the reduced risk of dying could even be as high as 9–13% of global GDP, or $20–$30 trillion (US). In addition, the researchers found that the economic benefit of reduced greenhouse gas emissions from dietary changes could be as much as $570 billion (US).'

The goal of scientists and governments who take part in international climate talks is now to stop the earth from warming a mere two degrees Celsius more. We are this close to inconceivably catastrophic problems like stronger heatwaves, longer droughts, reduced crop yields, critically risking delicate coral reefs, and rising sea level,[72] which would flood many of the world's coastal regions and cause large-scale damage and migration, especially in India and Bangladesh.

Already, scientists are warning we are set to reach this two additional degrees' mark by 2050 if human impact on climate change does not significantly vary. Sir Robert Watson, former head of the UN's Intergovernmental Panel for Climate Change (IPCC), warns, 'Climate change is happening now, and much faster than anticipated.[73]'

We should, therefore, consider it a relief that making a huge positive impact on climate change, and populations of wild animals like the tiger, can be as easy as making a simple diet change.

13

THE PRICE WE PAY

In my opinion there are definite drawbacks in taking milk or meat. In order to get meat we have to kill. And we are certainly not entitled to any other milk except the mother's milk in our infancy. Over and above the moral drawback, there are others, purely from the point of view of health.[1]

—Mahatma Gandhi

When I was in my early twenties, my mother's cousins, who were close to her age and most of whom lived in Gujarat, were in their early fifties. That's when we started receiving calls about them 'suddenly' dying of heart attacks—their families always described the attacks as a surprise. While it may sound strange that even though my father had a stroke in his thirties, when he also had a heart attack in his early fifties that he thankfully survived, we weren't expecting it. He considered himself to be healthy and thought the stroke was a mere fluke, a case of plain bad luck, and that's how we, his family, thought of it too. Doctors my father spoke to at the time encouraged this view.

Perhaps my father and my mother's cousins never experienced or simply didn't recognize early warning signs of a heart attack, dismissing them as something else. Those who believe themselves to be in decent health likely wouldn't expect to have an attack so young. But today, half the heart attacks in India strike in people younger than fifty, with a quarter occurring in those under the age of forty.[2]

In fact, these days, lifestyle diseases like cardiovascular disease, diabetes and cancers cause most deaths in India—over 60 per cent of them. Unhealthy diets are a major culprit, with tobacco use accounting for about 6 per cent of India's disease load.[3] Thanks undoubtedly to the awareness work of health advocates, a recent study indicates Indians are finally smoking less.[4] Yet while cigarette packs now contain graphic labels of certain cancers and other health problems linked to smoking—packets of meat, eggs and dairy carry no such warnings, considering the ailments doctors and health studies now tell us they are linked to, they should.

At the time of his attack, my father ate all of these foods, and while my mother's cousins in Gujarat did not eat meat or eggs, they consumed plenty of ghee and other dairy foods, fried foods and oil.

Experts like Dr T. Colin Campbell, who is globally renowned for his pioneering work in nutrition education and research; Dr Caldwell B. Esselstyn, who discovered a proven plant food-focused method for arresting and actually reversing even very advanced stages of heart disease; Dr Neal Barnard, president of Physicians Committee for Responsible Medicine (PCRM), based in Washington, DC and author of a book on using the power of plant foods to reverse diabetes; and Dr John McDougall, physician and nutrition specialist, were featured in the must-see health-related documentary *Forks Over Knives*.

Nowadays, they and numerous other health authorities warn animal-derived foods, oils and processed foods full of sugar, salt and fat—like the kind that usually come in packaging instead of their natural form—are making us awfully sick. Among the diseases which these experts list as diet-related are heart disease and stroke, like my father faced; hypertension and osteoporosis, like my mother suffers; diabetes, which my grandmother was plagued by; cancer that killed half of my grandparents, allergies and many more. Impotence is also on this list.

These doctors recommend what they call a whole-food, plant-based diet for good health, disease prevention and even arrest of disease progression and possible cure. This is eating focused on unprocessed plants like fruits, vegetables, whole grains and legumes.[5] And it's not just these doctors who are singing the praises of plant-based foods—recently, hundreds of them stood outside the White House in Washington, DC behind a banner that read, 'Go Vegan!'. A week later, they joined hands again for a similar stunt, but this time the banner read, 'Ditch the Dairy!' The doctors were in the city for an international conference on nutrition in medicine, co-hosted by PCRM and the George Washington University School of Medicine and Health Sciences.[6]

Becoming Heart-Attack Proof

Many of us tend to blame genetics, God and fate for a poor heart or lousy health. You know, bad luck, like my father thought about his stroke. This attitude makes us helpless victims who have no control over our own bodies. Those who feel they have no power over their own health also have little motivation to do anything different to try to improve matters—which likely contributed to my father's heart attack after having a stroke. But if anyone can prove that's not usually the case, that we are more often than not fully responsible for being healthy or ill, it is Dr Esselstyn. I had the good fortune of joining Dr Esselstyn on a speaking tour of medical schools and hospitals in India. What he presented blew the doctors away.

He described patients who came to him with progressed states of coronary artery disease for an initial study, and showed slides of their arteries before and after they went through his programme. The differences were profound. Not only did following his programme stop the advancement of their artery blockage, it reversed it. From the slides you could plainly see their arteries opened up. Prior to joining Dr Esselstyn's study, these patients' treatments had included bypasses and angioplasties, and several of them had been given the terrible news that they were going to die within a year. Dr Esselstyn used a plant-based, no-oil food programme, along with cholesterol-lowering medication, as needed, to become what he calls 'heart-attack proof'. As Dr Esselstyn describes in his book, *Prevent and Reverse Heart Disease*, twelve whole years later, seventeen of these formerly serious heart patients who continued with his programme had no further heart episodes and patients even lived more than twenty years without any more symptoms.[7] In other words, he *cured* these patients of heart disease.

Diabetes, like heart disease, can also be reversed according to Dr Neal Barnard who has written a book about it called *Dr Neal Barnard's Program for Reversing Diabetes*. Considering just how prevalent diabetes is among people I know, this is a book I have given to my parents, my parents' friends—basically anyone and everyone who will take it—to help them prevent or work to be in control of diabetes. I highly recommend picking it up along with the Esselstyn book. Dr Barnard's programme also involves working towards this goal with a low-fat vegan diet—that is, a diet of no animal-derived foods or added cooking oils. Barnard and his colleagues had embarked on numerous research studies from which the programme was born, with one finding his plant-based plan to be triply more effective than the dietary guidelines of the American Diabetes Association for controlling blood sugar.[8]

Letting Plants Be Thy Medicine

Alberta LeBlanc's case is a real-life example of a plant-based diet working magic. Alberta lives in Louisiana, US, and her son Robbie LeBlanc works for PETA Foundation in the UK. In a blog written by Alberta for the PETA US website,[9] she describes that following a lifelong meat, cheese and fried foods diet, she developed type-2 diabetes, high cholesterol, hypertension and numerous other serious ailments. In her late sixties, she was in and out of the emergency room.

Robbie told me[10] that his mother had started fainting, wasn't producing enough iron, 'was medicated up to the eyeballs', and began regularly haemorrhaging. She then stopped producing enough blood cells, and her heartbeat was irregular. Doctors had difficulty diagnosing what was wrong with her—it turns out she had developed aplastic anaemia—a condition that can cause frequent infections and other symptoms, and be fatal. Robbie visited Alberta during one of her many visits to the hospital in Louisiana where he says she was 'constantly receiving infusions and transfusions,' and noticed the dinner they gave her was a greasy pork chop and sugary blue drink. That's when he had enough.

Robbie was aware of the benefits of plant-based foods, having been vegan for many years. He complained to hospital staff that the foods they were feeding patients was making them more sick, went to his parents' place and threw out all of the food in the fridge and pantry that wasn't plant-based. He parked himself at his parents' house for weeks, consulted with Dr Barnard and taught his mother what to eat to be on a low-fat vegan diet. Although he had tried to convince her to eat healthier before, this time she was in a desperate enough situation to be willing to try.

The results were tremendous. Within four months, Alberta lost nearly fourteen kilos. She was due for a treatment that would have involved chemotherapy for the aplastic anaemia, but her oncologist advised to hold off, that things appeared to be improving. She never ended up having that treatment. Two years since the time she started eating plant-based, she lost a total of thirty kilos, had enough energy to take up daily exercise on her bike—a first in decades, and went back to work.

In the blog Alberta writes shortly after she switched to plant-based foods, her doctors were able to lower her insulin by 40 per cent and her cholesterol medication by 50 per cent. She says her new diet has meant 'reduced food bills, a much more diverse menu, a new-found interest in shopping for food and food preparation and lower prescription costs.'

Alberta and those who have worked with Esselstyn and Barnard are hardly the only ones to have benefited from eating plant-based. In India, Dr Nandita Shah, recipient of the prestigious Nari Shakti Award 2016 for her work in health and nutrition, and author of *Reversing Diabetes in 21 Days,* is among the professionals who encourage vegan oil-free eating. Dr Shah is the founder of Sanctuary for Health and Reconnection to Animals and Nature (SHARAN), an organization that helps people transition to nutritious foods. Testimonials on their website[11] include those from Shailaja Menon, a professor at TISS Hyderabad, who was diagnosed with early stage chronic kidney disease and whose husband suffers from diabetes. She came across Dr Shah's work and embarked on a whole-foods, plant-based way of eating. She reports they starting seeing significant health improvements within just weeks of eating this new way. Her husband was quickly able to reduce his medication from seven pills to two in consultation with his doctor, and her condition improved so much she shocked her nephrologist. Not only was her disease no longer progressing, but her kidney functioning was getting better.

Another testimonial is from Jaishree Kannan whose ovarian cancer had relapsed within nine months despite surgery and chemotherapy. Because her body couldn't take yet another round of chemo, she searched for an alternative and found SHARAN. Within just a few days of eating wholly plant-based, Jaishree's mouth ulcers began vanishing. That was ten years ago—Jaishree knocked out cancer and credits good food for saving her life.

Shammi Sethi, a cyclist, has also provided a testimonial. Sethi was vegetarian but consumed dairy and lived a very active lifestyle (we're talking 150-km cycle missions). Most would assume a person like this to be healthy but Shammi was diagnosed with high blood pressure. He was told by his doctor he would need to be on a cocktail of medications for life. Not liking that advice, he ended up meeting nutritionist Bhavna Kapoor from SHARAN and within four months of following their plant-based diet, he was well enough to be able to reduce his medication from four tablets a day to one.

Others have had such major health improvements that food has become their only medicine. Dr Suketu Shah is a general and laparoscopic surgeon at BCJ Hospital and Asha Parekh Research Centre in Mumbai. She reports that eating the way SHARAN recommends resulted in her reversing diabetes, hypertension and obesity in just four months and that now she needs no medications.

Mayavi Khandelwal, the founder of My Pure Path, a Mumbai-based tiffin service I often use that provides vegan, oil-free and even gluten-free lunches, reversed her diabetes, hyperthyroidism and high blood pressure and is medicine-free from eating the types of foods she now serves to others.[12]

India Leader in Diet-Related Ailments

India tops the charts in the kinds of diet-related ailments Alberta and others face. Cardiovascular diseases are the leading cause of deaths in India[13], and indeed the world (causing 31 per cent of all deaths worldwide, killing 17.7 million people a year).[14] And heart disease is not only ending the lives of the old: According to a *Trinity*

Hospital study, 900 people under 30 are dying every day from heart attacks in the country.[15]

It is no coincidence then that India was called the impotence capital of the world by sexual medicine expert Dr Sudhakar Krishnamurti[16]—impotence is considered an early warning sign of blocked arteries (not just to the heart, ahem!) and heart disease.[17] It's also not a matter of chance that as Indians are suffering from heart disease at earlier ages, they are also becoming impotent younger too. A few years ago, Ahmedabad-based sexologist Dr Paras Shah observed that one out of four of his patients with erectile dysfunction was under thirty, and that out of 400 men complaining of problems in this area, around hundred were just twenty-something.[18]

Stroke is a key cause of death and disability in India.[19] India is also the world leader in diabetes, with as many as 50 million of its citizens suffering from the type-2 variety.[20] High blood pressure is a major calamity in the country too, with it being projected to affect 214 million Indians in 2025.[21] One out of eight male and one out of three female Indians are reportedly suffering from osteoporosis.[22] The rise in lifestyle-related cancers,[23] such as of the breast, colon and prostate, in India are alarming. And while it is also the home to the most underweight people in the world, obesity is a growing epidemic, with 20 million obese women and 9.8 million obese men in India as per recent records.[24]

Childhood obesity is a crisis now in India too, with an expected 17 million obese children in the country by 2025,[25] and parents ought to worry. As explained in a paper that appeared in the *Indian Journal of Endocrinology and Metabolism*, 'Childhood obesity impacts all the major organ systems of the body and is well known to result in significant morbidity and mortality. Obesity in childhood and adolescence is associated with established risk factors for cardiovascular diseases and accelerated atherosclerotic processes, including elevated blood pressure (BP), atherogenic dyslipidemia, atherosclerosis, metabolic syndrome, type-2 diabetes mellitus, cardiac structural and functional changes and obstructive sleep apnea.[26'] According to another study, 70 per cent of obese youngsters already have at least one risk factor for cardiovascular disease.[27]

If you live in a city, watch out! People who live in Indian urban areas are at triple the risk of heart attacks than those living rurally.[28] Not only are many villagers getting more exercise through manual work than those with a sedentary lifestyle, but if you consider that more and more people in cities, especially kids, have access to the meat, egg or dairy-laden foods, like burgers and pizzas offered by fast-food chains, this may become less surprising. Kerala has tried to reduce the consumption of fatty foods by proposing a 14.5 per cent tax on fast-food chains[29], but that still doesn't address the growing amount of animal products children are being fed at home, including by parents who believe them to be good for health.

But Where Do You Get Your Protein?

It is commonly thought, thanks in large part to myths put out by the industries that produce animal-derived foods, that meat and/or eggs are required for protein and that animal milk is needed for calcium. While it is true that meat and eggs contain protein, they are also cholesterol heavy, and though milk contains calcium, like meat and eggs, it also contains animal protein which, unlike plant protein, is now known to seep calcium from our bones to pass through our urine.

Indeed, the meat and egg industries have been so successful at making consumers believe these foods are the ultimate and perhaps even the only sources of protein, while the dairy industry has been as effective in creating that impression about itself for calcium, that many people are surprised to hear whole foods, or plant foods in their natural form, contain all the protein[30] and calcium[31] we need, often containing just as much or more than animal-derived foods.

One large egg contains 6 grams of protein[32], but one cup of chickpeas contains 14.5 grams, that same portion of boiled lentils contains 17.9 grams, and a half cup of firm tofu contains 19.9 grams. Even two tablespoons of peanut butter, which contains 8 grams of protein[33], contains more protein than an egg. In a blog, Dr Scott Stoll, a healthy eating guide, explained, 'Broccoli contains more protein per calorie than steak and, per calorie, spinach is about equal to chicken and fish. Of course, you'll need to eat a lot more broccoli and spinach to get the same amount of calories that you do from the meat. Multiple studies have shown that if you are meeting your caloric needs through plant-based nutrition, you will satisfy your body's protein requirements.[34]'

As far as milk is concerned, the equivalent of 226 grams of non-fat milk contains 299 milligrams of calcium.[35] In contrast, one cup of calcium-fortified orange juice can contain 349 milligrams of calcium while a half cup of calcium-set tofu can contain 861 milligrams! Dark green, leafy vegetables like spinach and kale, as well as many types of beans, chickpeas, figs and soybeans are also particularly strong sources of calcium.[36]

The human body does not require excessive amounts of protein or calcium. Too much protein is, in fact, linked to kidney disease, certain cancers, osteoporosis and calcium stones and too much calcium is thought to be possibly linked to prostate cancer.[37] Thus, eating a whole-foods, plant-based diet easily suffices for our dietary requirements of both protein and calcium for good health.

Ande Ka True Funda

Cholesterol intake contributes to heart disease because when low-density lipoproteins (LDL) cholesterol becomes too high, it affects our arteries and can gradually hamper blood flow. Our own bodies already produce the cholesterol we need—we do not require it from an external source.[38] Unlike animals, plants do not have a liver and are unable to make cholesterol. Animal-based foods are chock-full of cholesterol, including the types of meats many people consider healthier, like the meat from chickens.

Many are surprised to hear chicken meat contains as much cholesterol as beef, 25 mg per ounce, and that shellfish is also often cholesterol-heavy. The physicians at PCRM say, 'Every 100 mg of cholesterol in your daily diet adds roughly five points to your cholesterol level, although this varies from person to person.' They caution 100 mg of cholesterol is contained in about 114 grams of beef or chicken, half an egg or three cups of milk, and advise, 'People can reduce their cholesterol levels dramatically by changing the foods they eat. For every 1 per cent you reduce your cholesterol level, you reduce your risk of heart disease by 2 per cent.[39]'

PCRM further emphasizes keeping a check on fat consumption helps reduce cholesterol and the risk of diet-related diseases, warning that all animal-derived foods, including so-called 'lean' meats as well as fried foods and vegetable oils, are extremely fatty with about 23 per cent of the calories of skinless chicken coming from fat; ice creams containing about 45 to 65 per cent calories from fat; most cheeses 60 to 80 per cent; and butter, margarine and oils usually containing 95 to 100 per cent of calories from fat. Plant foods in their natural form have less than 10 per cent of their calories coming from fat. What's more, meat, eggs and dairy foods and some vegetable oils also contain saturated fat, which, unlike unsaturated fats, causes the creation of more cholesterol in our bodies.[40]

The Indian National Egg Coordination Committee wants you to eat eggs every day. You'll remember their old sign-song advert that goes, 'Sunday *ho ya* Monday, *roz khao ande!*[41]' Unsurprising, really, considering they represent egg sellers. Research, however, shows us eating eggs every day, or any day, isn't the best idea.

Eggs contain a massive amount of cholesterol and more than 60 per cent of calories from fat, much of it saturated.[42] Studies published in various reputed journals have found that eggs are in fact so unhealthy that consumers who ate the most eggs increased their risk of cardiovascular disease by 19 per cent and their risk of diabetes by 68 per cent, and that diabetics who ate the most eggs increased their risk for developing heart disease by an incredible 83 per cent.[43]

Egg consumption has also been associated with colon, rectal, bladder and prostate cancers. Studies found that even people who consume a small amount of eggs, just one and a half eggs per week, have almost five times the risk for colon cancer than those who eat less than eleven eggs per year; modest egg consumption is said to triple the risk of developing bladder cancer; and the consumption of two and a half eggs per week by men was found to increase the risk of a deadly form of prostate cancer by 81 per cent in comparison those who consumed almost no eggs per week. Research has suggested that choline in eggs may aggravate the risk of heart disease, stroke and prostate cancer.[44]

The Myth of Dairy Consumption and Good Bone Health

In *Forks Over Knives,* Dr Campbell explains the reason why the consumption of animal protein such as that found in milk results in the leaching of calcium from our bones. In simple terms, it's because the consumption of it results in an acid-base imbalance in the human body. Our bodies then use the calcium from our bones to combat this condition.[45]

A University of North Carolina paper published in *The American Journal of Clinical Nutrition* explains, 'Osteoporotic bone fracture rates are highest in countries that consume the most dairy, calcium and animal protein.' Its researcher, Amy Joy Lanou, the current chair and professor of health and wellness for the university, found, 'Most studies of fracture risk provide little or no evidence that milk or other dairy products benefit bone.' The paper also warns, 'Accumulating evidence shows that consuming milk or dairy products may contribute to the risk of prostate and ovarian cancers, autoimmune diseases and some childhood ailments. Because milk is not necessary for humans after weaning and the nutrients it contains are readily available in foods without animal protein, saturated fat and cholesterol, vegetarians may have healthier outcomes for chronic disease if they limit or avoid milk and other dairy products.' It goes on to suggest, 'Bones are better served by attending to calcium balance and focusing efforts on increasing fruit and vegetable intakes, limiting animal protein, exercising regularly, getting adequate sunshine or supplemental vitamin D, and getting ≈500 mg Ca/d from plant sources.[46]'

A large Harvard Physicians' Health Study found that male consumers of just a little over two servings of dairy per day had 34 per cent more risk of developing prostate cancer than men who consumed no or almost no dairy products,[47] while Iowa Women's Health Study showed just drinking more than one glass of milk per day seemed to increase women's chances of ovarian cancer by 73 per cent over those who drank less than one glass per day. Dairy consumption is also thought to worsen the risk of breast cancer for the same reason it is linked to prostate cancer—a growth factor called IGF-1 that is found in cow's milk.[48]

Childhood onset diabetes, or rather type-1 diabetes, is also thought to be related to the consumption of animal milk. A study from Finland demonstrated that giving children cow's milk early increased their vulnerability to this type of diabetes. Supportively, the American Academy of Pediatrics found that refraining from giving babies cow's milk for at least until they are three months old lowered the risk of this diabetes by up to 30 per cent.[49]

As mentioned earlier, most of us also cannot properly digest milk because we are lactose intolerant. In fact, researchers at the Sanjay Gandhi Post Graduate Institute of Medical Sciences found that three out of four Indians cannot digest milk.[50] Although rare, even new-born babies can be lactose intolerant.[51]

Some people are allergic to animal milk, which is different from lactose intolerance. Symptoms can include hives, coughing, a runny nose, watery eyes, diarrhoea, among others. Like peanuts, for those who are allergic, milk can also result in anaphylaxis, which causes difficulty breathing and can even result in death.[52]

For babies, reaction to animal milk can include colic, which is noticed by long, intense crying, likely from tummy pain. The baby need not drink bovine milk directly to suffer colic. Mothers who drink milk can pass the animal's antibodies to their babies through their breast milk.[53]

How About a Side of Poison with Your Fish?

Speaking of mothers, the US Food and Drug Administration (FDA) and Environmental Protection Agency (EPA) have issued advice for expecting women and parents that list certain species like bigeye tuna, king mackerel, marlin, shark, swordfish and others as 'choices to avoid' for having the highest mercury levels.[54] Other fish too frequently contain significant levels of mercury. The advice from the FDA and EPA targets parents because the dangers of eating fish can be especially problematic in children in the womb.

The Delhi-based Centre for Science and Environment (CSE) warns, 'Mercury, a very toxic and dangerous substance, has severely contaminated land, water, air and the food chain throughout India … Mercury is poisonous in all forms—inorganic, organic or elemental. Methyl mercury is a neurotoxicant: It can damage the developing brain as it crosses the placental and blood-brain barriers easily. The threat to the unborn is, therefore, of particular concern. It can also trigger depression and suicidal tendencies, paralysis, kidney failure, Alzheimer's disease, speech and vision impairment, allergies, hypospermia and impotence. Even miniscule increases in methyl mercury exposures may adversely affect the cardiovascular system, says the UNEP's Global Mercury Assessment report. It is also a possible carcinogen for humans, according to the International Agency for Research on Cancer.[55']

At a conference organised by the CSE on the subject, Dr R.C. Srivastava, co-chairperson of the United Nations Environment Programme's (UNEP) Chemicals Working Group, described mercury contamination in India as reaching 'alarming levels'. This was blamed mostly on discharge of industrial waste containing more mercury than prescribed by Indian and World Health Organization (WHO) standards.

The CSE looked at numerous studies of mercury pollution in India finding especially high levels of mercury in fish caught in coastal areas, like those around Mumbai, Kolkata and areas of Karnataka and Bihar. It observed, 'The North Koel river showed mercury concentrations almost 600–700 times above the limits.'

Other serious pollutants can also be found in fish, including those that may be cancer causing in humans or lead to other health ailments like learning disabilities or other neurological problems, liver damage, reduced immunity, and more.

Fish consumption is unhealthy for other reasons too. Like other meats, eggs and dairy, it contains animal protein and is especially rich in it; much of the fat in fish is saturated; and certain fish are especially high in cholesterol. A PCRM factsheet on fish consumption,[56] therefore, cautions, 'Chinook salmon, for example, derives 52 per cent of its calories from fat, and swordfish derives 30 per cent. About one quarter of the fat in both types of fish is saturated. Fish and shellfish are also significant sources of cholesterol. Three ounces of shrimp have 166 milligrams of cholesterol, while the same amount of bass has about 80 milligrams; in comparison, a three-ounce steak has about 80 milligrams.'

According to one study of Japanese men, like milk, fish consumption also appears associated with the risk of prostate cancer. Many people consume fish believing they have to for their source of omega-3 fatty acids. PCRM offers the reassuring knowledge, 'Alpha-linolenic acid, the only essential omega-3 fatty acid, is found in many vegetables, beans, nuts, seeds and fruits.'

Delhi Belly

The consumption of animal-derived foods is also linked to various foodborne illnesses. Foodborne illnesses are a major global problem, with the WHO estimating nearly one in ten people falling sick every year and 4,20,000 dying from consuming contaminated food. Children are at particular risk of falling sick from eating bad food.[57]

India is so infamous for food poisoning among tourists that there is a name for it: 'Delhi Belly'. Vegetarians and vegans can also get food poisoning from unhygienic food, of course, but certain outbreaks are more commonly linked to animal-derived foods.

For example, egg consumption is a major factor for salmonella outbreaks and deaths. Other food-related infections often associated with meat or dairy products include campylobacter (chicken meat and milk)[58], *E. coli* (often ground beef) [59], staphylococcal (often pork)[60], listeriosis (meat or dairy)[61]. This list is far from exhaustive. To make matters worse, food-borne illnesses are becoming harder to treat because of antibiotic resistance.[62]

Ironically, food-borne illnesses and health problems arising out of a lack of a sanitary environment are a major reason why children in India, such as through government mid-day meal schemes, are fed eggs. Of course, the official justification given for feeding kids eggs is not this—it is to address malnutrition. Certainly, that would be the intention, but if we take a look at what causes malnutrition, it's easy to see eggs won't solve it.

According to the WHO, half of all malnutrition is linked to repeated diarrhoea or intestinal worm infections from dirty water and inadequate hygiene conditions. India is home to almost 62 million stunted kids, but this is not due to a lack of eggs or animal-derived foods in their diets. As an article by the Population Reference Bureau, which specializes in disseminating information on population, health and the environment, explains, 'Stunting in children can stem from enteropathy, a chronic illness caused by inflammation that keeps the body from absorbing calories and nutrients. Children who are exposed to open defecation or who don't have a clean water supply may ingest bacteria, viruses, fungi, or parasites that cause intestinal infection; chronic inflammation in a child's gastrointestinal track is linked to stunting and anaemia, and puts children at risk for poor early childhood development.[63]'

In other words, much of the answer to addressing malnutrition lies not in feeding India's children foods that are at high risk of contributing to food-borne illnesses and conditions like diarrhoea, but in working to ensure access to clean water, toilets and a hygienic environment.

Not all mid-day meals contain eggs, however, or even dairy. [64] Instead meals consist of chapati, rice, pulses and vegetables[65]— the perfect fuel for a growing person containing plant protein and other nutrients more easily absorbed and retained by the human body. Those states that serve eggs also often only do so once a week. However, as eating habits are set in childhood, a consortium of fifteen doctors and nutritionists recently approached states and union territories urging them to leave out all animal-derived foods here forward as a matter of policy.[66] They call for children to be provided a variety of healthy plant-based foods packed with the fibre, vitamins and minerals they need to help them be in the best position to avoid heart disease, diabetes and other ailments later in life.

Plant Power

So, the consumption of meat, eggs and dairy harms our health in various ways, but still not convinced plant-based eating is for you? Consider this:

The Academy of Nutrition and Dietetics is described as the world's largest organization of food and nutrition professionals. The group raises in a position paper, 'It is the position of the Academy of Nutrition and Dietetics that appropriately planned vegetarian, including vegan, diets are healthful, nutritionally adequate and may provide health benefits for the prevention and treatment of certain diseases. These diets are appropriate for all stages of the life cycle, including pregnancy, lactation, infancy, childhood, adolescence, older adulthood and for athletes ...Vegetarians and vegans are at reduced risk of certain health conditions, including ischemic heart disease, type-2 diabetes, hypertension, certain types of cancer and obesity. Low intake of saturated fat and high intakes of vegetables, fruits, whole grains, legumes, soy products, nuts, and seeds (all rich in fibre and phytochemicals) are characteristics of vegetarian and vegan diets that produce lower total and low-density lipoprotein cholesterol levels and better serum glucose control. These factors contribute to reduction of chronic disease. Vegans need reliable sources of vitamin B12, such as fortified foods or supplements.[67']

Dr Barnard recommends a B12 supplement for everyone, vegans and meat-eaters alike.[68] For vegans, B12 may be found in plant products from bacterial contamination, fortified foods and certain fermented foods like spirulina and miso, but taking a supplement is an easy way to ensure we are getting enough B12 (adults usually need about 2.4 micrograms a day) while still being protected from diseases linked to the consumption of animal-derived foods.[69] And a study published in *The American Journal of Clinical Nutrition* of nearly 45,000 people in the UK showed vegetarians were 32 per cent less likely to die or need hospitalisation from heart disease. These individuals experienced lower cholesterol levels, blood pressure and weight.[70]

Research published in the same journal concluded 'the incidence of all cancers combined was lower among vegetarians than among meat eaters[71]' while another study found 'vegan diets showed statistically significant protection for overall cancer incidence ... in both genders combined and for female-specific cancers.[72]' It also found vegetarians seem to have decreased risk of cancers of the gastrointestinal system. A look at the dietary habits of more than 70,000 people by Loma Linda University showed those who ate a vegetarian diet had a 22 per cent lower risk of colorectal cancer than those who were non-vegetarian.[73]

On diabetes, a study published in *Nutrition, Metabolism and Cardiovascular Diseases* of over 40,000 men and women who provided lifestyle and other data to researchers concluded vegetarian diets 'were associated with a substantial and independent reduction in diabetes incidence.[74]'

And to keep the kilos off, plant-based diets are the best. A study from Loma Linda University of over 71,000 men and women, with an average age of 59, found average body mass index was lowest among vegans and highest among those who eat meat. Specifically, researchers found that only 9.4 per cent of the vegans studied were obese while 33.3 per cent of the people who ate meat were obese.[75]

On a personal note, my father, who is now nearly vegan, has not suffered any major health problem since he stopped eating meat, and my mother, who is vegetarian and has stopped eating eggs, but still consumes some dairy, continues to have hypertension and osteoporosis. However, I suspect she may have long ago gone the route of her cousins if she had started eating meat like my father had.

There is the old saying, you are what you eat, and evidence shows when we avoid using our bodies as an animals' graveyard, we too stay alive and thrive.

14

THE MYTH OF HUMANE PRODUCTION

[M]ost meat is obtained from the slaughterhouse, a place of blood and offal and struggles and screams. If that is so humane, why don't we take the kids and make a day of it? Because it isn't humane, that's why.[1]

—*Ingrid Newkirk, founder, PETA affiliates worldwide*

Eyewitnesses reveal stolen dogs[2] and cats with collars still on and recognisable breeds like Dalmatians as among those that end up being transported by scooters and trucks to be killed for meat in China. Gangs tour city streets and collect dogs and cats they see, strays and companions alike.[3] These animals, many of whom were once kept in people's homes, are moved on the backs of vehicles crammed in often tiny, rusted metal or wooden crates like the kinds often used for transporting chickens. And like chickens, transporters deny them water, food and careful handling.

231

When they finally arrive to the market or slaughterhouse, most are made to wait confined, with some animals kept so crowded, they are piled on top of others. Crushed together in suffocating heat, they meow and howl in fear, confusion, discomfort and despair. Workers use iron tongs that clasp around the animals' necks to move them from the cage.

In China, dogs and cats are typically slayed by being clubbed repeatedly and then having their throats slit over a bucket or drain. Dogs have been secretly filmed by animal protection group Last Chance for Animals facing the horrifying ordeal of being trapped in a pen with a menacing man who clubs each of them over and over again, one by one. They try to escape, hide, cower and yelp in terror while their pen-mates' skulls are crushed.[4]

Many dogs and cats are also used for leather and fur. Items made of dog or cat fur or leather are often mislabelled as from other animals and sold to unsuspecting buyers around the world. As part of an investigation of China's leather trade, PETA Asia filmed screaming dogs being dragged by their necks into a room awash with blood and full of dead dogs' bodies to face a butcher who kicks them and bashes their heads repeatedly with a heavy stick. Their terrified screeches sound similar to the panicked squeals of pigs.[5]

Many dead and dying dog and cats' bodies are hung from hooks, burnt with blowtorches and boiled to remove fur[6], not unlike how chickens' bodies are scalded in hot water for feather removal in mechanized slaughterhouses around the world.

In Indonesia, dogs and cats are killed in similar ways to how they are in China. Dog Meat-Free Indonesia reveals many animals are still conscious when fire is applied all along their bodies[7], just as many chickens are still aware when they are thrown in hot water as numerous investigations have revealed. Their bodies are then cut up, sometimes frozen and packed to be sold.

The butchery of dogs and cats in China and other parts of Asia for meat, fur and leather has been the target of outrage by people around the world who consider these species of animals friends.

If in response the Chinese government pledged to ensure dogs and cats are no longer stolen or caged, are reared on farms with access to the outdoors, given decent food and clean water, transported under regulations, and killed only after being stunned with proper equipment, would most people consider that acceptable? Would China even be trusted to adhere to these promises? Or would global protests against dog and cat slaughter continue?

Often Meaningless, Confusing Labels

While this trend hasn't picked up much in India yet, in the West, due to increased consumer awareness of and objection to how animals used for food are typically treated, packets of meat, eggs and dairy foods are commonly labelled as humanely produced so to encourage people who care about animals to buy them with reduced guilt. Descriptions commonly used to indicate higher welfare than normal include 'free-range', 'organic', 'higher welfare indoors', and 'grass-fed' but numerous other labels are also used. These labels are supposed to indicate varying degrees of humaneness, superior to regular factory farm conditions.

In the US, however, there's no legal definition of 'humane', 'cage-free', 'free-range', 'free-roaming', 'natural' or other such terms frequently used to describe how animals are reared.[8] There, for instance, 'grass-fed' is regularly seen on packets of beef and other meat. It sounds nice—as if the meat is from cattle or other animals who were allowed to roam in fields, eating grass. In reality, it could mean that the animals were fed grass at some point but then ended up on a feedlot—an enclosed intensive farming system common in the US where cattle or other animals are reared, often by the thousands, to be fattened for slaughter. There, they would be fed their regular mix of grain, antibiotics and growth hormone gruel to get them to 'slaughter weight' as quickly as possible.[9] Poor legal definitions have contributed to certifications from third-party organizations being used by companies to build consumer trust in their claims.

In the UK, groups like Compassion in World Farming (CIWF) campaign for clearer food labels and there are some definitions and requirements under European law (most Grade A, or decent-quality eggs with shells intact, when sold whole and not as ingredients, have to be legally identified as from chickens reared in an organic, free-range, barn or cage system).[10] However, now, in the UK as well as the US, so many labels and third-party certifications are used for various animal-derived foods that are supposed to mean different things that many consumers can't help but be confused.

For instance, ninety-nine per cent of animals in the US are reared in factory farms but a couple of years ago, the Sentience Institute ran a survey of Americans that found 75 per cent of them claim they normally buy meat, milk and eggs 'from animals that are treated humanely.[11]' The math doesn't add up indicating many consumers there likely do not accurately understand the welfare implications of the foods they are eating.

In both countries, numerous investigations have shown humane labels can be essentially meaningless and that neither the labels nor the certification schemes can be fully trusted as guarantees of satisfactory animal welfare.

How Much Kindness Are You Willing to Afford?

In 2012, animal protection groups CIWF and OneKind joined hands to assess and compare the major schemes for farm assurance standards in England and Scotland to help consumers with their buying choices. The Red Tractor scheme is the UK's largest food labelling programme, but it was ranked lowest, expecting hardly more on animal welfare per its standards than what is already required at the bare minimum by law. The assessment revealed the Red Tractor's 'Assured Food Standards' scheme still allowed practices such as the cutting off of pigs' tails without anaesthetics, severely restricting animals' movement including refusing grazing opportunity for cows used for milk, genetically modifying or cloning animals, and more. An article in the *Independent* about it read, 'The 'good food' stamp barely worth the label it's printed on.[12]' CIWF and OneKind recommended other schemes like those endorsed by the British Royal Society for the Prevention of Cruelty to Animals (RSPCA) or Soil Association are better. Investigations into farms operating under those schemes too, however, have revealed cause for concern.

One of the many difficulties with animal welfare labelling and schemes is that rather than governments just legally requiring all farms to treat animals with as much compassion as possible, it is left up to the consumer to decide how much cruelty they are fine with or how much kindness they want to afford.

For example, in the UK, free-range reared hens are supposed to be cage-free and have access to the outdoors, while barn raised hens are cage-free but cannot go outside, and eggs from hens kept in cages are the cheapest. Hens used for eggs labelled organic are supposed to be free-range and have more access to the outdoors than those from non-organic free-range systems. They are also supposed to be kept in less crowded conditions. All of these hens would still suffer routine debeaking, except for those used for organic eggs certified as so by the Soil Association. Birds used for free-range British Blacktail eggs sold by British supermarket chain Waitrose also apparently escape debeaking.[13]

How and whether the chickens are caged or debeaked, of course, is just part of the problem—these birds would still face other horrors such as the trauma of transport and the misery of the slaughterhouse.

And are the free-range birds as free as the description sounds? UK-based animal protection group Viva! is among those that say no.

Not So Happy Hens for Happy Eggs

Noble Foods is the UK's largest supplier of eggs.[14] It prides itself on higher hen welfare. Among the eggs it sells are those under its Happy Egg label. You would think a company that says on its website, 'At Noble Foods, animal welfare is at the cornerstone of everything we do[15]' would steer clear of eggs from caged hens, but it also uses the Big and Fresh brand and keeps 4.3 million hens in cages[16].

Rising demand for free-range eggs in the UK by well-meaning consumers (52 per cent of eggs produced in the UK in the fourth quarter of 2018 were from hens kept on farms defined as free-range[17]) seems to have translated into crowded conditions on some farms.

Viva! documented hens used for eggs sold under the Happy Egg label housed by the thousands in sheds until they are eighteen to twenty-one weeks old. The group believes this was to get them used to staying indoors to make egg collection easier. Viva! also found that electric wires were used to shock young hens to avoid them defecating in areas where their food was kept.

They report farmworkers handling garbage bags full of dead birds, visiting a shed plagued with red mites and, though the hens are debeaked, being told that hens in a shed peck each other to death. All this on farms certified as adhering to certain standards by a highly respected third party—the RSPCA under its Freedom Food scheme (now improved and changed to RSPCA Assured).[18]

The RSPCA has come under fire many times for documented conditions on Freedom Food-monitored farms. Some years ago, Animal Aid visited a Double Gate Farm in Somerset, UK operated by Millard Poultry Ltd where it said more than 30,000 birds were held in a 2,300 square metres unit with no access to the outdoors. Animal Aid visited the farm three times over the course of the chickens' shortened lives and reported finding 'numerous chickens immobilised and often dying from hunger, because agonising leg and hip injuries prevented them from reaching feed and water stations.[19'] Other problems were also found such as perches kept in a way that most birds couldn't use them, disease, injury and more. The farm was suspended from the Freedom Food scheme.

It's not just chickens. Viva! documented conditions at an Attwells and Seafield Pedigrees farm in the Midlands, UK, rearing turkeys whose staff member asserted it was RSPCA Freedom Food-approved. There, on this supposedly higher welfare farm, the group found typical factory farm conditions: sheds so overcrowded with turkeys they could not even spread a wing. They reported that many birds were found trampled, there were no perches or hay for the birds despite the RSPCA requirements, a turkey suffering with a severe bloody facial abscess and more.[20]

In April 2013, McDonald's announced it was transitioning to selling only Freedom Food pork in the UK[21], and thus supposedly from pigs reared as per RSPCA standards. By September of that same year, news was out of a Hillside Animal Sanctuary investigation of pigs at Wood Common Farm near Congleton, UK, which supplied McDonald's and was part of the Freedom Food scheme. Hillside's investigation found malnourished, crippled and semi-paralyzed pigs lying collapsed in faecal slurry. One veterinarian said it was the worst case of cruelty in pig farming he had ever come across.[22] The RSPCA's response was to suspend this farm from the Freedom Food scheme too, but due to exposé after exposé of conditions that do not meet the RSPCA's own criteria, consumers couldn't help but wonder what was happening on other Freedom Food scheme farms too.

This wasn't the first time problems were found on a Freedom Food monitored pig farm either. Hillside Animal Sanctuary had previously documented conditions at Manor Farm in Yaxham, UK also monitored by the Freedom Food scheme. There pigs spent their days in faeces, urine and mud muck in a dark barn. The group reported rats having a feast on piles of dead pigs. An investigator told the media outlet *Sunday People*, 'Thousands of distressed pigs were sleeping in their own filth. There was no sign of dry space—just a pool of slurry. A few yards away was a huge bin full of dead pigs swarming with maggots that spilled out on to the barn floor … On one visit there were so many carcasses the bin was overflowing, and eight or nine dead pigs had just been dumped next to it. It was horrible for the pigs—and a huge health risk.[23]' Farm owners Easey Pigs Ltd supplied supermarket chain Tesco via various food processors. Here too, Freedom Food suspended the farm and Tesco stopped selling its products.

Label Schemes Under the Scanner

Following the name change of their programme from Freedom Food to RSPCA Assured, the RSPCA improved its welfare requirements. It still allows certain treatment such as indoor systems, mutilations like teeth clipping and tail cutting (albeit in what they call 'exceptional' circumstances), space allowances that do not allow for all natural behaviours and so on common to factory farming systems.[24] Their efforts are, however, with noble motive to reduce suffering. But worryingly for consumers seeking guarantee of welfare standards, as past investigations have shown, even lower standards were often not met.

Soil Association has come under the scanner for violations of its certification scheme standards too. Animal Aid secretly investigated a Soil Association-approved slaughterhouse in Devon, UK resulting in the suspension of three butchers and a condemnation by the UK's Meat Hygiene Service, which called conditions 'clear evidence of breaches of animal welfare legislation'. The slaughterhouse handled pigs and sheep. Animal Aid reports animals there were 'being kicked, slapped and thrown; improperly stunned; and even decapitated while they may still have been alive.[25]'

This Is No 'Chicken Disneyland'

The American Humane Association runs a certification programme in the US that, like the Red Tractor scheme in the UK, has been condemned for offering the bare minimum standards, not much better than factory farming.

Consumer Reports, an American magazine well-regarded for providing unbiased product ratings and reviews, said, '[M]any of the requirements in the American Humane standards mirror the conventional industry's practices, and livestock producers do not have to meet all of the requirements to be certified. The program does not require producers to meet certain requirements that consumers may expect from a welfare label, such as providing access to the outdoors, access to fresh air and indoor enrichment that relieve boredom and allow animals to engage in natural behaviours. The standards do not prohibit physical alterations such as teeth filing and tail docking of pigs or beak trimming of chickens. The American Humane Association welfare program allows livestock producers to administer antibiotics to an entire flock or herd (at the discretion of the veterinarian—for example, if at least one animal in the flock or herd is sick).[26]'

This programme covers more than one billion animals in the US, and Mercy for Animals warns on its website AmericanHumaneScam.com, 'American Humane Association has certified many of the cruellest factory farms in North America, including Butterball, Weaver Brothers, Burnbrae Farms, Rose Acre Farms, Cal-Maine, Eggland's Best and Hillandale Farms. Many of these AHA-certified companies have been caught on hidden camera abusing animals.'[27]

American supermarket chain Whole Foods describes itself on its website as the company that 'seek[s] out the finest natural and organic foods available, maintain the strictest quality standards in the industry, and have an unshakeable commitment to sustainable agriculture.[28]' Indeed, many consumers view Whole Foods as trustworthy, wholesome. It offers products with varying degrees of better welfare than regular factory farming—again, leaving it to consumers to decide how much cruelty they find acceptable or how much kindness they want to afford instead of requiring all of its suppliers to meet the highest possible welfare standards.

A few years ago, a PETA US investigator spent over two months documenting conditions at a pig farm, Sweet Stem Farm, in the American state of Pennsylvania that supplies Whole Foods and says it produces 'happy meat.'[29] This farm was certified as 'Step 2,' more humane than 'Step 1,' as per Whole Foods certifications that go up to Step 5. Most farms supplying pig meat to Whole Foods only meet Step 1, that is the lowest requirements. 'Step 2' farms are supposed to be spacious and have an enriched environment to mentally stimulate pigs.

PETA US' eyewitness documented the pigs at Sweet Stem Farm were nearly always crammed into crowded sheds or made to live on concrete floors and that some pigs were kept in semi-darkness. A bit of straw was strewn over the floor and some pigs were provided less than half a square metre of floor space each. For 200 pigs, a few chains or rubber hoses were provided for play but Whole Foods-supported standards list these as 'not … acceptable enrichments' because they are not 'valuable/satisfying to the pigs,' as 'extensive research' demonstrates. 'Thermal comfort' is mentioned as important in the Whole Foods standards, but PETA US reports finding one water sprinkler for hundreds of pigs to use during hot months.

But it doesn't just stop there. PETA US's eyewitness reported sick or injured pigs being left to have their conditions worsen instead of being promptly euthanized—what should have happened under the Whole Foods standards. This included a pig with a recurrent fever and another who was lame—both were ultimately shot. Seven pigs were left to suffer bloody huge rectal prolapses for up to nearly a month.

And it gets worse. The report found workers hit pigs, a manager allowed twenty pigs to be kept packed in a metal trailer during a hot day for more than twenty-four hours, a manager lifted heavy pigs by their ears, pigs who had been given antibiotics were loaded on to a truck destined for a slaughterhouse (despite Whole Foods pledge that it doesn't sell meat from animals who have been given them)[30] and dead pigs who were diagnosed with contagious salmonellosis. (Salmonella infection can be spread to humans who eat improperly cooked meat or eggs. Symptoms can include vomiting, abdominal pains, fever, diarrhoea, blood in the stool and more. The infection can even become life threatening.[31])

In December 2018, PETA US released the findings of an eyewitness who visited a cage-free facility at Hilliker's Ranch Fresh Eggs near San Diego, California.[32] The farm's owner Frank Hilliker called it 'Chicken Disneyland.' More like street artist Banksy's nightmarish and creepy Dismaland pop-up exhibit, described as 'a sinister twist on Disneyland,'[33] if you ask me.

The eyewitness found hens were crammed chock-a-block in the shed, so much so the floor was hardly visible. The shed reeked of waste and the hens' constant calls would put all the birds at risk of further distress. Hilliker's idea of providing 'toys' was to hang four nets from the rafters that only the socially dominant birds could access, that too after climbing across a sea of others. Upon observing the footage, a veterinarian remarked, 'It is my professional opinion that these hens experienced stress as a result of being unable to freely engage in natural behaviours, owing to the high stocking density and conditions in this shed.'

Recently, in Germany, chicken producers tried to block German public broadcaster *Mitteldeutsche Rundfunk* (MDR) from airing footage shot undercover of organic chicken farms. Germany's Federal

Court of Justice ruled that the footage could be aired in the public interest. The footage showed dreary conditions, partly featherless birds and some birds dead, but dismal as it may be, the court also ruled the chicken producers hadn't violated the law.[34]

Indian Producers Joining the 'Humane' Bandwagon

Indian producers of animal-derived foods are starting to join the 'humane' bandwagon. Mullipatti-based Happy Hens sells eggs from free-range birds and says it does not use antibiotics.[35]

However, in India, there is absolutely no legal definition of free-range. The company boasts on its website: 'We have implemented standards set by the Royal Society for the Prevention of Cruelty to Animals (RSPCA), the highest animal welfare standard, while raising our hens. Our birds do not have their beaks trimmed nor their wings clipped. They enjoy a minimum of 45 sq. ft. per bird of range, which means every hen has plenty of space to roam. We adopt a method of rotating them through green pastures, so they have constant access to greens. Comfortable, clean nesting boxes are provided to the hens. It allows them to lay eggs and brood in privacy in a secure place.'[36]

The RSPCA Assured scheme is, however, a UK scheme and its inspectors are UK based. A look at the packaging reveals Happy Hens' carton simply claims 'RSPCA (UK) Standards implemented' but it is missing the official RSPCA Assured certifying logo. And so, without a legal definition of free-range, government inspections or the RSPCA authorised stamp, Indian consumers may simply be left to take Happy Hens' word for how they treat the birds they use.

An article in the *Hindu* about Happy Hens discloses the company produces 4,000–5,000 eggs *per day*,[37] and has twenty franchisee farmers in Ariyalur, Perambalur and Tiruchirappalli. Chickens specially bred to lay eggs can lay many in a year, usually between 200–320, depending on the breed.[38] Taking into account breeds with the highest egg laying capacity, it still does not add up to one every day. That means Happy Hens raises far more than 5,000 birds to produce up to 5,000 eggs per day. Consider how large the farms would have to be to provide each bird nearly 4.2 square metres (or 45 square feet) space. Remember how in the UK, growing consumer interest in free-range eggs led to increasingly crowded conditions? Will this company endlessly keep buying land to meet increased demand for its eggs, or will it put a cap on the number of eggs it can produce to ensure it sticks to its own space standards?

The *Hindu* article also reveals there has been trial and error involved with the setting up of Happy Hens, leading to a loss of many chickens' lives. A co-founder, Ashok Kannan, lost 800 of the 1,000 chickens he started out with because he fed them the wrong food.

These aren't the only Happy Hens chickens who have died though. They all ultimately do. It is unclear how the company deals with male chicks who cannot lay eggs, but its hens end up at the butcher—200 of them per week. Kannan was quoted by the *Hindu* as explaining, 'The hen can actually live up to fifteen years in its natural state. But in our poultry farming model, the fertile period of the bird gets over in twenty months.' Then, off they go to be slaughtered. I bet the hens are not very 'happy' about that.

In India, many people consider milk from *gaushalas* slaughter-free and, therefore, humane, but too often these cow shelters focus on life, rather than quality of life. As previously mentioned, many unwanted cattle end up at here, where they are often used for dairy.

For example, the notorious Hingonia gaushala, where more than 8,000 cows died in a seven-month span due to neglect, is now, instead of being shut down, home to even more cows, nearly 15,000 of them, many of whom are used for milk, and who are, therefore, made to reproduce. Today, rather than being run by the government, its routine operations are handled by a non-governmental organization (NGO).[39] But nearly 15,000 cows crammed together in one space, many producing calves—with these numbers, it is nothing short of a dairy factory farm. Besides, can a gaushala with that kind of past death rate really be considered slaughter-free? Can other gaushalas where cattle often succumb to untreated or poorly treated health conditions?

'Better Than Nothing' Bad for the Planet

Certain certifiers have very close relationships with animal-derived foods industries, leaving the public to question where their loyalties really lie, but organizations like the RSPCA do not have ill intent. Rather, as stated before—they are genuinely trying to push producers of animal-derived foods to treat the animals they raise or kill more kindly and would have created their standards taking into account how far they feel they can reasonably push these businesses to improve. But trying to find a balance between what's better for animals and what the industries may be willing to do can leave standards lower than what many consumers would likely expect from humane certification. And though the RSPCA monitors those who use its label, its inspectors cannot be everywhere all of the time.

Proponents of humane labelling argue that consumers buying products with the labelling helps improve conditions on farms and that it is 'better than nothing'. This is hardly a ringing endorsement, but improved conditions, if and when they are even achieved, tend to be marginal and do not typically translate into elimination of practices that most concerned people would find unacceptable to support if they knew exactly what went on.

Moreover, higher-welfare farms, and those that claim to be, are still disastrous for the environment and, in some ways, can even be more damaging, including because there is not enough land on Earth for all farms rearing animals for food to be shifted to free-range. Already, we are clearing huge swathes of rainforest and other land to raise animals and the food to feed them and affecting the chances of many wild animals to survive in the process. Systems dealing with animals used for food already take up almost half of the global surface area—do we really wish to make it closer to 100 per cent, leaving room only for these animals and high-rise flats for us to live? We would be foolish to think that type of transition to a deforested planet, with nearly nothing but farms rearing animals, wouldn't negatively impact our own health and survival.

Domesticated cattle exist in the huge numbers they do (over 1.4 billion)[40] because humans breed, use and kill them for food. A *Mother Jones* article warned of a situation if all dairies in the US became slaughter-free: '... we'd need three to four times as many dairy cows to produce the same amount of milk, which would mean adding at least 27 million additional cows to our herds. Those added cows would each year produce greenhouse gas emissions equivalent to four large coal-fired power plants.'[41] In India, scientists have already warned that methane produced by its existing livestock population alone can considerably raise global temperatures.[42]

Speaking of methane, Jacy Reese, co-founder of Sentience Institute, points out grass-fed rearing of cattle for beef results in up to four times more methane production than animals fed grain, and in addition to using more land, it requires more water and fossil fuels.[43]

Would support of hypothetical 'humane' or 'higher-welfare' rearing and slaughter of dogs and cats be okay as it would be 'better than nothing' or would support of such a practice keep those species of animals entrenched in suffering a cruel and unnecessary system? I suspect most people who care about dogs and cats would say the latter. Many opponents of humane labelling feel the same when it comes to cows, buffaloes, sheep, goats, pigs, chickens and fish.

15

MAKING THE TRANSITION
∽

When the suffering of another creature causes you to feel pain, do not submit to the initial desire to flee from the suffering one, but on the contrary, come closer, as close as you can to him who suffers, and try to help.[1]

—*Leo Tolstoy*, A Calendar of Wisdom

If this book has inspired you to become vegan, vegetarian or to eat less meat, eggs or dairy foods, this chapter is for you. You'd be in plenty of company. Today, with increased awareness of what happens to animals for food, the environmental impact of producing such foods and the health effects of consuming them, vegan eating is taking India and the world by storm. A recent article on a website run by Franchise India Holdings Limited, Asia›s largest integrated franchise solution company, reads the number of vegans in India has risen by 360 per cent in the past decade[2].

I am a former meat, egg and dairy consumer and my first reaction to a friend suggesting I stop eating meat was that I never would—and yet for over twenty years now, I have been eating only plant-based foods. The vast majority of the now vegan colleagues I have had at PETA affiliates around world are former meat-eaters too. They come from a variety of backgrounds and religions—with most growing up in households where meat consumption was the deep-rooted cultural norm. But, they know that no religion *requires* meat-eating even if it allows it, and that just because things have long been a certain way in their families or communities doesn't mean they have to be that way for them now.

In preparation for this chapter, I spoke to colleagues, supporters and volunteers of various PETA affiliates as well as many others who grew up eating meat or consuming dairy foods about what led them to make the switch to eating vegan, what obstacles they faced and how they made the transition. Common challenges they described included having initial difficulty staying resolute in their decision to eat plant-based; unsupportive family members, partners or friends; not being initially convinced eating plant-based is healthy; not knowing what to cook or where to buy vegan foods; feeling alone; wrongly believing being vegan would make it hard for them to eat at a restaurant or in social engagements; and incorrectly thinking eating vegan has to be expensive. I have kept their experiences, and my own, in mind in providing the five steps towards eating vegan, vegetarian or less animal-derived foods you will find in this chapter.

However, more than difficulties, what these individuals shared is how happy they are in their decision to eat vegan, and how easy they find eating plant-based, now. I wholeheartedly share this view.

It's amazing how quickly new habits form and how fast our bodies adjust to a different way of eating—in a shorter time than you probably think, your cravings change and you soon start to relish healthy vegan foods. You speedily transform from thinking about what you're giving up, to realizing what you're gaining: a clean conscience, good health, and a whole new world of plant-

based foods and recipes to try. Like with doing anything new, it's
an adventure! Through eating plant-based and getting hooked into
social networks of other vegans, you make new friends. You explore
different ways of cooking, and try new restaurants. You may even
come up with a hot new ethical business idea, like my good friend
Stephanie Downs who helped create Good Dot, a vegan 'meat'
business out of Udaipur. And for extra good news, every person I
have ever met who has gone vegetarian or vegan have all said they
ultimately felt repelled by the very animal-derived foods they once
used to devour which means for most, eventually missing these
foods does not remain an issue.

Most of these individuals also had something positive to share
about the effect of eating plant-based on their health or on the well-
being of those they know. Many revealed eating vegan helps them
maintain a healthy weight, be active, has cleared up their skin, seems
to prevent them from getting ill, and more.

As for me, I am forty-three years old, but most people are
surprised to learn that—many comment that I look much younger.
I can count on one hand the number of sick days I have taken in the
past two decades. And I haven't suffered the awful stomach aches
or coughs that were so regular for me in my childhood and teenage
years for even a single day since I stopped having dairy.

Inspired? Feeling ready? Here are the five steps:

Step 1: Know Eating Vegan Is Easy Peas-y

Think of all of the trying things you have overcome in your life and
the challenges you have conquered—you likely passed countless
exams; gained entry into university; became a professional; raised
wonderful children and more. But choosing to have soya chunks or
vegetables instead of chicken in a subzi, tofu (soya paneer) instead of
paneer, margarine instead of butter, soya milk instead of dairy milk
and so on are not mountains to climb. They are just simple, easy food
choices that often do not even alter the taste or texture of the dish

much, if at all. In Indian cooking especially, it's usually the spice, not the vegetable or meat, providing much of the taste, and that flavour doesn't change greatly between meat and vegetable dishes.

Worried you'll miss meat or cow's milk too much? Don't. Maxwell Maltz was a plastic surgeon and in the 1950s, he observed it took about 21 days for patients to get used to their cosmetic surgery, and that it took him about this amount of time to establish a new habit too. He concluded through this and other observations it takes a minimum of about 21 days to form a new habit, while other researchers later said they think it takes about 66 days[3]. Of course, this varies from person to person, but the point is, the time is not long. The biggest hurdle is in just deciding to eat vegan, and once that's done, it becomes easier and easier day by day until you forget you were trying to form a new habit at all because your new way of eating simply becomes routine.

PCRM runs a 21-day vegan web resource for Indians to kick-start their foray into the vegan lifestyle at www.21dayKickstartIndia. org. The western version of the programme, which can be found on www.pcrm.org, has helped hundreds of thousands of people to improve their health through easy recipes, advice from nutrition experts, success stories and other resources. On the India-specific page, visitors can find similar tools.

And there's more support! In India, SHARAN holds 21-day health retreats each year; offer a number of health programmes such as Diabetes Reversal, Hypertension Reversal, Weight Release and more; provide consultations and can facilitate support groups; arrange cooking classes in various cities; give talks and more. Check them out on sharan-india.org.

Step 2: Get and Stay Schooled

You being on this page of this book means you have already started acquiring knowledge on the benefits of eating plant-based. However, this book isn't the only resource for that of course.

Watching documentaries is a great way to become more committed to your goal of protecting animals and eating vegan and hosting a movie night can help your friends and family members appreciate your new eating choices too. There are many documentaries on vegan eating, animal rights, environmental protection and good health to choose from, but here are some of my favourites:

1. *Earthlings*: This is a great one to show to anyone you want to introduce to animal rights. It covers how animals are used by various large industries: in the pet trade, for food, clothing, entertainment and experimentation and helps the viewer consider that it is a similar type of rationale against those who are different that allows people to be sexist or racist, which allows them to be speciesist (ranking members of one species more worthy than another for better treatment).

2. *Dominion*: This one was released in 2018. It is a feature-length film directed by Chris Delforce and co-produced by *Earthlings* director Shaun Monson which covers various ways animals are exploited and examines humanity's 'superiority complex' over the animal kingdom. Joaquin Phoenix, Rooney Mara, Sia, Kat Von D and Sadie Sink help narrate the film.

3. *Cowspiracy, The Sustainability Secret*: I've mentioned this one earlier in this book, and this must-see film focuses on the environmental toll of raising animals for meat, eggs and dairy.

4. *Forks Over Knives*: This one too I've mentioned before, but it's so good, I must mention it again here. This documentary's tagline is, 'A film that can save your life'. Here's a description from its own website: It 'examines the profound claim that most, if not all, of the degenerative diseases that afflict us can be controlled, or even reversed, by rejecting our present menu of animal-based and processed foods'[4].

5. *What the Health*: This one is from the makers of *Cowspiracy* and is just as ground-breaking. Its website says, '*What the*

Health exposes the collusion and corruption in government and big business that is costing us trillions of healthcare dollars, and keeping us sick ... Audiences will be shocked to learn the insidious roles played by pharmaceutical companies, agribusiness, and processed animal food companies in the nation's health, especially in the most vulnerable communities, and will cheer at the transformation and recovery of those who took their lives into their own hands.[5] It is US-focused but the kinds of truths it exposes are not limited to being relevant only to US audiences.

6. *The Game Changers*: This film, executive produced by James Cameron, Arnold Schwarzenegger, Jackie Chan, Lewis Hamilton, Novak Djokovic and Chris Paul and directed by Louie Psihoyos, is a game changer indeed. In it, renowned athletes share their experiences of using plant-power for optimal performance.

7. *Fast Food Nation*: This is a film inspired by the book of the same name that examines the fast-food industry. It covers everything from cruelty to animals to the treatment of employees.

8. *Gods in Shackles*: This one is not food related, but is about the shocking cruelty to elephants for processions and use in temples in Kerala. I find anything that helps us empathize with the plight of any animal can increase our sensitivities to the suffering of all animals.

9. *Blackfish*: Though this too is not about animals used for food, I recommend it for the same reason I recommend *Gods in Shackles*—it's useful to generally raise our awareness about the plight of animals in people who you are introducing to the concept of eating vegan. This is about Tilikum, a captive orca at the US-based captive animal marine-park SeaWorld, who has since died. The powerful film resulted in a tremendous backlash against SeaWorld, once one of America's most famous parks.

10. *Okja*: Last but certainly not least, this Netflix original movie directed by *Snowpiercer's* Bong Joon Ho and starring Ahn Seo-hyun, Tilda Swinton, Paul Dano and Jake Gyllenhaal is fiction, but has helped many people consider the plight of real animals and led them to eat vegan. The movie follows Mija, a young girl who fights to save her best friend—a massive 'super pig' hybrid named Okja—from meat company Mirando.

If you're more of a book person, try these:

1. *Animal Liberation* by Peter Singer: If you only ever read one other book on animal rights, make this it. This book was first published in 1975, a year before I was born, and it's the book that inspired Ingrid Newkirk to start PETA in the US in 1980. Now there are PETA affiliates around the world. She writes, 'It forever changed the conversation about our treatment of animals. It made people—myself included—change what we ate, what we wore, and how we perceived animals.'[6]

2. *The PETA Practical Guide to Animal Rights* by Ingrid Newkirk: Need ideas on how to help animals? This guide would be perfect for you.

3. *Committed: A Rabble-Rouser's Memoir* by Dan Mathews: Dan is senior vice president for PETA US, and knowing him personally I can tell you, he's a riot. It's no surprise then that his book on his adventures of being an animal rights activist is a fun, funny and entertaining read.

4. *Eating Animals* by Jonathan Safran Foer: This *New York Times* bestseller is about the author's personal and emotional pursuit to question and consider what goes behind eating animals.

5. *Skinny Bitch* by Rory Freedman and Kim Barnouin: This sassy, hilarious book for women on eating right to look great is a rollicking read.

6. *Skinny Bastard: A Kick-in-the-Ass for Real Men Who Want to Stop Being Fat and Start Getting Buff* by the same authors is a similar book but for men. As Amazon puts it, 'What's good for the bitch is good for the bastard', they say.

7. *The Cheese Trap: How Breaking a Surprising Addiction Will Help You Lose Weight, Gain Energy, and Get Healthy* by Dr Neal Barnard. Here, Dr Barnard explains in detail how cheese is full of calories, fat, and cholesterol, linked to health problems, and why and how addiction to it must be broken.

8. *How Not to Die: Discover the Foods Scientifically Proven to Prevent and Reverse Disease* by Dr Michael Greger and Gene Stone. Really, the name says it all.

9. *What a Fish Knows: The Inner Lives of Our Underwater Cousins* by Jonathan Balcombe. This *New York Times* bestseller uses science to describe the emotional and intellectual competencies of fish.

10. *The Animals' Agenda: Freedom, Compassion, and Coexistence in the Human Age* by Marc Bekoff and Jessica Pierce. The book is described as 'a compelling argument that the time has come to use what we know about the fascinating and diverse inner lives of other animals on their behalf'.[7] It is a call for action.

Step 3: Find Support

Feel like the only vegan in the village? Don't worry. There are other ways to find social support.

Vegan groups are popping up all over India. SHARAN lists some on their website (https://sharan-india.org/join-sharan-vegan-related-facebook-groups-in-your-area/), but you can also simply Google or Facebook search the name of your city with the word 'vegans' after it, and you may come across a local group. If you don't find a group to join, why not start one on Facebook for your area? You'll probably be surprised at how fast the group grows. You can also try using meetup.com to find and meet vegans, or people who are curious about going vegan or eating vegan foods near you.

You may also like to opt for a vegan mentor. The organization Vegan Outreach runs a programme through which they connect volunteer mentors with individuals interested in going vegan (veganoutreach.org/vegan-mentorship-program/). As they describe, your mentor 'will help you with anything from navigating the grocery store aisles to figuring out how to respond when people ask you questions'. The mentor programme has been a huge success. They boast, 'The Vegan Mentor Program now has 2,300 mentors in 1,150 cities in 60 countries. Over 4,300 mentees have been matched so far.'[8]

If you would prefer information from or the support of people of your own religion or community, there are resources for that too. This includes websites run by PETA US' Christian and Muslim supporters like jesuspeopleforanimals.com and animalsinislam.com. There are also websites run by others like www.jewishveg.org, christianveg.org and jainvegans.org. Through Facebook, other groups like Vegetarian Muslim Society, Muslim Vegans, Christian Vegans, Jain Vegans and more can be found. Here too, if you don't see one that's right for you, why not just start one?

You can also keep up with the latest on what's happening in the vegan world in India, including new products to try, via VeganFirst.com where you can use the 'Ask Our Experts' section of nutritionists and others to clear your doubts.

Step 4: Cook, Eat and Experiment

With the vegan food options available today, you won't even have a chance to miss your favourite meat, egg and dairy foods. Some common ingredient replacements for traditionally meat or dairy containing dishes are mentioned in Step 1 of this chapter, and others include vegetarian 'meat'—made from soya or other plants but with the texture and taste of meat—or soya *chaap* instead of animal meat; vegetable oil instead of ghee; vegan mayonnaise instead of non-vegan mayonnaise (read the ingredient labels—many eggless mayonnaises are dairy-free too); and hummus, almond butter, cashew spread or peanut butter instead of a buttery spread. There are many yummy varieties of plant-based milks that can be used instead of animal milk. Almond, peanut, pistachio, coconut, oat and rice milk are among the plant milks available in India through various companies, as is vegan buttermilk by Nutriva. Abroad, there are even more varieties such as milk made from macadamia nuts, hazelnuts, hemp, peas, chickpeas and more.

Vegetarian meat is available in India from companies like Good Dot (which deliberately prices its products as low as meat), Vezlay, Vegetagold, Veggie Champ and more. Various vegetarian 'meat' products can be purchased from Godrej Nature's Basket, Foodhall, online (Good Dot takes online orders or you can try the vegan online store: VegaDukan.com). Sometimes the plant-based 'meat' is vegetarian, not vegan, so read the labels if you only want the vegan variety.

You will likely be able to find plant-based milks at your neighbourhood corner shop, while established grocery chains like Godrej Nature's Basket, HyperCITY Fresh and more also carry these products. Plant-based milk can also be ordered online from Big Basket and several others who provide a delivery service. GoodMylk (goodmylk.in) can be contacted to deliver vegan peanut milk or curd priced to be light on the wallet.

If you have a blender, you can also make these milks and other plant-based versions of dairy products at home on the cheap. SHARAN's website is a good resource for wonderful recipes for vegan versions of dairy products, including vegan cheese, yogurt, milks, cream and butter; as well as egg replacers; and faux meat.

Certain fruits and vegetables like jackfruit and mushrooms have a meaty texture and are good replacers for meat in dishes too. If you ever get your hands on a can of ackee fruit (popular in Jamaica and originally from West Africa), it can be used to make an eggless

version of scrambled eggs (recipes can be found on the internet). I
had the pleasure of tasting it at a Jamaican restaurant in London and
it is creamy, cheesy and delicious. It is best to use ackee from a can
because the raw fruit can be poisonous if eaten unripe, and its seeds
are poisonous too. Scrambled 'eggs' can also be made with tofu (just
Google to find your favourite tofu scramble recipe), and there are
also recipes online for vegan omelettes (often made with chickpea
flour). Urbanplatter.in sells various egg replacers, vegan parmesan
cheese and other exciting vegan products.

If you have a sweet tooth and are worried about having to give
up cakes and ice-cream by eating vegan, worry no more. Human
beings are great at discovery, and one fabulous finding is that the
liquid in cans of chickpeas (and other beans apparently, though I
haven't tried this), or the liquid leftover from cooking chickpeas
yourself, is an excellent egg replacer in making desserts and other
dishes that call for eggs. Aquafaba, as this chickpea juice is called, is
so effective as an egg replacement, there's a popular Facebook group:
facebook.com/groups/VeganMeringue/ about dishes that can be
made using it. Other egg replacers include bananas, applesauce,
ground flaxseed mixed with water (if you put 1 tablespoon flaxseed
put 3 tablespoons water), chia seeds (same ratio), and tofu depending
on whether the dish is sweet or savoury.

Readymade vegan ice cream is available from White Cub. It can
be found in Godrej Nature's Basket freezers. Papacream also makes
vegan ice cream, and in Hyderabad, Frozera runs a delivery service
for it. Sorbets are typically fruit-based and do not contain milk.

Alternatively, there are several vegan ice cream recipe books
available—just search 'vegan ice cream' in Amazon or Flipkart's
search feature—and many vegan ice cream recipes are also available
online. The books include *N'ice Cream: 80+ Recipes for Healthy
Homemade Vegan Ice Creams* and *Vegan Ice Cream: Over 90 Sinfully
Delicious Dairy-Free Delights*.

And brie, step aside. Delightful 'cheeses' can be made from nuts and seeds! Books like *Vegan Cheese: 75 of The Most Delicious Vegan Cheese Recipes: Created By Expert Vegan Chef To Curb Your Cheese Cravings* and *Artisan Vegan Cheese* are there to show you how. Numerous vegan cheese recipes are also available online. Nutritional yeast, which can be ordered online from Amazon or Urban Platter and which is also available through certain health food retailers, resembles parmesan cheese, is packed full of vitamins, and can be sprinkled on pizza and popcorn or other foods, or used in cooking in place of cheese. Many 'cheesy' vegan recipes have it as an ingredient.

If this sounds like too much work, don't worry. Readymade vegan cheese from foreign brands Violife and Verys is now available in India, and Indian companies offering plant cheese include Urban Platter, Soft Spot Foods, Bombay Cheese Company and Cowvathi.

Speaking of cookbooks, there are numerous vegan recipe books available. The *Guilt-Free Vegan Cookbook: Oil, Sugar, Gluten and Dairy Free Vegetarian Recipes* by Mala Barua and Nandini Gulati is an excellent resource for delicious food to help you thrive. Pramoda Chitrabhanu's *Rainbow Food for the Vegan Palate!* is also a favourite.

Of course, these days, you don't have to buy cookbooks at all. You can find countless vegan recipe blogs, YouTube channels and websites on the internet. Here are some suggestions: Bosh.tv for simple delicious recipes, veganricha.com for Indian and Indian-inspired vegan recipes, minimalistbaker.com for 'plant-based recipes requiring 10 ingredients or less, 1 bowl, or 30 minutes or less to prepare', ohsheglows.com for recipes largely free of gluten and processed foods, and cookingwithplants.com for oil-free ideas. The website manjulaskitchen.com also has a vegan section.

If you'd rather eat out or order in, the Happy Cow app has got you covered. Wherever you are in the world, use it to find a vegan, vegetarian or veg-friendly restaurant near you. In India, if using Zomato, type in the word 'vegan' in the search and you'll see restaurants that offer vegetarian or vegan food come up (you'll need to carefully look at the menu though, and specify to the restaurant that your order should be vegan). To be honest, I do not use Zomato to find vegan-friendly restaurants myself because it's so easy to go to just about *any* restaurant in India and find vegan options. Restaurant vegetarian options can often easily be made vegan by asking the chef to simply leave out the butter or ghee, paneer, or cream.

Still need more help? PETA India's free Vegan Starter Kit contains recipes, recommendations for what you can use in the place of various animal-derived ingredients and other tips. It can be ordered from PETAIndia.com.

Step 5: Get Involved

Working on projects to help animals, raise awareness about healthy eating or to protect the environment is an excellent way to keep motivated to eat vegan, make friends and inspire others to be kind. Whether you have a little or a lot of time, there's so much you can do. Here are some ideas.

- Speak up. It sounds simple enough, but so often we hesitate to do this. If a neighbour is hitting his dog, if you don't ask him to stop, who will? Other society members are likely to support you if you get the discussion started.
- Sign up for PETA India's Activist Network from its website to receive regular emails with ideas on getting active for animals. Also check out the action alerts on the front page of PETA India's website—with a few clicks, you can sign petitions and appeals requesting authorities to help animals.
- Keep numbers of local animal rescue groups handy. A directory of animal protection groups can be found on worldanimal.net. PETA India's 24/7 emergency response number is (0)98201 22602. Most of their rescuers are based in the Andheri West suburb of Mumbai but they can connect callers to local groups.

- Keep an animal rescue kit in your car. This can include a dog/cat carrier, dog/cat food, food/water bowls, gloves (to protect from potential scratches and bites from frightened animals), a collar and leash, towels and gauze bandages. This way, if you see an animal who needs help you are prepared and can transport the animal to a veterinary clinic or shelter or have the animal in the carrier until help arrives. Often, if you simply put food in the carrier, the animal will walk inside his or hers if they are able. Getting an animal protection group on the 'phone to further guide you would be useful.

- Share videos of what happens to animals for food, for the leather trade, in laboratories, for entertainment and for other uses on social media. Many videos can be found on PETA India's official YouTube page (www.youtube.com/officialPETAIndia).

- Consider joining your local animal shelter for an adoption drive or to walk and play with dogs. If you come across a shelter that is lacking in some facility due to a lack of resources, for example perhaps they need an ambulance, run a fundraising drive to help them out.

- If you have the time, patience and resources to adopt a dog or cat, opt to adopt an animal in need from an animal shelter. Obtain a copy of the Animal Welfare Board of India (AWBI) pet and street dogs circular from their website to know your rights as a companion animal guardian or request a copy from PETA India by writing to info@petaindia.org.

- Put out clean water for strays especially during hot weather. Strays also often rely on our mercy for other nourishment, so if you're able to feed strays, do, but outside of your society's gate to avoid unnecessary conflict. Be careful to avoid becoming the animals' only source of food if you are unable to commit to feeding them every day. The AWBI provides colony caretaker cards to those who would like official identification to show to anyone who might complain, but you do not need this card to feed strays.

- Know the law and report cases of illegal cruelty to animals to the police and work with them to file a First Information Report (FIR). Contact your local animal protection group or PETA India for guidance. The Prevention of Cruelty to Animals Act, 1960, can be found on the Animal Welfare Board of India's website (awbi.org) though there may be other laws that apply to the case.

- Use your profession to help animals. For example, if you are a doctor, why not speak to your patients about the benefits of plant-based eating? If you are a teacher, connect with Compassionate Citizen (compassionatecitizen.com/), PETA India's free humane education programme for children aged 8–12 to encourage kindness to animals. If you are a business person, perhaps you will want to explore creating a new vegan food product, or shoes made out of apple leather, or non-animal tested and environmentally friendly cleaning detergents. If you are a business owner, contact PETA India or your favourite animal protection group for leaflets to display that customers can pick up.

- Set up an information table or give a talk at your school, college or corporate office. PETA India can be contacted for materials, video, or guidance.

- Contact Vegan Outreach to become a vegan mentor or teach others how to cook vegan. Invite friends over for a dinner party to show them how delicious vegan food can be.

- Pledge to say no to plastic as much as possible and encourage others to also do the same. Plastic garbage is accidentally ingested by cows and other animals, including those who live in the sea. Small animals easily get trapped in plastic garbage too. This leads to a great deal of suffering and often death. Use reusable bags, say no to straws and single-use bottles, and dispose of trash keeping risk to animals in mind. For example, dogs and cats can easily get their heads stuck in jars so put the caps firmly back on before disposing.

- Join a clean-up drive. Versova was one of the most polluted beaches in Mumbai. This led local lawyer Afroz Shah to launch a citizens' clean-up drive. Shah got so much help that they removed 5 million kilograms of garbage from a 2.7 km shoreline, and now their clean-up efforts continue. As a result, after almost a decade, Olive Ridley turtles started appearing on Versova beach.
- Write letters to your local newspaper in response to stories of cruelty to animals, health and the environment for possible print in the letters to the editor section. Be sure to study the style and length of letters they print before submission. And if you see a television show, advertisement or film that depicts cruelty to animals, write to the director, producer or company to complain.
- Help SHARAN organize a healthy eating event in your city or at your corporate office. Contact the group via sharan-india.org.

If you feel there are concerns that I have not explicitly covered in this chapter, your vegan mentor, Facebook group or new friends who may have been through similar experiences are sure to be great sounding boards for ideas, and good suppliers of additional tips.

Hollywood actor Joaquin Phoenix, a longtime vegan activist, famously said, 'It takes nothing away from a human to be kind to an animal.[9]' Instead, as doctors are increasingly telling us, humans are healthiest by consuming whole foods like fruits, vegetables, nuts and pulses. Today, with all of the vegetarian meats, egg replacers and plant-based milks and other tasty vegan products available, what Joaquin said is especially true. We do not even need to compromise on tastes and textures we are used to by choosing to eat vegan, leaving us with fewer and fewer excuses for causing tens of billions of animals to suffer every year—for a moment of taste.

NOTES

❧

Introduction

1. Devi, Subramaniam Mohana, Vellingiri Balachandar, Sang In Lee, and In Ho Kim. 2014. 'An Outline of Meat Consumption in the Indian Population: A Pilot Review.' *Korean Journal for Food Science of Animal Resources* 34(4): 507–15.

2. Guilford, Gwynn, and Ritchie King. 2013. *Peak Meat? The World Eats 7-Times More Animals Than We Did in 1950*. 13 June. Accessed January 19, 2019. https://www.theatlantic.com/business/archive/2013/06/peak-meat-the-world-eats-7-times-more-animals-than-we-did-in-1950/276846/.

3. Indiaspend. 2015. *Chicken Is India's First Love, but Beef Consumption Is Rising Too*. 23 October. Accessed January 19, 2019. https://www.thequint.com/news/india/chicken-is-indias-first-love-but-beef-consumption-is-rising-too.

4. Esselborn, Priya. 2013. *Vegetarians developing a taste for meat*. 2 January. Accessed January 19, 2019. https://www.dw.com/en/vegetarians-developing-a-taste-for-meat/a-16490496.

5. Humane Society International. n.d. *Eating for the Environment*. Accessed January 19, 2019. http://www.hsi.org/issues/eating/meatfree_

guide/eating_for_the_environment.html?referrer=https://www.
google.co.in/.

6. Fishcount.org.uk. n.d. *Fish count estimates.* Accessed January 19, 2019.
    http://fishcount.org.uk/fish-count-estimates.

7. Old Dominion University. n.d. *Desegregation of Virginia Education.*
    Accessed January 19, 2019. https://www.odu.edu/library/special-
    collections/dove/timeline.

8. Samuels, Alexandra. 2016. *U.Va. report: Med students believe black
    people feel less pain than whites.* 5 April. Accessed January 19, 2019.
    https://www.usatoday.com/story/college/2016/04/05/uva-report-med-
    students-believe-black-people-feel-less-pain-than-whites/37416037/.

9. Gabbatiss, Josh. 2018. *Meat and dairy companies to surpass oil industry
    as world's biggest polluters, report finds.* 18 July. Accessed January 19,
    2019.   https://www.independent.co.uk/environment/meat-dairy-
    industry-greenhouse-gas-emissions-fossil-fuels-oil-pollution-iatp-
    grain-a8451871.html.

10. Steinfeld, H., P. Gerber, T. Wassenaar, V. Castel, M, Rosales, and C. de
    Haan. 2006. *Livestock's Long Shadow: Environmental Issues and Options.*
    Rome: Food and Agriculture Organization of the United Nations.

11. Ravindran, Shruti. 2014. *Mumbai will likely flood again – and nobody's
    doing much about it.* 27 November. Accessed January 19, 2019. https://
    www.theguardian.com/cities/2014/nov/27/mumbai-flood-rain-
    monsoon-city-planning.

12. Wu, Huizhong. 2016. *Mercury rising: India records its highest
    temperature ever.* 23 May. https://edition.cnn.com/2016/05/20/asia/
    india-record-temperature/.

13. Parfitt, Tom. 2018. *UK heatwave turns KILLER: 1,000 more people die
    this summer than average as temps soar.* 6 August. Accessed January 19,
    2019.   https://www.express.co.uk/news/weather/999586/UK-weather-
    forecast-heatwave-death-Met-Office-latest-temperatures.

14. TNN. 2016. *70% of Indians eat non-veg, but veg diet getting popular.*
    9 June. Accessed June 19, 2019. https://timesofindia.indiatimes.com/
    india/70-of-Indians-eat-non-veg-but-veg-diet-getting-popular/
    articleshow/52663492.cms.

15. Rowland, Michael Pellman. 2018. *Millennials Are Driving The
    Worldwide Shift Away From Meat.* 23 March. Accessed January 19, 2019.

https://www.forbes.com/sites/michaelpellmanrowland/2018/03/23/
millennials-move-away-from-meat/.

16. Animal Charity Evaluators. 2015. *How Many Animals Does a Vegetarian Save in the UK?* 1 April. Accessed January 19, 2019. https://animalcharityevaluators.org/blog/how-many-animals-does-a-vegetarian-save-in-the-uk/.

17. Gallagher, James. 2013. *Vegetarians 'cut heart risk by 32%'.* 30 January. Accessed January 19, 2019. https://www.bbc.co.uk/news/health-21258509.

18. Petter, Olivia. 2018. *Veganism is 'single best way' to reduce our environmental impact on planet, study finds.* 1 June. Accessed January 19, 2019. https://www.independent.co.uk/life-style/health-and-families/veganism-environmental-impact-planet-reduced-plant-based-diet-humans-study-a8378631.html.

Chapter 1: The Individual on Your Plate

1. The University of Adelaide. 2013. *Humans Not Smarter Than Animals, Just Different.* 5 December. Accessed January 19, 2019. https://www.adelaide.edu.au/news/news67182.html.

2. Schelling, Ameena. 2015. *Crying Mother Cow Greets Lost Baby In Breathtaking Reunion.* 6 August. Accessed January 19, 2019. https://www.thedodo.com/mother-cow-baby-reunited-1284650070.html.

3. —. 2015. *Mother Cow Hides Baby In Desperate Act Of Love.* 4 August. Accessed January 19, 2019. https://www.thedodo.com/mother-cow-hides-baby-1281641475.html.

4. Schlosberg, Jason. 2007. *Battle at Kruger.* 3 May. Accessed January 19, 2019. https://www.youtube.com/watch?v=LU8DDYz68kM.

5. Agrawal, Keshav. 2015. *Buffalo herd saves man from tiger.* 8 May. Accessed January 19, 2019. http://timesofindia.indiatimes.com/city/bareilly/Buffalo-herd-saves-man-from-tiger/articleshow/47207137.cms.

6. Edgar, Joanne, Suzanne Held, Charlotte Jones, and Camille Troisi. 2016 January. 'Influences of Maternal Care on Chicken Welfare.' *Animals (Basel)* 6(1): 2.

7. Hatkoff, Amy. 2009. *The Inner World of Farm Animals.* New York: Stewart, Tabori & Chang.

8. Farm Sanctuary. 2015. *6 Farm Animal Moms Who Will Do Anything For Their Babies.* 8 May. Accessed January 19, 2019. https://www.thedodo.com/farm-animals-moms-babies-affection-1132949239.html.

9. Ingham, John. 2018. *Grieving whale finally lets baby go after 17 days of mourning for lost calf.* 15 August. Accessed January 19, 2019. https://www.express.co.uk/news/nature/1003522/mother-whale-end-grieving-and-releases-dead-baby-environment.

10. Masson, Jeffrey, and Susan McCarthy. 1994. *When Elephants Weep: The Emotional Lives of Animals.* London: Vintage, Random House.

11. International Business Times. 2015. *Mothers' Love: Even after 4 years, this cow continues to hound a bus that killed its offspring [VIDEO].* 15 December. Accessed January 19, 2019. https://www.ibtimes.co.in/mothers-love-even-after-4-years-this-cow-continues-hound-bus-that-killed-its-offspring-video-659569.

12. Singer, Peter, and Jim Mason. 2006. *Eating: What We Eat and Why It Matters.* p. 58. London: Arrow Books, Random House.

13. Bates, Mary. 2014. *The Emotional Lives of Dairy Cows.* 30 June. Accessed January 19, 2019.

14. https://www.wired.com/2014/06/the-emotional-lives-of-dairy-cows/.

15. von Keyserlingk, Marina A.G., and Daniel M. Weary. 2007. 'Maternal behavior in cattle.' *Hormones and Behavior* 52; 106–113.

16. King, Barbara J. 2016. *WATCH: Ensnared Porcupinefish's Pal 'Keeps Vigil' As Snorkeler Sets It Free.* 31 March. Accessed January 19, 2019. http://www.npr.org/sections/13.7/2016/03/31/472500225/popular-video-of-porcupinefish-rescue-hinges-on-his-companion.

17. Hatkoff, Amy. 2009. *The Inner World of Farm Animals.* New York: Stewart, Tabori & Chang.

18. Radford, Tim. 2004. *All anxious sheep want is a picture of ewe.* 25 August. Accessed January 19, 2019. https://www.theguardian.com/science/2004/aug/25/science.research.

19. BBC News, 2004. *Sheep like smiles say researchers.* 11 June. Accessed January 19, 2019. http://news.bbc.co.uk/2/hi/uk_news/england/cambridgeshire/3796017.stm.

20. Bekoff, Mark. 2015. *Pigs are Intelligent, Emotional, and Cognitively Complex.* 12 June. Accessed January 19, 2019. https://www.

psychologytoday.com/blog/animal-emotions/201506/pigs-are-intelligent-emotional-and-cognitively-complex.

21. O'Connell, Sanjida. 2005. *This little piggy has depression*. 16 February. Accessed January 19, 2019. https://www.independent.co.uk/news/science/this-little-piggy-has-depression-483522.html.

22. Leake, Jonathan. 2005. *Cows hold grudges, say scientists*. 28 February. Accessed January 19, 2019. http://www.freerepublic.com/focus/news/1352692/posts (originally from news.com.au).

23. Jabr, Ferris. 2017. *Fowl Language: AI Decodes the Nuances of Chicken 'Speech'*. 11 December. Accessed January 19, 2019. https://www.scientificamerican.com/article/fowl-language-ai-decodes-the-nuances-of-chicken-ldquo-speech-rdquo/.

24. Edgar, Joanne, Suzanne Held, Charlotte Jones, and Camille Troisi. 2016 January. 'Influences of Maternal Care on Chicken Welfare.' *Animals (Basel)* 6(1): 2.

25. Ray, C. Claiborne. 2015. *How Fish Communicate, Even Using Noise*. 13 December. Accessed January 19, 2019. http://www.nytimes.com/2015/12/15/science/how-fish-communicate-even-using-noise.html.

26. Breithaupt, Thomas, and Martin Thiel. 2011. *Chemical Communication in Crustaceans*. Springer.

27. Agencies. 2009. *http://www.chinadaily.com.cn/world/2009-01/11/content_7385430.htm*. 11 January. Accessed January 19, 2019. http://www.chinadaily.com.cn/world/2009-01/11/content_7385430.htm.

28. Burghardt, Gordon M., Vladimir Dinets, and James B. Murphy. 2014. 'Highly Repetitive Object Play in a Cichlid Fish (Tropheus duboisi).' *Ethology* DOI: 10.1111/eth.12312.

29. Brown, C. 2015. 'Fish intelligence, sentience and ethics.' *Animal Cognition* 18(1): 1–17.

30. Matthews, Robert. 2004. *Fast-learning fish have memories that put their owners to shame*. 3 October. Accessed January 19, 2019. https://www.telegraph.co.uk/news/uknews/1473210/Fast-learning-fish-have-memories-that-put-their-owners-to-shame.html.

31. Power, Julie. 2015. *Cows master maze, making mice look like dimwits*. 23 July. Accessed January 19, 2019. https://www.smh.com.au/national/

nsw/cows-master-maze-making-mice-look-like-dimwits-20150723-gij1l7.html.

32. Gray, Richard. 2011. *Sheep are far smarter than previously thought.* 20 February. Accessed January 19, 2019. https://www.telegraph.co.uk/news/science/science-news/8335465/Sheep-are-far-smarter-than-previously-thought.html.

33. Radford, Tim. 2004. *All anxious sheep want is a picture of ewe.* 25 August. Accessed January 19, 2019. https://www.theguardian.com/science/2004/aug/25/science.research.

34. Hugo, Kristin. 2017. *Cow Science: Cattle are intelligent, emotional and they have eureka moments–so should we be killing them?* 11 November. Accessed January 19, 2019. https://www.newsweek.com/cow-cattle-animal-intelligence-science-personalities-emotion-697979.

35. Nuwer, Rachel. 2014. *Never Underestimate a Goat; It's Not As Stupid As It Looks.* 25 March. Accessed January 19, 2019. http://www.smithsonianmag.com/science-nature/never-underestimate-goat-not-stupid-looks-180950265/?no-ist.

36. BBC News. 2004. *Crafty sheep conquer cattle grids.* 30 July. Accessed January 19, 2019. http://news.bbc.co.uk/2/hi/uk_news/3938591.stm.

37. Gray, Richard. 2011. *Sheep are far smarter than previously thought.* 20 February. Accessed January 19, 2019. https://www.telegraph.co.uk/news/science/science-news/8335465/Sheep-are-far-smarter-than-previously-thought.html.

38. Stanley, T.L. 2014. *A New Reason Not to Eat Pigs: They Rule at Video Games.* 25 March. Accessed January 19, 2019. https://mashable.com/2014/03/25/pigs-video-games/?europe=true#UZgwP7QysGqz.

39. Marino, Lori, and Christina M. Colvin. 2015. 'Thinking Pigs: A Comparative Review of Cognition, Emotion, and Personality in Sus.' *International Journal of Comparative Psychology* 28(1).

40. Viegas, Jen. 2015. *IQ Tests Suggest Pigs Are Smart as Dogs, Chimps.* 11 June. Accessed January 19, 2019. https://www.seeker.com/iq-tests-suggest-pigs-are-smart-as-dogs-chimps-1769934406.html.

41. Smith, Carolynn L., and Sarah L. Zielinski. February 2014. *Brainy Bird.* Scientific American.

42. Marino, Lori. 2017. 'Thinking chickens: a review of cognition, emotion, and behavior.' *Animal Cognition* 20: 127–147.

43. The University of Adelaide. 2013. *Humans Not Smarter Than Animals, Just Different.* 5 December. Accessed January 19, 2019. https://www.adelaide.edu.au/news/news67182.html.

44. Live Science. 2012. *How Do Birds Navigate?* 15 November. Accessed January 19, 2019. https://www.livescience.com/32276-how-do-birds-navigate.html.

45. Amos, Jonathan. 2015. *Seismology of elephants investigated.* 18 December. Accessed January 19, 2019. https://www.bbc.com/news/science-environment-35129175.

Chapter 2: Why Did I Eat Animals?

1. Foer, Jonathan Safran. 2009. *Eating Animals.* p. 67. London: Penguin.

2. Loughnan, Steve, Boyka Bratanova, and Elisa Puvia. 2012. 'The Meat Paradox: How are we able to love animals and love eating animals.' *In-Mind Italia* 1, 15–18.

3. Reilly, Nicholas. 2014. *Supermarket butcher pranks customers into believing that he's making sausages from live pigs.* 30 November. Accessed January 25, 2019. https://metro.co.uk/2014/11/30/supermarket-butcher-pranks-customers-into-believing-that-hes-making-sausages-from-live-pigs-4967985/.

4. Loughnan, Steve, Boyka Bratanova, and Elisa Puvia. 2012. 'The Meat Paradox: How are we able to love animals and love eating animals.' *In-Mind Italia* 1, 15–18.

5. ibid.

6. Loughnan, Steve, Boyka Bratanova, and Elisa Puvia. 2012. 'The Meat Paradox: How are we able to love animals and love eating animals.' *In-Mind Italia* 1, 15–18.

7. Sea Shepherd. 2018. *Largest Fish Factory Vessel in the World Arrested and Seized in Peru Pending Criminal Charges.* 31 May. Accessed January 26, 2019. https://seashepherd.org/2018/05/31/largest-fish-factory-vessel-in-the-world-arrested-and-seized/.

8. Joy, Dr Melanie. Joy. 2010. *Why We Love Dogs, Eat Pigs and Wear Cows.* p. 14. San Francisco: Conari Press.

9. Brannen, Aimee. 2016. *How to become a vegetarian: Heartbreaking moment a little boy begs his mother not to cook a chicken for lunch as he*

wants to 'take care of her'. 15 March. Accessed January 26, 2019. https://www.dailymail.co.uk/femail/article-3493269/Little-boy-begs-mother-not-cook-chicken-lunch-wants-care-her.html.

10. PETA US. 2015. *Proof That Kids Don't Want to Eat Meat*. 5 August. Accessed January 26, 2019. https://www.peta.org/living/food/proof-that-kids-dont-want-to-eat-meat/.

11. *3 year old kid fighting to save his animal friend goat*. 9 July 2015. Accessed January 26, 2019. https://www.youtube.com/watch?v=TwIK7cjfVpg.

12. Hackett, Conrad, and David Mcclendon. 2017. *Christians remain world's largest religious group, but they are declining in Europe*. 5 April. Accessed March 13, 2019. http://www.pewresearch.org/fact-tank/2017/04/05/christians-remain-worlds-largest-religious-group-but-they-are-declining-in-europe/.

13. Horn, Charles. 2014. *Meat Logic: Why Do We Eat Animals?* Charles Horn.

14. n.d. *Carnism*. Accessed January 26, 2019. https://www.carnism.org/carnism.

15. Vranica, Suzanne. 2017. *McDonald's To Review Its $2 billion Global Media Buying Account*. 26 October. Accessed January 26, 2019. https://www.wsj.com/articles/mcdonalds-to-review-its-2-billion-global-media-buying-account-1509036600.

16. Figus, Cinzia. 2017. *375 million vegetarians worldwide. All the reasons for a green lifestyle*. 27 October. Accessed January 26, 2019. http://www.expo2015.org/magazine/en/lifestyle/375-million-vegetarians-worldwide.html.

17. Petter, Olivia. 2018. *Number of Vegans in UK Soars to 3.5 Million, Survey Finds*. 3 April. Accessed January 26, 2019. https://www.independent.co.uk/life-style/food-and-drink/vegans-uk-rise-popularity-plant-based-diets-veganism-figures-survey-compare-the-market-a8286471.html.

18. Chiorando, Maria. 2018. *Plant-Based Doctors Tell The Government To 'Ditch Dairy' With Sign Outside White House*. 16 August. Accessed March 10, 2019. https://www.plantbasednews.org/post/plant-based-doctors-tell-government-ditch-dairy-sign-white-house.

19. Cumberland and Westmorland Herald. 2003. *A country of vegetarians by 2047? Hard cheese, say Eden's farmers.* 24 May. Accessed January 26, 2019. http://www.cwherald.com/a/archive/a-country-of-vegetarians-by-2047-hard-cheese-say-eden-s-farmers.278716.html.

20. Smithers, Rebecca. 2018. *Third of Britons have stopped or reduced eating meat - report.* 1 November. Accessed January 26, 2019. https://www.theguardian.com/business/2018/nov/01/third-of-britons-have-stopped-or-reduced-meat-eating-vegan-vegetarian-report.

21. Kaushik, Himanshu. 2016. *'Veg' Gujarat has 40% non-vegetarians.* 10 June. Accessed January 26, 2019. https://timesofindia.indiatimes.com/city/ahmedabad/Veg-Gujarat-has-40-non-vegetarians/articleshow/52681704.cms.

22. n.d. *Carnism.* Accessed January 26, 2019. https://www.carnism.org/carnism.

23. Milton R. Mills, M.D. 21. *The Comparative Anatomy of Eating.* 2009 November. Accessed January 26, 2019. http://www.vegsource.com/news/2009/11/the-comparative-anatomy-of-eating.html.

24. Fenton, Siobhan. 2016. *Vegans Live Longer Than Those Who Eat Meat or Eggs, Research Finds.* 2 August. Accessed January 26, 2019. https://www.independent.co.uk/life-style/health-and-families/health-news/vegan-meat-life-expectancy-eggs-dairy-research-a7168036.html.

25. Klaper, Dr Michael. 2017. *Dr. Klaper's Take on Dairy.* 29 June. Accessed January 26, 2019. https://www.doctorklaper.com/dairy-free.

26. Suarez, F, C Shannon, S Hertzler, and D Savaiano. 2003. 'Food Intolerance | Lactose Intolerance.' *Encyclopedia of Food Sciences and Nutrition (Second Edition)* 2634–642.

27. 2010. In *Why We Love Dogs, Eat Pigs and Wear Cows*, by Dr Melanie Joy, 14. San Francisco: Conari Press.

28. Lancaster University. 2015. *How people defend eating meat.* 15 May. Accessed January 26, 2019. https://www.lancaster.ac.uk/news/articles/2015/how-people-defend-eating-meat/.

Chapter 3: Fast Food and Factory Farms

1. Masson, In Jeffrey Moussaieff. 2009. *The Face on Your Plate: The Truth About Food*, p. 99. New York: W.W. Norton and Company.

2. Guenette, Ryan. 2013. *Five things you didn't know about McDonald's*. 19 November. Accessed January 26, 2019. https://eu.usatoday.com/story/money/markets/2013/11/19/five-things-about-mcdonalds/3643557/.

3. Lubin, Gus, and Mamta Badkar. 2011. *15 Facts About McDonald's That Will Blow Your Mind*. 25 November. Accessed January 26, 2019. https://www.businessinsider.com/facts-about-mcdonalds-blow-your-mind-2011-11?r=US&IR=T#e-only-place-in-the-lower-48-that-is-more-than-100-miles-from-a-mcdonalds-is-a-barren-plain-in-south-dakota-12.

4. 2009. In *Eating Animals*, by Jonathan Safran Foer, 67. London: Penguin.

5. Davies, Madlen. 2018. *Indian poultry firm Venky's in new furore*. 23 May. Accessed January 26, 2019. https://www.thebureauinvestigates.com/stories/2018-05-23/venkys-asked-to-withdraw-advert.

6. BBC News. 2018. *'Don't call police over KFC crisis'*. 21 February. Accessed January 26, 2019. https://www.bbc.co.uk/news/uk-england-43140836.

7. Farm Animal Investment Risk and Return (FAIRR), A Coller Initiative. 2016. *Factory Farming: Assessing Investment Risks*. London: Farm Animal Investment Risk and Return (FAIRR).

8. Guilford, Gwynn. 2016. *The future is here: People are now eating more farmed fish than wild-caught fish*. 14 July. Accessed January 26, 2019. https://qz.com/730794/the-future-is-here-people-are-now-eating-more-farmed-fish-than-wild-caught-fish/.

9. Food and Agriculture Organization of the United Nations. n.d. *Poultry Production*. Accessed January 26, 2019. http://www.fao.org/docrep/article/agrippa/657_en-04.htm.

10. Conklin, Tina. 2014. *An animal welfare history lesson on the Five Freedoms*. 25 February. Accessed January 26, 2019. https://www.canr.msu.edu/news/an_animal_welfare_history_lesson_on_the_five_freedoms.

11. Farm Animal Welfare Council (UK). 2009. *Five Freedoms*. 16 April. Accessed January 26, 2019. https://webarchive.nationalarchives.gov.uk/20121010012427/http://www.fawc.org.uk/freedoms.htm.

12. OIE), World Organisation for Animal Health. n.d. *Animal Welfare*. Accessed January 26, 2019. http://www.oie.int/en/animal-welfare/animal-welfare-at-a-glance/.

13. Kumar, Jagdish. 2015. *Can Pork Consumption Fix India's Cheap Protein Link?* 18 May. Accessed January 26, 2019. http://thepigsite.com/news/2015/05/can-pork-consumption-fix-indias-cheap-protein-link-1.

14. Indian Council of Agricultural Research. n.d. *Commercial Goat Farming.* Accessed January 26, 2019. https://icar.org.in/node/8040.

15. Tamil Nadu Agricultural University (TNAU). 2019. *Housing of sheep and goats.* 26 January. Accessed January 26, 2019. http://www.agritech.tnau.ac.in/expert_system/sheepgoat/Housing%20of%20sheep%20and%20goats.html.

16. Department of Animal Husbandry, Dairying and Fisheries. n.d. *Biosecurity guidelines for piggery.* Accessed January 26, 2019. http://dahd.nic.in/sites/default/filess/Biosecurity%20guidelines%20for%20piggery_0.pdf.

17. Punjab, Department of Animal Husbandry. n.d. *Innovative Pig Breeding Centre Gurdaspur.* Accessed January 26, 2019. http://husbandrypunjab.org/institutionsdetails.aspx?inst_innovativepigbreedingcentregurdaspur.

18. Department of Animal Husbandry and Veterinary, Government of Mizoram. 2017. *Pig AI.* 21 June. Accessed January 26, 2019. https://ahvety.mizoram.gov.in/page/ped240516110549.

19. Kerala Veterinary and Animal Sciences University. n.d. *Pig Breeding Farm, Mannuthy.* Accessed January 26, 2019. http://www.kvasu.ac.in/researchcategory/7.

20. Tamil Nadu Agricultural University. 2015. *Piggery Farming.* Accessed January 26, 2019. http://agritech.tnau.ac.in/farm_enterprises/Farm%20enterprises_%20piggery.html.

21. Royal Livestock Farms. n.d. *Farrowing Crate-Livestock Farms.* Accessed January 26, 2019. http://www.royallivestock.com/livestock-farm-farrowing-crate.php.

22. Schweig, Sarah V. 2016. *It's Totally Legal To Keep A Mother Pig And Her Babies Like This.* 15 July. Accessed January 26, 2019. https://www.thedodo.com/mother-pig-farrowing-crate-1924497542.html.

23. Compassion in World Farming (CIWF). n.d. *Farm Animals Pig Welfare.* Accessed January 26, 2019. https://www.ciwf.org.uk/farm-animals/pigs/pig-welfare/.

24. Director Animal Husbandry, P. C. (2014, August 12). Animal Welfare Issue–Use of gestation crates in pigs. *Letter.* Directorate Animal Husbandry, Punjab, Chandigarh (Development Branch).

25. Compassion in World Farming (CIWF). n.d. *Farm Animals Pig Welfare.* Accessed January 26, 2019. https://www.ciwf.org.uk/farm-animals/pigs/pig-welfare/.

26. Woods, Judy. n.d. *Libby's Story.* Accessed January 26, 2019. http://www.pigspeace.org/stories/libby.html.

27. Mitra, Sounak. 2016. *Delhi to get a taste of Parag Milk's premium brand Pride of Cows.* 14 June. Accessed January 27, 2019. https://www.livemint.com/Consumer/8ELznahcCRK4iec1YxN7BO/Delhi-to-get-a-taste-of-Parag-Milks-premium-brand-Pride-of.html.

28. Reflections video. 2014. *Gowardhan Milk Products: Corporate FILM.* 12 March. Accessed January 27, 2019. https://www.youtube.com/watch?v=DdwXzd–cJA.

29. Bhattacharya, Ananya. 2017. *Thousands of Indian cows have been fitted with tiny sensors to give farmers real-time data.* 7 December. Accessed January 27, 2019. https://qz.com/india/1148120/thousands-of-cows-across-india-have-been-fitted-with-sensors-to-provide-dairy-farmers-with-real-time-data/.

30. n.d. *Aquaculture.* Accessed January 27, 2019. https://indianfisheries.icsf.net/en/page/624-Aquaculture.html.

31. Moyer, Melinda Wenner. 2016. *How Drug-Resistant Bacteria Travel from the Farm to Your Table.* 1 December. Accessed January 27, 2019. https://webcache.googleusercontent.com/search?q=cache:CEr1jXWWm6AJ:https://www.scientificamerican.com/article/how-drug-resistant-bacteria-travel-from-the-farm-to-your-table/+&cd=1&hl=en&ct=clnk&gl=uk.

32. Stockton, Ben, Madlen Davies, and Rahul Meesaraganda. 2018. *World's biggest animal drugs company sells antibiotics to fatten livestock in India despite superbug risk.* 12 October. Accessed February 2, 2019. https://www.thebureauinvestigates.com/stories/2018-10-12/worlds-biggest-animal-drugs-company-sells-antibiotics-to-fatten-livestock-in-india-despite-superbug-risk.

33. foodsafetyhelpline.com. 2018. *Antibiotic Substances in Food Products and FSSAI Regulations.* 31 January. Accessed February 2, 2019. https://foodsafetyhelpline.com/2018/01/antibiotic-substances-in-food-products-and-fssai-regulations/.

34. R-Biopharm AG. 2016. *Antibiotics in meat: 5 facts about residues in food.* 13 January. Accessed January 27, 2019. https://food.r-biopharm.com/news/antibiotics-in-meat-5-facts-about-residues-in-food/.

35. World Health Organization. 2018. *Antibiotic resistance.* 5 February. Accessed January 27, 2019. https://www.who.int/en/news-room/fact-sheets/detail/antibiotic-resistance.

36. Harris, Gardiner. 2014. *'Superbugs' Kill India's Babies and Pose an Overseas Threat.* 3 December. Accessed January 27, 2019. https://www.nytimes.com/2014/12/04/world/asia/superbugs-kill-indias-babies-and-pose-an-overseas-threat.html.

37. DW. 2018. *Superbugs kill 33,000 in Europe each year, says study.* 6 November. Accessed January 27, 2019. https://www.dw.com/en/superbugs-kill-33000-in-europe-each-year-says-study/a-46167151.

38. Pearson, Natalie Obiko, and Sharang Limaye. 2016. *Antibiotic Apocalypse Fear Stoked by India's Drugged Chickens.* 29 March. Accessed January 27, 2019. https://www.bloomberg.com/news/features/2016-03-29/antibiotic-apocalypse-fear-stoked-by-india-s-drugged-chickens.

39. Rijksdienst voor Ondernemend Nederland. 2017. *Poultry Sector: Opportunities and Challenges in India.* Hyderabad, India: Rijksdienst voor Ondernemend Nederland.

40. Pearson, Natalie Obiko, and Sharang Limaye. 2016. *Antibiotic Apocalypse Fear Stoked by India's Drugged Chickens.* 29 March. Accessed January 27, 2019. https://www.bloomberg.com/news/features/2016-03-29/antibiotic-apocalypse-fear-stoked-by-india-s-drugged-chickens.

41. Kaul, Rhythma, and Malavika Vyawahare. 2017. *Antibiotic resistance among bacteria high in India, reveals report.* 1 November. Accessed January 27, 2019. https://webcache.googleusercontent.com/search?q=cache:qg69fqGJ-DcJ:https://www.hindustantimes.com/health/antibiotic-resistance-among-bacteria-high-in-india-reveals-report/story-S8hGExYKzzFD1GGQS6pbAP.html+&cd=1&hl=en&ct=clnk&gl=uk.

42. Khullar, B. (2019, August 16). *FSSAI implements ban on colistin use.* Retrieved from Down to Earth: https://www.downtoearth.org.in/news/food/fssai-implements-ban-on-colistin-use-66162.

43. Sinha, R. (2019, February 18). *New report flags use of antibiotics on animals.* Retrieved from Down to Earth: https://www.downtoearth.org.in/news/health/new-report-flags-use-of-antibiotics-on-animals-63265.

44. Keim, Brandon. 2009. *Swine Flu Ancestor Born on US Factory Farms.* 1 May. Accessed January 27, 2019. https://www.wired.com/2009/05/swineflufarm/.

45. Game Management Authority. n.d. *Avian flu.* Accessed January 27, 2019. http://www.gma.vic.gov.au/education/fact-sheets/avian-flu.

46. Firstpost. 2018. *Bird flu scare in Bengaluru: 900 fowls culled after H5N1 avian influenza virus is detected; Karnataka govt starts awareness campaign.* 7 January. Accessed January 27, 2019. https://www.firstpost.com/india/bird-flu-scare-in-bengaluru-900-fowls-culled-after-h5n1-avian-influenza-virus-is-detected-karnataka-govt-starts-awareness-campaign-4291145.html.

47. Indo Asian News Service. 2017. *India declares itself free from H5N1 and H5N8 bird flu.* 6 July. Accessed January 27, 2019. https://www.hindustantimes.com/india-news/india-declares-itself-free-from-h5n1-and-h5n8-bird-flu/story-XC2H6cZzD9B50GUp0JLbfP.html.

48. WebMD. n.d. *Frequently Asked Questions About Bird Flu.* Accessed January 27, 2019. https://www.webmd.com/cold-and-flu/flu-guide/what-know-about-bird-flu#1.

49. World Health Organization. 2005. *No bird flu risk for consumers from properly cooked poultry and eggs.* 5 December. Accessed January 27, 2019. https://www.who.int/mediacentre/news/releases/2005/pr66/en/.

50. Mullin, Gemma. 2016. *Footage reveals gruesome FOAM suffocation method used to kill chickens infected with bird flu.* 18 July. Accessed January 27, 2019. https://www.mirror.co.uk/news/world-news/footage-reveals-gruesome-foam-suffocation-8445728.

51. Watts, Kerean. 2018. *Swine flu alert in India, first cases reported this year.* 2 August. Accessed January 27, 2019. https://www.thenewsminute.com/article/swine-flu-alert-india-first-case-reported-year-85827.

52. Keim, Brandon. 2009. *Swine Flu Ancestor Born on US Factory Farms.* 1 May. Accessed January 27, 2019. https://www.wired.com/2009/05/swineflufarm/.

53. Parry, Lizzie. 2018. *'Flu is Biggest Threat to Mankind': Killer flu pandemic 'could hit any time' – wiping out 300 million across the globe.* 6 March. Accessed January 27, 2019. https://www.thesun.co.uk/news/5738866/killer-flu-pandemic-could-hit-any-time-killing-300-million/.

54. Boseley, Sarah. 2017. *Poor diet is a factor in one in five deaths, global disease study reveals.* 14 September. Accessed January 27, 2019. https://www.theguardian.com/society/2017/sep/14/poor-diet-is-a-factor-in-one-in-five-deaths-global-disease-study-reveals.

55. World Heart Federation. n.d. *The costs of CVD.* Accessed January 27, 2019. http://www.championadvocates.org/en/champion-advocates-programme/the-costs-of-cvd.

56. Adams, Jill U. 2012. *Hog Farm Stink Raises Neighbors' Blood Pressure.* 7 November. Accessed January 27, 2019. http://www.sciencemag.org/news/2012/11/hog-farm-stink-raises-neighbors-blood-pressure.

57. Bishnoi, Arvind. 2017. *Poultry woes: Flies rule in Raipurrani, Barwala.* 25 September. Accessed January 27, 2019. https://timesofindia.indiatimes.com/city/chandigarh/poultry-woes-flies-rule-in-raipurrani-barwala/articleshow/60824795.cms.

58. The Humane Society of the United States. n.d. *Factory Farming in America: The True Cost of Animal Agribusiness for Rural Communities, Public Health, Families, Farmers, the Environment, and Animals.* The Humane Society of the United States.

59. Food Empowerment Project. n.d. *Factory Farm Workers.* Accessed January 29, 2019. http://www.foodispower.org/factory-farm-workers/.

60. Mustain, Patrick. 2015. *Swine, Superbugs, and the Meat We Choose to Eat.* 7 May. Accessed January 29, 2019. https://blogs.scientificamerican.com/food-matters/swine-superbugs-and-the-meat-we-choose-to-eat/.

61. Boyles, Salynn. 2007. *More U.S. Deaths From MRSA Than AIDS.* 16 October. Accessed January 29, 2019. https://www.webmd.com/skin-problems-and-treatments/news/20071016/more-us-deaths-from-mrsa-than-aids#1.

62. MRSA Survivors Network. 2014. *MRSA is a Major Global Health Threat.* 13 August. Accessed January 29, 2019. https://www.prnewswire.com/news-releases/mrsa-is-a-major-global-health-threat-271062591.html.

63. Stromberg, Joseph. 2013. *Factory Farms May Be Ground-Zero For Drug Resistant Staph Bacteria.* 2 July. Accessed January 29, 2019. https://www.smithsonianmag.com/science-nature/factory-farms-may-be-ground-zero-for-drug-resistant-staph-bacteria-6055013/.

64. K.S.Sudhi. 2017. *New clone of MRSA identified in Kerala aquatic environment.* 11 March. Accessed January 29, 2019. http://www.thehindu.com/sci-tech/science/new-clone-of-mrsa-identified-in-kerala-aquatic-environment/article17448716.ece.

65. International Union of Food, Agricultural, Hotel, Restaurant, Catering, Tobacco and Allied Workers' Associations (IUF). 2012. *India: Barefoot slaughterhouse workers fight for rights in the world's third largest beef exporter.* 2 January. Accessed January 29, 2019. http://cms.iuf.org/?q=node/1318.

66. PETA US. 2000. *Investigation of North Carolina Pig Farm Results in Historic Felony Cruelty Convictions.* April. Accessed January 29, 2019. https://www.peta.org/about-peta/victories/investigation-north-carolina-pig-farm-results-historic-felony-cruelty-convictions/.

67. DH Vancouver Staff. 2017. *Live chickens ripped apart, forced into violent sexual acts at Chilliwack farm (VIDEO).* 12 June. Accessed January 29, 2019. https://dailyhive.com/toronto/bc-spca-chilliwack-chicken-farm-abuse.

68. Perring, Rebecca. 2015. *Barbaric torment of farm animals inside family butchers' slaughterhouse.* 8 February. Accessed January 29, 2019. https://www.express.co.uk/news/uk/556946/Slaughterhouse-farm-animals-slaughtered-undercover-investigation.

69. Fitzgerald, Amy J., Linda Kalof, and Thomas Dietz. 2009. 'Slaughterhouses and Increased Crime Rates: An Empirical Analysis of the Spillover From 'The Jungle' Into the Surrounding Community.' *Organization & Environment.*

70. Shepherd, Tory. 2013. *Slaughterhouse workers are more likely to be violent, study shows.* 24 January. Accessed January 29, 2019. https://www.

news.com.au/national/slaughterhouse-workers-are-more-likely-to-be-violent-study-shows/news-story/f16165f66f38eb04a289eb8bd7f7f273.

71. Gandhi, Maneka. 2011. *Slaughter houses and increased crime rates.* 17 February. Accessed January 29, 2019. http://www.bihartimes.in/Maneka/Slaughter_houses_and_increased_crime_rates.html.

72. Kumar, Sanjiv, and Shakti Ranjan Panigrahy. December 2016. 'Farmers' Perspective Towards Existing Poultry Contract Farming Model in Anand District of Gujarat.' *Economic Affairs* Vol. 61(4): 741–46.

73. Humane Society International. 2011. *The impact of industrial farm animal production on food security in the developing world.* 14 November. Accessed January 29, 2019. http://www.hsi.org/assets/pdfs/hsi-fa-white-papers/the_impact_of_industrial_farm.pdf.

74. Pew. 2013. *The Business of Broilers: Hidden Costs of Putting a Chicken on Every Grill.* 20 December. Accessed January 29, 2019. https://www.pewtrusts.org/en/research-and-analysis/reports/2013/12/20/the-business-of-broilers-hidden-costs-of-putting-a-chicken-on-every-grill.

75. Kessler, Carson. 2018. *KFC Plans to Test Out Vegetarian Fried Chicken in the U.K.* 6 June. Accessed January 29, 2019. http://fortune.com/2018/06/06/kfc-fried-chicken-vegetarian/.

76. Toliver, Zachary. 2018. *We'd Love Some Vegan KFC Over Here, Y'all. Is That Too Much to Ask?* 7 August. Accessed January 29, 2019. https://www.peta.org/living/food/vegan-kfc-chicken/.

77. Burger King (2019, September 28). *Impossible.* Retrieved from https://impossiblefoods.com/burgerking/.

78. *After Success of First Vegan Slider, White Castle Offers Second Vegan Patty.* (2019, September 28). Retrieved from PETA: https://www.peta.org/living/food/white-castle-veggie-sliders-vegan/.

79. Chiorandomay, M. (2019, May 14). *Papa John's Launches Vegan Hot Dog Pizza With Cheese.* Retrieved from Plant Based News: https://www.plantbasednews.org/lifestyle/papa-johns-vegan-hot-dog-pizza-cheese.

80. S., Meenakshi. (2019, September 28). *Pizza Express Launches Vegan Cheese Pizzas Across India!* Retrieved from VeganFirst: https://www.veganfirst.com/article/pizza-express-launches-vegan-cheese-pizzas-across-india.

81. Starostinetskaya, A. (2018, October 2). *Domino's New Zealand Permanently Adds Vegan Cheese to Menu.* Retrieved from Veg News: https://vegnews.com/2018/10/dominos-new-zealand-permanently-adds-vegan-cheese-to-menu.

82. O'Malley, K. (2019, August 7). *Subway Launches Vegetarian Plant-based Meatball Sub to 'Offer Something for Everyone'.* Retrieved from Independent: https://www.independent.co.uk/life-style/food-and-drink/subway-meatless-meatball-sub-vegan-launch-plant-based-a9045666.html.

83. BusinessToday.In. 2018. *Domino's outlets in Gujarat take non-vegetarian pizzas out of the menu.* 10 October. Accessed January 30, 2019. https://www.businesstoday.in/latest/trends/dominos-outlets-in-gujarat-take-non-vegetarian-pizzas-out-of-the-menu/story/284578.html.

Chapter 4: Born to Die

1. Crimmins, James E. 2019. 'Jeremy Bentham.' *The Stanford Encyclopedia of Philosophy.* 28 January. Accessed February 2, 2019. https://plato.stanford.edu/archives/spr2019/entries/bentham/.

2. Singh, Vijay. 2007. *George, the calf, survives Eid slaughter in Mumbai.* 3 January. Accessed February 2, 2009. https://www.pressreader.com/india/the-times-of-india-new-delhi-edition/20070103/281827164284226.

3. Bender, Kelli. 2018. *Baby Cow Escapes Slaughterhouse and Is Raised by Deer Family in Snowy Forest.* 26 June. Accessed February 2, 2019. https://people.com/pets/cow-raised-by-deer-farm-sanctuary/.

4. Woodstock Farm Sanctuary. 2007. *Calfway to the Rescue.* 5 March. Accessed February 2, 2019. http://woodstocksanctuary.org/calfway-to-the-rescue/.

5. Investigator. 2016. 'video clip from fish farm.' *Hatcheries Notes.* Anonymous for Animal Rights & PETA India.

6. PETA India & Anonymous for Animal Rights. 2017. *From Shell to Hell: The Plight of Chicks in the Indian Egg and Meat Industries.* Mumbai: PETA India & Anonymous for Animal Rights.

7. Ramaa Incubators Pvt Ltd. n.d. *Incubator & Hatcher Machine.* Accessed February 2, 2019. http://www.ramaaincubators.net/incubator-hatcher-machine.html.

8. Cobb. n.d. *The Chick Quality Versus Quantity Conundrum*. Accessed February 2, 2019. https://www.cobb-vantress.com/academy/articles/article/academy/2015/04/04/the-chick-quality-conundrum.

9. United Poultry Concerns (UPC). n.d. *Debeaking*. Accessed February 2, 2019. https://www.upc-online.org/merchandise/debeak_factsheet.html.

10. American Veterinary Medical Association (AVMA). 2010. *Literature Review on the Welfare Implications of Beak Trimming*. 7 February. Accessed February 2, 2019. https://www.avma.org/KB/Resources/LiteratureReviews/Documents/beak_trimming_bgnd.pdf.

11. American Veterinary Medical Association (AVMA). 2010. *Literature Review on the Welfare Implications of Beak Trimming*. 7 February. Accessed February 2, 2019. https://www.avma.org/KB/Resources/LiteratureReviews/Documents/beak_trimming_bgnd.pdf.

12. Pickett, Heather. 2011. *Controlling Feather Pecking & Cannibalism in Laying Hens Without Beak Trimming*. Compassion in World Farming.

13. Pickett, Heather. 2011. *Controlling Feather Pecking & Cannibalism in Laying Hens Without Beak Trimming*. Compassion in World Farming.

14. Express News Service. 2018. *What a fowl way to go! 'Attractive' packaging suffocates chicks*. 31 October. Accessed February 2, 2019. http://www.newindianexpress.com/cities/hyderabad/2018/oct/31/what-a-fowl-way-to-go-attractive-packaging-suffocates-chicks-1892355.html?fbclid=IwAR0Z8VNYZqgQQLjGwCzQbVBBYZIJlBTcskXhXTbPVe91OyzEERmJOfoasRo.

15. Khan, Hasnain. 2016. *How to colour in chick*. 17 December. Accessed February 2, 2019. https://www.youtube.com/watch?v=K-MAIF5WA4E.

16. Saraswathy, M. 2014. *Crushing the chicks right after they are hatched*. 24 September. Accessed February 2, 2019. https://www.business-standard.com/article/companies/crushing-the-chicks-right-after-they-are-hatched-114092200497_1.html.

17. Jayathilakan, K., Khudsia Sultana, K. Radhakrishna, and A. S. Bawa. 2012. 'Utilization of byproducts and waste materials from meat, poultry and fish processing industries: a review.' *Journal of Food Science and Technology* 49(3): 278–93.

18. PETA India & Anonymous for Animal Rights. 2017. *From Shell to Hell: Cruel Treatment of Baby Chicks in the Indian Egg and Meat Industries*.

20 February. Accessed February 2, 2019. https://www.youtube.com/watch?v=hFJPWknSEtk.

19. United Egg Producers. 2018. *SELEGGT Announces Breakthrough for In-Ovo Sexing.* 29 November. Accessed February 2, 2019. https://unitedegg.com/seleggt-announces-breakthrough-for-in-ovo-sexing/.

20. OIE. 2010. 'Terrestrial Animal Health Code.' *Killing of Animals for Disease Control Purposes.* World Organisation for Animal Health. http://www.oie.int/fileadmin/Home/eng/Health_standards/tahc/current/chapitre_aw_killing.pdf.

21. Department of Animal Husbandry, Dairying and Fisheries. 2012. *19th Livestock Census-2012 All India Report.* New Delhi: Ministry of Agriculture.

22. Adak, Baishali. 2016. *Holy cow, unholy practice: Illegal dairies use gaumata as cash cows.* 9 August. Accessed February 2, 2019. https://www.indiatoday.in/mail-today/story/holy-cow-unholy-practice-illegal-dairies-use-gaumata-as-cash-crops-334117-2016-08-09.

23. Karuna Society for Animals and Nature. n.d. *The Plastic Cow Project.* Accessed February 2, 2019. https://www.karunasociety.org/the-plastic-cow-project.

24. Reuters. (2019, August 29). *India may ban single-use plastic products from October 2.* Retrieved from India Today: https://www.indiatoday.in/india/story/india-ban-singleuse-plastic-products-october2-1592850-2019-08-29.

25. Kurien, Dr V. 1972. *Dairying as an Instrument of Change.* 16 December. Accessed February 2, 2019. http://drkurien.com/content/december-16-1972.

26. Agricultural and Processed Food Products Export Development Authority. n.d. *Chapter 1 Livestock Resources.* Accessed February 2, 2019. http://apeda.gov.in/apedawebsite/MEAT_MANUAL/Chap1/chap1.pdf.

27. PETA India. n.d. *Inside the Indian Dairy Industry: A Report on the Abuse of Cows and Buffaloes Exploited for Milk.* Mumbai: PETA India.

28. Kedia, Shruti. 2017. *The white lies of the dairy industry that no one wants you to know.* 6 March. Accessed February 2, 2019. https://yourstory.com/2017/03/dairy-industry/.

29. Vishal, Anoothi. 2017. *Goa All Out: The new restaurant O Pedro by the Bombay Canteen team is a hat-tip to the swinging state.* 8 October. Accessed February 2, 2019. https://economictimes.indiatimes.com/magazines/panache/goa-all-out-the-new-restaurant-o-pedro-by-the-bombay-canteen-team-is-a-hat-tip-to-the-swinging-state/articleshow/60987660.cms.

30. USDA Foreign Agricultural Service. 2017. *India Livestock and Products Annual.* 1 September. Accessed February 2, 2019. http://agriexchange.apeda.gov.in/MarketReport/Reports/Livestock%20and%20Products%20Annual_New%20Delhi_India_9-1-2017.pdf.

31. Council for Leather Exports. n.d. *Leather manufacturers in India.* Accessed February 2, 2019. http://leatherindia.org/leather-manufacturers-in-india/.

32. The Humane Society of the United States (HSUS). July 2012. *An HSUS Report: The Welfare of Animals in the Veal Industry.* The Humane Society of the United States.

33. Garner, Robert. 2005. *Animal Ethics.* p. 108. Cambridge: Polity Press.

34. The Humane Society of the United States (HSUS). July 2012. *An HSUS Report: The Welfare of Animals in the Veal Industry.* The Humane Society of the United States.

35. Compassion in World Farming. n.d. *About Calves Reared for Veal.* Accessed February 2, 2019. https://www.ciwf.org.uk/farm-animals/cows/veal-calves/.

36. Vyawahare, Malavika. 2017. *Gender bias: India promotes sex selection in cattle to limit birth of male calves.* 12 July. Accessed February 2, 2019. http://www.hindustantimes.com/india-news/gender-bias-india-promotes-sex-selection-in-cattle-to-limit-birth-of-male-calves/story-OhAaNuiDaaqBH2L1YySYhK.html.

37. The Bullvine. (2019, March 28). *Sexing Technologies® opens second sorting lab in India.* Retrieved from The Bullvine: http://www.thebullvine.com/news/sexing-technologies-opens-second-sorting-lab-in-india/.

38. Pioneer News Service. 2019. *Sexed semen production lab to be a game-changer.* 10 March. Accessed March 23, 2019. https://www.dailypioneer.com/2019/state-editions/sexed-semen-production-lab-to-be-a-game-changer.html.

39. Jha, Prashant. 2018. *State signs MoU with US firm to produce sex-sorted semen doses for cattle.* 12 August. Accessed February 2, 2019. https://timesofindia.indiatimes.com/city/dehradun/state-signs-mou-with-us-firm-to-produce-sex-sorted-semen-doses-for-cattle/articleshow/65370073.cms.

40. Katiyar, P. 9 February 2019. *India testing a new way to deal with stray cattle: Eliminate male bovine before conception.* Retrieved from The Economic Times: https://economictimes.indiatimes.com/news/politics-and-nation/india-testing-a-new-way-to-deal-with-stray-cattle-eliminate-male-bovine-before-conception/articleshow/67918649.cms?utm_source=contentofinterest&utm_medium=text&utm_campaign=cppst.

41. Pandey, N. 4 September 2019. *Artificial insemination of cows will help end mob lynching in India, says Giriraj Singh.* Retrieved from The Print: https://theprint.in/india/mob-lynching-will-end-by-2025-thanks-to-100-artificial-insemination-of-cows-giriraj-singh/286742/.

42. Tamil Nadu Agricultural University. n.d. *Broilers.* Accessed February 2, 2019. http://agritech.tnau.ac.in/animal_husbandry/ani_chik_broilers.html.

43. —. n.d. *Chicken Breeds.* Accessed February 2, 2019. http://agritech.tnau.ac.in/animal_husbandry/ani_chik_breeds%20of%20chicken.html.

44. Gopinathan, A., S.M.K. Karthickeyan, J. Ramesh, R. Narendra Babu, and S.N. Sivaselvam. 2015. 'Evaluation of optimum slaughter age based on carcass traits of crossbred pigs.' *Indian Journal Of Animal Research* 49 (3): 416–17.

45. Aussie Farms. n.d. *Age of animals slaughtered.* Accessed February 2, 2019. https://www.aussieabattoirs.com/facts?s=age-slaughtered.

Chapter 5: Motherhood on the Farm

1. In *Eating*, by Peter Singer and Jim Mason, p. 58. London: Arrow Books, Random House. 2006.

2. Vila, Denis. 2013. 'Happy Cows' *Kuhrettung Rhein Berg.* 22 July. Accessed February 2, 2019. https://www.youtube.com/watch?v=kUZ1YLhIAg8.

3. BBC News. 2017. *Vegetarian beef farmer gives herd to animal sanctuary.* 13 June. Accessed February 2, 2019. https://www.bbc.co.uk/news/uk-england-40253429.

4. FIAPO. 2018. *Gau Gaatha Tale of the Cow.* New Delhi: Federation of Indian Animal Protection Organisations.

5. Tamil Nadu Agricultural University. n.d. *Artificial Insemination.* Accessed February 2, 2019. http://agritech.tnau.ac.in/animal_husbandry/animhus_cattle_AI.html.

6. Tamil Nadu Agricultural University. n.d. *Artificial Insemination.* Accessed February 2, 2019. http://agritech.tnau.ac.in/animal_husbandry/animhus_cattle_AI.html.

7. National Dairy Development Board. n.d. *Calf Nutrition.* Accessed February 2, 2019. https://www.nddb.coop/services/animalnutrition/cn.

8. Chakrapani, Saranya. 2017. *Desi cow may be holy, but low milk yield still a spoiler.* 8 February. Accessed February 2, 2019. https://timesofindia. indiatimes.com/blogs/tracking-indian-communities/desi-cow-may-be-holy-but-low-milk-yield-still-a-spoiler/.

9. Chaba, Anju Agnihotri. 2015. *Punjab Dairy farmers see no economic benefits in switching from Holsteins to Sahiwal.* 20 August. Accessed February 2, 2019. https://indianexpress.com/article/india/india-others/punjab-dairy-farmers-see-no-economic-benefits-in-switching-from-holsteins-to-sahiwal/.

10. FIAPO. 2017. *Cattle-ogue: Unveiling the Truth of the Indian Dairy Industry.* New Delhi: The Federation of Indian Animal Protection Organisations.

11. Viva!! 2014. *The Dark Side of Dairy.* Bristol: Viva!!

12. Mazoomdaar, Jay. 2013. *The Desi Cow – Almost Extinct.* 24 January. Accessed February 2, 2019. http://old.tehelka.com/the-desi-cow-almost-extinct/.

13. Tribune News Service. 2017. *Urgent need to improve local breeds, say experts.* 9 April. Accessed February 2, 2019. https://www.tribuneindia. com/news/sunday-special/perspective/urgent-need-to-improve-local-breeds-say-experts/389136.html.

14. FIAPO. 2017. *Cattle-ogue: Unveiling the Truth of the Indian Dairy Industry*. New Delhi: The Federation of Indian Animal Protection Organisations.
15. Priyanka, & Panigrahi, Sumitra & Sheoran, Maninder & Ganguly, Subha. (2017). Antibiotic residues in milk, a serious public health hazard. *Journal of Environment and Life Sciences* (iMedPharm Publications, Odisha, India). 2. 99–102.
16. Menon, Vinod Kumar, and Ranjeet Jadhav. 2013. *Banned drug injected into cattle is poisoning your milk*. 11 June. Accessed February 2, 2019. http://archive.mid-day.com/news/2013/jun/110613-banned-drug-injected-into-cattle-is-poisoning-your-milk.htm.
17. TNN. 2012. *Oxytocin triggers early puberty among girls: Expert*. 17 April. Accessed February 2, 2019. https://timesofindia.indiatimes.com/city/lucknow/Oxytocin-triggers-early-puberty-among-girls-Expert/articleshow/12697535.cms.
18. Menon, Vinod Kumar, and Ranjeet Jadhav. 2013. *Banned drug injected into cattle is poisoning your milk*. 11 June. Accessed February 2, 2019. http://archive.mid-day.com/news/2013/jun/110613-banned-drug-injected-into-cattle-is-poisoning-your-milk.htm.
19. Thacker, T. (2017, February 4). *Govt moves Supreme Court against Delhi HC order over Oxytocin ban*. Retrieved from Live Mint: https://www.livemint.com/news/india/govt-moves-supreme-court-against-delhi-hc-order-over-oxytocin-ban-1549292969839.html.
20. Tamil Nadu Agricultural University. n.d. *Economic Character in Dairy Cattle*. Accessed February 3, 2019. http://agritech.tnau.ac.in/animal_husbandry/animhus_economic%20character.html.
21. Breyer, Melissa. 2017. *21 things you didn't know about cows*. 26 January. Accessed February 3, 2019. https://www.mnn.com/earth-matters/animals/stories/20-things-you-didnt-know-about-cows.
22. FIAPO. 2017. *Cattle-ogue: Unveiling the Truth of the Indian Dairy Industry*. New Delhi: The Federation of Indian Animal Protection Organisations.
23. Viva!! 2014. *The Dark Side of Dairy*. Bristol: Viva!
24. FIAPO. 2017. *Cattle-ogue: Unveiling the Truth of the Indian Dairy Industry*. New Delhi: The Federation of Indian Animal Protection Organisations.

25. World Animal Protection. n.d. *Suffering in the Dairy Industry.* Accessed February 3, 2019. https://www.worldanimalprotection.org.in/cruelty-free-dairies-delhi.
26. Rediff. 2005. *Black rain claims 2,500 buffaloes.* 29 July. Accessed February 3, 2019. https://www.rediff.com/news/2005/jul/29jcm.htm.
27. FIAPO. 2017. *Cattle-ogue: Unveiling the Truth of the Indian Dairy Industry.* New Delhi: The Federation of Indian Animal Protection Organisations.
28. Viva!! 2014. *The Dark Side of Dairy.* Bristol: Viva!!
29. Krishnan, Suhasini. 2017. *Amid Calls for Gau Raksha, Old Cows Attacked With Acid & Abandoned.* 14 July. Accessed February 3, 2019. https://www.thequint.com/news/gau-raksha-old-cows-abandoned.
30. Jain, Dr. Abhishek. 2011. *Management of Diarrhoea in Dairy animals.* 14 February. Accessed February 3, 2019. https://en.engormix.com/dairy-cattle/articles/diarrhoea-in-dairy-t34751.htm.
31. Tamil Nadu Agricultural University. n.d. *Mastitis.* Accessed February 3, 2019. http://agritech.tnau.ac.in/expert_system/cattlebuffalo/Mastitis-Diseases.html.
32. Viva!!. n.d. *Suffering in Silence.* Accessed February 3, 2019. https://www.Viva!.org.uk/dark-side-dairy/suffering-silence.
33. PETA India. n.d. *Inside the Indian Dairy Industry: A Report on the Abuse of Cows and Buffaloes Exploited for Milk.* Mumbai: PETA India.
34. Viva!!. n.d. *Suffering in Silence.* Accessed February 3, 2019. https://www.Viva!.org.uk/dark-side-dairy/suffering-silence.
35. 2005. In *Animal Welfare: Limping Toward Eden,* by John Webster, 139. Oxford: Blackwell Publishing.
36. Tamil Nadu Agricultural University. n.d. *Economic Character in Dairy Cattle.* Accessed February 3, 2019. http://agritech.tnau.ac.in/animal_husbandry/animhus_economic%20character.html.
37. Agricultural and Processed Food Products Export Development Authority. n.d. *Chapter 2 Indian Meat Industry.* Accessed February 3, 2019. http://apeda.gov.in/apedawebsite/MEAT_MANUAL/Chap2/Chap2.pdf.
38. BT Online. 2017. *Five more BJP-ruled states crack down on illegal meat shops.* 29 March. Accessed February 3, 2019. https://www.businesstoday.

in/current/economy-politics/meat-ban-yogi-adityanath-bjp-ruled-states-crack-down/story/248878.html.

39. Debroy, Bibek. 2016. *Who has the licence to kill?* 1 September. Accessed February 3, 2019. https://indianexpress.com/article/opinion/columns/who-has-the-licence-to-kill-3006789/.

40. Agricultural and Processed Food Products Export Development Authority. n.d. *Chapter 2 Indian Meat Industry.* Accessed February 3, 2019. http://apeda.gov.in/apedawebsite/MEAT_MANUAL/Chap2/Chap2.pdf.

41. Sharma, Shantanu Nandan. 2019. *Great Indian cattle count: An inside story.* 27 January. Accessed February 3, 2019. https://economictimes.indiatimes.com/news/politics-and-nation/how-a-team-of-experts-are-conducting-indias-first-tech-aided-livestock-census/articleshow/67704952.cms.

42. Hashmi, Rasia. 2018. *'Cow is our mother': India becomes world's top beef exporter.* 3 August. Accessed February 3, 2019. https://www.siasat.com/news/cow-our-mother-india-becomes-worlds-top-beef-exporter-1387975/.

43. Singh, Harsha Kumari. 2016. *500 Cows Starve To Death In Rajasthan Shelter, Their Hooves Stuck In Muck.* 7 August. Accessed February 3, 2019. https://www.ndtv.com/india-news/500-cows-starve-to-death-in-rajasthan-shelter-their-hooves-stuck-in-muck-1440923.

44. Tribune India. 2016. *8,122 cows died since Jan at Hingonia gaushala: Rajasthan govt.* 6 August. Accessed February 3, 2019. https://www.tribuneindia.com/news/nation/8-122-cows-died-since-jan-at-hingonia-gaushala-rajasthan-govt/276859.html.

45. Singh, Ajay. 2017. *Fund crunch, growing cattle hit Hingonia gaushala hard.* 8 September. Accessed February 3, 2019. https://timesofindia.indiatimes.com/city/jaipur/fund-crunch-growing-cattle-hit-hingonia-gaushala-hard/articleshow/60418538.cms.

46. Misra, Savvy Soumya. 2015. *Most Indians drinking adulterated milk, finds FSSAI survey.* 4 July. Accessed February 7, 2019. https://www.downtoearth.org.in/news/most-indians-drinking-adulterated-milk-finds-fssai-survey-35646.

47. Qureshi, Siraj. 2016. *At least 127 children ill and three dead after consuming mid-day meal milk in Mathura.* 6 May. Accessed February 7, 2019. https://www.indiatoday.in/india/north/story/at-least-127-children-ill-and-three-dead-after-consuming-mid-day-meal-milk-in-mathura-322086-2016-05-06.

48. Sushma, Meenakshi. 2018. *Only 10% of milk in India unsafe for human consumption, says FSSAI.* 15 November. Accessed February 7, 2019. https://www.downtoearth.org.in/news/food/only-10-of-milk-in-india-unsafe-for-human-consumption-says-fssai-62116.

49. ANI. (18 October 2019). *The Economic Times.* Retrieved from 41% milk samples of poor quality, 7% samples unfit to consume: FSSAI survey. Accessed December 14, 2019. https://economictimes.indiatimes.com/industry/cons-products/food/41-milk-samples-of-poor-quality-7-samples-unfit-to-consume-fssai-survey/articleshow/71647497.cms.

50. Chatterjee, Badri. 2017. *Two-year undercover study reveals cruel side of India's dairy industries.* 25 November. Accessed February 7, 2019. https://www.hindustantimes.com/mumbai-news/two-year-undercover-study-reveals-cruel-side-of-india-s-dairy-industries/story-7icLDyv1Rq2tVV2kbYKccN.html.

51. World Animal Protection. n.d. *Suffering in the Dairy Industry.* Accessed February 3, 2019. https://www.worldanimalprotection.org.in/cruelty-free-dairies-delhi.

52. Chatterjee, Badri. 2017. *Two-year undercover study reveals cruel side of India's dairy industries.* 25 November. Accessed February 7, 2019. https://www.hindustantimes.com/mumbai-news/two-year-undercover-study-reveals-cruel-side-of-india-s-dairy-industries/story-7icLDyv1Rq2tVV2kbYKccN.html.

53. Curry, Andrew. 2013. *Archaeology: The milk revolution.* 31 July. Accessed February 7, 2019. https://www.nature.com/news/archaeology-the-milk-revolution-1.13471.

54. Viva!. 2014. *Foreword: Professor T. Colin Campbell.* February. Accessed February 7, 2019. https://www.Viva!.org.uk/white-lies/foreword.

55. Lewis, Martin W. 2016. *Mapping the Consumption of Milk and Meat in India.* 8 March. Accessed February 7, 2019. https://thewire.in/uncategorised/mapping-the-consumption-of-milk-and-meat-in-india.

56. Nozaki, Yukiko. 2017. *Future Trends of Growing Demand for Milk and Dairy Products and Milk Supply in India.* September. Accessed February 7, 2019. https://www.mitsui.com/mgssi/en/report/detail/__icsFiles/afieldfile/2017/12/22/170907x_nozaki_e.pdf.

57. Deccan Chronicle. 2017. *India ranks highest in death from heart attacks.* 2 October. Accessed February 7, 2019. https://www.deccanchronicle.com/lifestyle/health-and-wellbeing/021017/india-ranks-highest-in-death-from-heart-attacks.html.

58. Malik, Rakesh. 2016. *India is the diabetes capital of the world!* 28 January. Accessed February 7, 2019. https://timesofindia.indiatimes.com/lifestyle/health-fitness/health-news/India-is-the-diabetes-capital-of-the-world/articleshow/50753461.cms.

Chapter 6: Confinement

1. 1996. In *Prisoned Chickens, Poisoned Eggs: An Inside Look at the Modern Poultry Industry,* by Dr Karen Davis, 19-20. Summertown, Tennessee: Book Publishing Company.

2. Humane Society International. 2013. *Hope for Hens: India Agrees That Battery Cages Are Illegal.* 13 May. Accessed February 7, 2019. http://www.hsi.org/world/india/news/news/2013/05/victory_hens_india_051413.html.

3. Humane Society International (India). 2017. *When Small Egg Farmers in India Win Big, Hens Benefit Too!* 21 July. Accessed February 7, 2019. https://www.thebetterindia.com/109210/when-small-egg-farmers-in-india-win-big-hens-benefit-too/.

4. Bureau of Indian Standards (BIS). 2015. 'Proceedings of the Meetings on 'Code of practices for raising egg laying hens' (BIS).' Bureau of Indian Standards (BIS), 7 October.

5. Horne, P.L.M. Van, and T.J. Achterbosch. n.d. *Animal welfare in poultry production systems: impact of European Union standards on world trade.* Accessed February 7, 2019. http://www.fao.org/Ag/againfo/home/events/bangkok2007/docs/part2/2_5.pdf.

6. Shields PhD, Sara, and Ian J.H. Duncan PhD. n.d. *An HSUS Report: A Comparison of the Welfare of Hens in Battery Cages and Alternative Systems.* The Humane Society of the United States.

7. Gartech. n.d. *GE Ultima - Layer Battery.* Accessed February 7, 2019. https://www.gartech.co.in/g-e-ultima.aspx.

8. Humane Society International. n.d. *An HSI Report: The Welfare of Animals in the Egg Industry.* Humane Society International.

9. Humane Society International. n.d. *An HSI Report: The Welfare of Animals in the Egg Industry.* Humane Society International.

10. Allana. n.d. *Poultry Feed Supplement, Animal Fats, Sterile Bone Meal.* Accessed February 7, 2019. http://www.allana.com/rendered-products/.

11. Kotaiah, Dr T. 2013. *India's Poultry Market is Booming.* 26 July. Accessed February 7, 2019. http://www.thepoultrysite.com/poultrynews/29581/indias-poultry-market-is-booming/.

12. Horne, P.L.M. Van, and T.J. Achterbosch. n.d. *Animal welfare in poultry production systems: impact of European Union standards on world trade.* Accessed February 7, 2019. http://www.fao.org/Ag/againfo/home/events/bangkok2007/docs/part2/2_5.pdf.

13. Karen Davis, Ph.D. n.d. *The Life of One Battery Hen.* Accessed February 16, 2019. http://www.upc-online.org/thinking/lifeofhen.htm.

14. Chow, Edward, and Emily Chan. 2015. *Shocking images show 7,000 chickens that suffocated to death when power cut shut off ventilation at Chinese battery farm.* 12 May. https://www.dailymail.co.uk/news/peoplesdaily/article-3077973/7-000-chickens-suffocated-power-cut-shut-ventilation-battery-farm.html.

15. WorldPoultry. 2012. *India: mob cuts power to poultry farm, 700,000 birds die.* 6 July. Accessed February 16, 2019. https://www.poultryworld.net/Broilers/Health/2012/7/India-mob-cuts-power-to-poultry-farm-700000-birds-die-WP010604W/.

16. Canadian Coalition for Farm Animals. October 2005. *Battery Cages and the Welfare of Hens.* Canadian Coalition for Farm Animals.

17. Karen Davis, Ph.D. n.d. *The Battery Hen: Her Life Is Not For The Birds.* Accessed February 16, 2019. https://www.upc-online.org/batthen.html.

18. Karen Davis, Ph.D. 2005. *Keep chickens out of wire-floored cages.* 19 August. Accessed February 16, 2019. https://www.upc-online.org/fall05/wirecages.html.

19. Shields PhD, Sara, and Ian J.H. Duncan PhD. n.d. *A Comparison of the Welfare of Hens in Battery Cages and Alternative Systems.* Accessed February 16, 2019. http://www.hsi.org/assets/pdfs/a-comparison-of-the-welfare-of-hens-in-battery-cages-and-alternative-systemshsi.pdf.

20. Humane Society International. n.d. *An HSI Report: The Welfare of Animals in the Egg Industry.* Humane Society International.

21. Humane Society International. n.d. *An HSI Report: The Welfare of Animals in the Egg Industry.* Humane Society International.

22. Humane Society International. n.d. *An HSI Report: The Welfare of Animals in the Egg Industry.* Humane Society International.

23. Humane Society International. n.d. *An HSI Report: The Welfare of Animals in the Egg Industry.* Humane Society International.

24. Shields PhD, Sara, and Ian J.H. Duncan PhD. n.d. *A Comparison of the Welfare of Hens in Battery Cages and Alternative Systems.* Accessed February 16, 2019. http://www.hsi.org/assets/pdfs/a-comparison-of-the-welfare-of-hens-in-battery-cages-and-alternative-systemshsi.pdf.

25. United Poultry Concerns (UPC). 1998. *Subject: Forced Molting of Laying Birds.* 1 April. Accessed February 16, 2019. http://www.upc-online.org/980401moltrpt.html.

26. United Poultry Concerns. 2003. *AVMA's Forced Molting Position Still Unacceptable.* http://www.upc-online.org/spring03/avma.htm.

27. Kharb, Dr RM. 2011. *forced molting circular.* Chennai: Animal Welfare Board of India, 9 March.

28. PETA India and Anonymous for Animal Rights. 2018. *What's Wrong With Eating Eggs and Chicken Flesh?* Mumbai: People for the Ethical Treatment of Animals (PETA) India and Anonymous for Animal Rights.

29. Livelaw News Network. 2017. *Law Commission Suggests New Rules To Stop Cruel Practices Against Egg-laying Hens (layers) & Broiler Chickens [Read 269th Report].* 3 July. Accessed February 16, 2019. http://www.livelaw.in/law-commission-suggests-new-rules-stop-cruel-practices-egg-laying-hens-layers-broiler-chickens-read-269th-report/.

30. Mandhani, Apoorva. 2018. *Uttarakhand HC Issues Directions For Humane Treatment Of Poultry Animals [Read Order].* 17 August. Accessed February

16, 2019. https://www.livelaw.in/uttarakhand-hc-issues-directions-for-humane-treatment-of-poultry-animals-read-order/.

31. Press Trust of India (PTI). 2018. *Hens ought to be kept in bigger cages with freedom of movement, says HC.* 5 November. Accessed February 16, 2019. Hens ought to be kept in bigger cages with freedom of movement, says HC.

32. Law Commission of India. (July 2017). *Report No. 269: Transportation and House-keeping of Egg-laying.* New Delhi: Government of India.

33. 5m Editor (2005, November 2). *International Egg and Poultry Review: Germany.* Retrieved from The Poultry Site: https://thepoultrysite.com/news/2005/11/international-egg-and-poultry-review-germany.

34. European Commission. n.d. *Laying hens.* Accessed February 17, 2019. https://ec.europa.eu/food/animals/welfare/practice/farm/laying_hens_en.

35. Kerswell, Justin. 2011. *Battery egg hens still face hell as 'enriched' cages phased in.* 8 September. Accessed February 17, 2019. https://theecologist.org/2011/sep/08/battery-egg-hens-still-face-hell-enriched-cages-phased.

36. Viva!!. n.d. *'Enriched Cages' Investigation.* Accessed February 17, 2019. https://www.Viva!.org.uk/resources/video-library/enriched-cages-investigation.

37. Animal Aid. 2014. *New investigation reveals the reality of 'enriched' cages.* 16 January. Accessed February 17, 2019. https://www.animalaid.org.uk/new-investigation-reveals-reality-enriched-cages/.

38. PETA India. 2015. *PETA Founder to Transform Herself into a Bloodied, Dying 'Chicken' for World Vegan Month.* 18 November. Accessed March 23, 2019. https://www.petaindia.com/media/peta-founder-tld-vegan-month/.

39. National Bank For Agriculture And Rural Development (NABARD). n.d. *Poultry Broiler Farming.* Accessed February 17, 2019. http://agritech.tnau.ac.in/banking/nabard_pdf/Animal%20husbandry/3.Poultry_Broiler_Farming.pdf.

40. Bureau of Indian Standards. 1986. 'IS: 2732-1985.' *Indian Standard: Code of Practice for Poultry Housing (Second Revision).* New Delhi: Indian Standards Institution, July.

41. Pickett, Heather. 2007. *Alternatives to the Barren Battery Cage For the Housing of Laying Hens in the European Union.* Godalming: Compassion in World Farming.

42. The Poultry Site. 2007. *Cannibalism by Poultry.* 4 June. Accessed February 17, 2019. http://www.thepoultrysite.com/articles/830/cannibalism-by-poultry/.

43. Sunstars Poultry. n.d. Accessed February 17, 2019. http://sunstarspoultry.com/product.php?id=2.

44. Kansas State University. n.d. *Management Practices.* Accessed February 17, 2019. https://www.asi.k-state.edu/doc/poultry/management-practices.pdf.

45. The Humane Society of the United States. 2013. *An HSUS Report: The Welfare of Animals in the Chicken Industry.* December. Accessed February 17, 2019. https://www.humanesociety.org/sites/default/files/docs/hsus-report-welfare-chicken-industry.pdf.

46. Kotaiah, Dr T. 2013. *India's Poultry Market is Booming.* 26 July. Accessed February 7, 2019. http://www.thepoultrysite.com/poultrynews/29581/indias-poultry-market-is-booming/.

47. Investigator, interview by Poorva Joshipura. 2016. *Investigation of treatment of chickens in Andhra Pradesh and Telengana.*

48. Compassion in World Farming (CIWF). n.d. *About Chickens.* Accessed February 17, 2019. https://www.ciwf.com/farm-animals/chickens/.

Chapter 7: Mutilation and Manipulation

1. Lawrence, Felicity. 2016. *If consumers knew how farmed chickens were raised, they might never eat their meat again.* 24 April. Accessed February 17, 2019. https://www.theguardian.com/environment/2016/apr/24/real-cost-of-roast-chicken-animal-welfare-farms.

2. Brulliard, Karin. 2016. *Dogs are born with ears and tails. They should get to keep them.* 8 September. Accessed February 17, 2019. https://www.washingtonpost.com/news/animalia/wp/2016/09/08/what-many-americans-dont-understand-about-designer-dogs/.

3. Kerns, Ben. 2015. *Why People Cut Their Dog's Ears (And Why You Shouldn't).* 23 June. Accessed February 17, 2019. https://www.thedodo.com/ear-cropping-cruel-1212872917.html.

4. Kavin, Kim. 2018. *A celebrated breeder cut dogs' ears. Now she's charged with felony torture.* 3 October. Accessed February 17, 2019. https://www.washingtonpost.com/science/2018/10/03/celebrated-breeder-cut-dogs-ears-now-shes-charged-with-felony-torture/?utm_term=.04a9edbd9909.

5. Becker, Dr Karen. 2010. *Top Two Painful Procedures Your Puppy Should Never Have to Endure.* 27 January. Accessed February 17, 2019. https://healthypets.mercola.com/sites/healthypets/archive/2010/01/27/is-tail-docking-and-ear-cropping-harmful-to-dogs.aspx.

6. Sinmez, Çağrı, Ali Yigit, and Gokhan Aslim. 2017. 'Tail docking and ear cropping in dogs: a short review of laws and welfare aspects in the Europe and Turkey.' *Italian Journal of Animal Science* 16, 431–437.

7. Langley, Liz. 2016. *Bizarre Horns of the Animal Kingdom.* 6 August. Accessed February 17, 2019. https://news.nationalgeographic.com/2016/08/animals-science-horns-africa-rhinos/.

8. Research Institute of Organic Agriculture and Demeter Association Inc. 2016. *Why cows have horns.* Accessed February 17, 2019. https://www.demeter-usa.org/downloads/why-cows-have-horns.pdf.

9. Tamil Nadu Agricultural University. n.d. *Daily Operations Schedule.* Accessed February 17, 2019. http://agritech.tnau.ac.in/animal_husbandry/animhus_cattle_daily%20operation.html.

10. PETA US. n.d. *Dehorning Revealed: Photos.* Accessed February 17, 2019. https://www.peta.org/features/dehorning-revealed-photos/.

11. Hopkins, Fred M., James B. Neel, and F. David Kirkpatrick. n.d. *Dehorning Calves.* Accessed February 17, 2019. https://extension.tennessee.edu/publications/Documents/PB1684.pdf.

12. PETA US. n.d. *Dehorning: Dairy's Dark Secret.* Accessed February 17, 2019. https://www.peta.org/issues/animals-used-for-food/factory-farming/cows/dairy-industry/dehorning/.

13. Hopkins, Fred M., James B. Neel, and F. David Kirkpatrick. n.d. *Dehorning Calves.* Accessed February 17, 2019. https://extension.tennessee.edu/publications/Documents/PB1684.pdf.

14. PETA US. n.d. *Dehorning: Dairy's Dark Secret.* Accessed February 17, 2019. https://www.peta.org/issues/animals-used-for-food/factory-farming/cows/dairy-industry/dehorning/.

15. Nosowitz, Dan. 2018. *Swiss Farmer's Plea to Save Cattle Horns Fails.* 29 November. Accessed February 17, 2019. https://modernfarmer. com/2018/11/swiss-farmers-plea-to-save-cattle-horns-fails/.

16. Valliyate, Dr Manilal, interview by Poorva Joshipura. 2018. *CEO PETA India* (24 November).

17. PETA India. 2012. *PETA Report Prompts Animal Welfare Board Directive On Humane Cattle Castration.* 28 May. Accessed February 17, 2019. https://www.petaindia.com/media/peta-report-prompts-animal-welfare-board-directive-humane-cattle-castration/.

18. PETA India. 2015. *Taking Pain Out of Cattle Castration is Among Animal Welfare Reforms Now Required in India.* 7 January. Accessed February 17, 2019. https://www.petaindia.com/media/taking-pain-cattle-castration-among-animal-welfare-reforms-now-required-india/.

19. Valliyate, Dr Manilal, interview by Poorva Joshipura. 2018. *CEO PETA India* (24 November).

20. raithai. 2011. *Castration of a Piglet.* 12 August. Accessed February 17, 2019. https://www.youtube.com/watch?v=WiNLNf8qSD0.

21. F.r.S Tv. 2018. *Villages goat castration by free hand..OMG..* 5 January. Accessed February 17, 2019. https://www.youtube.com/watch?v=Zl88IHR1ZI8.

22. Animal Husbandry: A Beneficial Occupation. 2018. *Type of Castrating the Male Goat (Banding of Goat) I Khassi Bakara.* 28 October. Accessed February 17, 2019. https://www.youtube.com/watch?v=zUyP3l176pg.

23. The Think Center. 2017. *Nose Piercing.* 23 February. Accessed February 17, 2019. https://www.youtube.com/watch?v=U9UCg-hjV_4.

24. Virginia Cooperative Extension: Virginia State University. 2009. *Cattle Identification: Freeze Branding.* 1 May. Accessed February 17, 2019. https://pubs.ext.vt.edu/400/400-301/400-301.html.

25. Valliyate, Dr Manilal, interview by Poorva Joshipura. 2018. *CEO PETA India* (24 November).

26. Griffiths, Sarah. 2014. *Dogs are NOT descended from modern wolves but split from common ancestor 34,000 years ago.* 16 January. Accessed February 17, 2019. http://www.dailymail.co.uk/sciencetech/article-2540737/Dogs-closely-related-wolves-evolved-common-ancestor-34-000-years-ago.html.

27. petMD. n.d. *Breathing Problem in Short-Nose Breed Dogs.* Accessed February 17, 2019. https://www.petmd.com/dog/conditions/respiratory/c_multi_brachycephalic_airway_syndrome.

28. Rooney, Dr Nicola, and Dr David Sargan. n.d. *Pedigree dog breeding in the UK: a major welfare concern?* Horsham: Royal Society for the Prevention of Cruelty to Animals (RSPCA).

29. BBC One. 2008. *BBC One reveals shocking truth about pedigree dog breeding in UK.* 19 August. Accessed February 17, 2019. http://www.bbc.co.uk/pressoffice/pressreleases/stories/2008/08_august/19/dogs.shtml.

30. Universities Federation for Animal Welfare. 2011. *Genetic Welfare Problems of Companion Animals.* Accessed February 17, 2019. https://www.ufaw.org.uk/dogs/english-bulldog-dystocia.

31. Compassion in World Farming Trust. 2005. *The Welfare of Broiler Chickens in the European Union.* Petersfield: Compassion in World Farming Trust.

32. Animals Australia. n.d. *Broiler Chickens Fact Sheet.* Accessed February 17, 2019. https://www.animalsaustralia.org/documents/factsheets/BroilerChickensFactSheet.pdf.

33. Grillo, Robert. 2014. *Esperanza: Story of a Rescued Broiler Chicken.* 3 January. Accessed February 17, 2019. https://freefromharm.org/animal-rescue-stories/esperanza-story-rescued-broiler-chicken/.

34. Compassion in World Farming Trust. 2005. *The Welfare of Broiler Chickens in the European Union.* Petersfield: Compassion in World Farming Trust.

35. Compassion in World Farming Trust. 2005. *The Welfare of Broiler Chickens in the European Union.* Petersfield: Compassion in World Farming Trust.

36. The Humane Society of the United States. 2013. *An HSUS Report: The Welfare of Animals in the Chicken Industry.* December. Accessed February 17, 2019. https://www.humanesociety.org/sites/default/files/docs/hsus-report-welfare-chicken-industry.pdf.

37. The Poultry Site. n.d. *Spondylolisthesis, Kinky-back.* Accessed February 17, 2019. http://www.thepoultrysite.com/diseaseinfo/141/spondylolisthesis-kinkyback/.

38. Animals Australia. n.d. *Broiler Chickens Fact Sheet.* Accessed February 17, 2019. https://www.animalsaustralia.org/documents/factsheets/BroilerChickensFactSheet.pdf.

39. The Humane Society of the United States. 2013. *An HSUS Report: The Welfare of Animals in the Chicken Industry.* December. Accessed February 17, 2019. https://www.humanesociety.org/sites/default/files/docs/hsus-report-welfare-chicken-industry.pdf.

40. Compassion in World Farming Trust. 2005. *The Welfare of Broiler Chickens in the European Union.* Petersfield: Compassion in World Farming Trust.

41. The Humane Society of the United States. 2013. *An HSUS Report: The Welfare of Animals in the Chicken Industry.* December. Accessed February 17, 2019. https://www.humanesociety.org/sites/default/files/docs/hsus-report-welfare-chicken-industry.pdf.

42. The Poultry Site. n.d. *Ascites.* Accessed February 17, 2019. http://www.thepoultrysite.com/diseaseinfo/6/ascites/.

43. Compassion in World Farming Trust. 2005. *The Welfare of Broiler Chickens in the European Union.* Petersfield: Compassion in World Farming Trust.

44. 2014. In *Critical Animal Studies: Thinking the Unthinkable*, by John Sorenson, 174. Toronto: Canadian Scholars' Press.

45. The Humane Society of the United States. n.d. *An HSUS Report: The Welfare of Animals in the Broiler Chicken Industry.* Accessed February 17, 2019. http://journeytoforever.org/farm_library/welfare_broiler.pdf.

46. Compassion in World Farming Trust. 2005. *The Welfare of Broiler Chickens in the European Union.* Petersfield: Compassion in World Farming Trust.

47. National Dairy Development Board. n.d. *Genetic Improvement.* Accessed February 17, 2019. https://www.nddb.coop/services/animalbreeding/geneticimprovement.

48. Rousseau, Oscar. 2016. *India to bolster pork industry.* 16 June. Accessed February 17, 2019. https://www.globalmeatnews.com/Article/2016/06/17/India-to-bolster-pork-industry.

49. Animal Resources Development Department, Government of Tripura. n.d. *Piggery Development.* Accessed February 17, 2019. https://ardd. tripura.gov.in/?q=piggery.

50. Humane Society of the United States (HSUS). n.d. *An HSUS Report: The Welfare of Animals in the Pig Industry.* Accessed February 17, 2019. https://www.humanesociety.org/sites/default/files/docs/hsus-report-pig-industry-welfare.pdf.

51. Farm Sanctuary. n.d. *Pig Care.* Accessed February 17, 2019. https:// www.farmsanctuary.org/wp-content/uploads/2012/06/Animal-Care-Pigs.pdf.

52. D'Silva, Joyce, and Peter Stevenson. July 1995. *Modern Breeding Technologies and the Welfare of Farm Animals.* Petersfield: Compassion in World Farming Trust.

53. Humane Society of the United States (HSUS). n.d. *An HSUS Report: The Welfare of Animals in the Pig Industry.* Accessed February 17, 2019. https://www.humanesociety.org/sites/default/files/docs/hsus-report-pig-industry-welfare.pdf.

54. National Animal Disease Information Service (NADIS). n.d. *Tail biting.* Accessed February 17, 2019. https://www.nadis.org.uk/disease-a-z/pigs/tail-biting/.

55. Humane Society of the United States (HSUS). n.d. *An HSUS Report: The Welfare of Piglets in the Pig Industry.* Accessed February 17, 2019. https://www.humanesociety.org/sites/default/files/docs/hsus-report-piglets-industry-welfare.pdf.

56. Humane Society of the United States (HSUS). n.d. *An HSUS Report: The Welfare of Animals in the Pig Industry.* Accessed February 17, 2019. https://www.humanesociety.org/sites/default/files/docs/hsus-report-pig-industry-welfare.pdf.

57. D'Silva, Joyce, and Peter Stevenson. July 1995. *Modern Breeding Technologies and the Welfare of Farm Animals.* Petersfield: Compassion in World Farming Trust.

58. Baines, Dr Julia. 2018. *PETA Condemns 'Frankenscience' Horror Show as Monkey Is Cloned for the First Time.* 24 January. Accessed February 17, 2019. https://www.peta.org.uk/blog/peta-condemns-frankenscience-horror-show-monkey-cloned-first-time/.

59. Duhaime-Ross, Arielle. 2016. *Scientists are one step closer to using pig hearts for human transplants.* 5 April. Accessed February 17, 2019. https://www.theverge.com/2016/4/5/11360702/xenotransplant-pig-heart-baboon-revivicor-nih.

60. Ormandy, Elisabeth H., Julie Dale, and Gilly Griffin. May 2011. 'Genetic engineering of animals: Ethical issues, including welfare concerns.' *Canadian Veterinary Journal* 52(5): 544–50.

61. Physicians Committee for Responsible Medicine (PCRM). 2015. *Get Omega-3s from Plants—Not Fish Oil.* 26 August. Accessed February 17, 2019. https://www.pcrm.org/news/blog/get-omega-3s-plants-not-fish-oil.

Chapter 8: Worked to Death

1. Yancy, George, and Peter Singer. 2015. *Peter Singer: On Racism, Animal Rights and Human Rights.* 27 May. Accessed March 18, 2019. https://opinionator.blogs.nytimes.com/2015/05/27/peter-singer-on-speciesism-and-racism/.

2. Natarajan, Akila, Mahesh Chander, and N. Bharathy. 2016. 'Relevance of draught cattle power and its future prospects in India: A review.' *Agricultural Reviews* 37 (1): 49–54.

3. Upreti, Dr Naresh, interview by Poorva Joshipura. 2017. *Chief Operating Officer, Animal Rahat* (30 April).

4. National Dairy Development Board (NDDB). n.d. *Managing dairy animals during Summer.* Accessed February 23, 2019. http://dairyknowledge.in/article/managing-dairy-animals-during-summer.

5. Gould, Kevin. 2011. *Heat stress in cattle – Know the warning signs!* 22 July. Accessed February 23, 2019. https://www.canr.msu.edu/news/heat_stress_in_cattle_know_the_warning_signs.

6. Nair, Dr Sudheesh S. 2014. *A Note on the Real Suffering Bulls in India.* 16 December. Accessed February 23, 2019. http://drssnairvet.blogspot.com/2014/12/the-real-suffering-bulls-in-india.html.

7. Valliyate, Dr Manilal, interview by Poorva Joshipura. 2017. *CEO, PETA India* (30 April).

8. Zoetis. n.d. *Pneumonia-Bovine Respiratory Disease-Dairy (BRD).* Accessed February 23, 2019. https://www.zoetis.com.au/diseases/ pneumonia-bovine-respiratory-disease-dairy-_brd_.aspx.

9. Upreti, Dr Naresh, interview by Poorva Joshipura. 2017. *Chief Operating Officer, Animal Rahat* (30 April).

10. Upreti, Dr Naresh. 2015. *Vellore leather investigation notes.* Animal Rahat, 27–29 October.

11. Valliyate, Dr Manilal, interview by Poorva Joshipura. 2017. *CEO, PETA India* (30 April).

12. PETA India. 2013. *PETA India's 2013 Bull Race Investigation.* 8 May. Accessed February 23, 2019. https://www.youtube.com/ watch?v=PMPXp5Rqc1A&t=180s.

13. PETA India. 2018. *Rekla Races: Kadaikutty Singam Makers Probably Don't Want You to See This.* 25 July. Accessed February 23, 2019. https:// www.youtube.com/watch?v=x0NP9obvrkA&t=41s.

14. PETA India. n.d. *Shocking Kambala Investigations Show Buffaloes Still Need Your Help.* Accessed February 23, 2019. https://www.petaindia. com/features/kambala-investigation/.

15. Goa Trip. n.d. *Bullfights Goa.* Accessed February 23, 2019. http://www. goatrip.co.in/travel-guide/sports-recreation/bullfights.html.

16. Surendran, Vivek. 2017. *All you need to know about Jallikattu.* 19 January. Accessed February 23, 2019. https://www.indiatoday.in/ fyi/story/jallikattu-ban-tamil-nadu-protest-supreme-court-bull-taming-955819-2017-01-19.

17. PETA India. 2013. *Jallikattu Investigation (Jan 2013).* 12 February. Accessed February 23, 2019. https://www.youtube.com/ watch?v=coZvTRHt2m4&t=3s.

18. Express News Service. 2018. *Tamil Nadu: Bull dies of cardiac arrest during Jallikattu.* 5 February. Accessed February 23, 2019. http://www. newindianexpress.com/states/tamil-nadu/2018/feb/05/tamil-nadu-bull-dies-of-cardiac-arrest-during-jallikattu-1768498.html.

19. Rohit, T.K. 2017. *43 lives lost to jallikattu: AWBI.* 14 January. Accessed February 23, 2019. https://www.thehindu.com/news/national/tamil-nadu/43-lives-lost-to-jallikattu-AWBI/article17037922.ece.

20. Somu, Balakumar. 2015. *Jallikattu: Suffocation by Law.* 12 January. Accessed February 23, 2019. http://jallikattu.in/?p=4126.

21. Press Trust of India (PTI). 2017. *Students held for burning PETA CEOs effigy.* 9 January. Accessed February 23, 2019. https://www.indiatoday.in/pti-feed/story/students-held-for-burning-peta-ceos-effigy-854050-2017-01-09.

22. Vandhana, M. 2014. *Jallikattu bulls go for a pittance.* 21 May. Accessed February 23, 2019. https://www.thehindu.com/news/cities/Madurai/jallikattu-bulls-go-for-a-pittance/article6030716.ece.

23. Food and Agriculture Organization of the United Nations (FAO). 2006. *Livestock a major threat to environment.* 29 November. Accessed February 23, 2019. http://www.fao.org/newsroom/en/news/2006/1000448/index.html.

24. Scully, Matthew. 2003. *Dominion: The Power of Man, the Suffering of Animals, and the Call to Mercy.* St. Martin's Press.

Chapter 9: The Final Journey

1. Daragahi, Borzou. 2018. *'This one has heat stress': the shocking reality of live animal exports.* 30 July. Accessed February 24, 2019. https://www.theguardian.com/environment/2018/jul/30/this-one-has-heat-stress-the-shocking-reality-of-live-animal-exports.

2. Kassam, Ashifa. 2017. *Judge dismisses case of woman who gave water to pigs headed to slaughter.* 4 May. Accessed February 24, 2019. https://www.theguardian.com/world/2017/may/04/canada-anita-krajnc-pigs-water-case-dismissed.

3. PETA India. 1999. *The Skins Trade in India.* 8 October. Accessed February 24, 2019. https://www.youtube.com/watch?v=3hCpz89WlUY&t=381s.

4. —. n.d. *PETA India's First Campaign: Taking on the Leather Industry.* Accessed February 24, 2019. https://www.petaindia.com/blog/peta-indias-first-campaign-taking-leather-industry/.

5. Hugo Boss. n.d. *Piñatex® Shoes from Boss.* Accessed February 24, 2019. https://www.hugoboss.com/uk/men-vegan-shoes/.

6. Rediff. 2000. *PM tells states to prevent cruel practices in leather trade.* 5 June. Accessed February 24, 2019. http://inwww.rediff.com/money/2000/jun/05pm.htm.

7. Haridas, Neena. 2000. *Maran to the rescue of leather traders.* 12 June. Accessed February 24, 2019. https://www.rediff.com/business/2000/jun/12leath.htm.

8. Lukose, Anjali. 2014. *State animal welfare board hasn't met in 11 yrs.* 6 February. Accessed February 24, 2019. http://indianexpress.com/article/cities/mumbai/state-animal-welfare-board-hasnt-met-in-11-yrs/.

9. Outlook Web Bureau. 2017. *After Supreme Court Slap, Centre Plans To Withdraw Notification Banning Cattle Sale For Slaughter In Market: Report.* 30 November. Accessed February 24, 2019. https://www.outlookindia.com/website/story/after-supreme-court-slap-centre-plans-to-withdraw-notification-banning-cattle-sa/304984.

10. TNN. 2018. *Govt finally dilutes rules on cattle sale.* 11 April. Accessed February 24, 2019. https://timesofindia.indiatimes.com/india/govt-finally-dilutes-rules-on-cattle-sale/articleshow/63705093.cms.

11. Upreti, Dr Naresh, interview by Poorva Joshipura. 2017. *Chief Operating Officer, Animal Rahat* (12 November).

12. Singh, Virat A. 2016. *No awareness about new rules for livestock transportation.* 16 February. Accessed February 24, 2019. http://www.dnaindia.com/mumbai/report-no-awareness-about-new-rules-for-livestock-transportation-2178181.

13. Khan, Hamza. 2018. *Rajasthan: 7 held for 'transporting' cattle for slaughter.* 20 August. Accessed February 24, 2019. http://indianexpress.com/article/india/india-news-india/seven-arrested-in-pratapgarh-for-transporting-bullocks-for-slaughter-2829806/.

14. Express News Service. 2016. *Mathura tense after 22 dead cows found in truck.* 24 June. Accessed February 24, 2019. http://indianexpress.com/article/india/india-news-india/delhi-mathura-highway-cows-dead-truck-beef-ban-lynching-2872205/.

15. Express News Service. 2016. *Haryana: Villagers catch truck with dead cattle in Hisar.* 26 August. Accessed February 24, 2019. http://indianexpress.com/article/india/india-news-india/haryana-villagers-catch-truck-with-dead-cattle-2997062/.

16. Behl, Manka. 2016. *Stuffed in truck, over 100 cattle died in one week.* 6 September. Accessed February 24, 2019. http://timesofindia.

indiatimes.com/city/nagpur/Stuffed-in-truck-over-100-cattle-died-in-one-week/articleshow/54022095.cms.

17. PETA India. (10 August 2019). *PETA India Finds Appalling Cruelty at Mumbai's Deonar Slaughterhouse Before Eid.* Retrieved from PETA India: https://www.petaindia.com/blog/peta-india-finds-appalling-cruelty-at-mumbais-deonar-slaughterhouse-before-eid/.

18. Khan, Hamza. 2018. *Rajasthan: 7 held for 'transporting' cattle for slaughter.* 20 August. Accessed February 24, 2019. http://indianexpress.com/article/india/india-news-india/seven-arrested-in-pratapgarh-for-transporting-bullocks-for-slaughter-2829806/.

19. Ghosh, Palash. 2014. *Cattle Smuggling: A Dangerous, Illegal And Highly Profitable Trade Between India And Bangladesh.* 4 February. Accessed February 24, 2019. http://www.ibtimes.com/cattle-smuggling-dangerous-illegal-highly-profitable-trade-between-india-bangladesh-1553155.

20. Oppili, P. 2015. *Mob forcibly drives away seized truck full of sheep.* 8 March. Accessed February 24, 2019. http://timesofindia.indiatimes.com/city/chennai/Mob-forcibly-drives-away-seized-truck-full-of-sheep/articleshow/46489674.cms.

21. Khakhariya, N. (18 September 2019). *Times of India.* Retrieved from Fresh guidelines on livestock export keep trade hanging. Accessed December 14, 2019. https://timesofindia.indiatimes.com/city/rajkot/fresh-guidelines-on-livestock-export-keep-trade-hanging/articleshow/71175083.cms

22. Pawar, Tushar. 2016. *12,000 sheep, goats flown to Sharjah in two months.* 12 September. Accessed February 24, 2019. https://timesofindia.indiatimes.com/city/nashik/12000-sheep-goats-flown-to-Sharjah-in-two-months/articleshow/54286738.cms.

23. Price, Shawn. 2016. *121 Irish sheep die of suffocation on flight to Singapore.* 11 September. Accessed February 24, 2019. http://www.upi.com/Top_News/World-News/2016/09/11/121-Irish-sheep-die-of-suffocation-on-flight-to-Singapore/2211473638733/.

24. Animals Australia. 2018. *What's it like on board a live export ship?* 3 December. Accessed February 24, 2019. https://www.animalsaustralia.org/features/whats-it-like-on-a-live-export-ship.php.

25. Briefrel, Roland. 2015. *Stop the Cruel Live Export Trade.* August. Accessed February 24, 2019. http://online.anyflip.com/ourh/iuik/ mobile/index.html#p=12.

26. Animals Australia. 2018. *What's it like on board a live export ship?* 3 December. Accessed February 24, 2019. https://www.animalsaustralia. org/features/whats-it-like-on-a-live-export-ship.php.

27. Michalopoulos, S. (26 November 2019). *Euractiv.* Retrieved from Andriukaitis questions live animal transport after Romanian sheep tragedy. Accessed December 14, 2019. https://www.euractiv.com/ section/agriculture-food/news/andriukaitis-questions-live-animal-transport-after-romanian-sheep-tragedy/

28. Kadyan, Naresh. 2014. *Cruel animal shifting: 40 pigs abused in goods transport vehicles - Sukanya Kadyan.* 4 April. Accessed February 24, 2019. https://www.youtube.com/watch?v=HzaCvSb9aNs.

29. Investigator. 2016. *Notes of Investigation of Poultry Farms in Andhra Pradesh and Telengana.*

30. Food and Agriculture Organization of the United Nations (FAO). n.d. *CHAPTER 6: Transport of livestock.* Accessed February 24, 2019. http:// www.fao.org/3/x6909e/x6909e08.htm.

Chapter 10: Slaughter

1. Hodson, Gordon, and Kimberly Costello. 2012. *The link between devaluing animals and discrimination.* 12 December. Accessed February 25, 2019. https://www.newscientist.com/article/mg21628950-400-the-link-between-devaluing-animals-and-discrimination/.

2. Gripper (BSc MRCVS), John, and Miriam Parker. 2000. *Transport and Slaughterhouse Conditions in India.* World Society for the Protection of Animals.

3. IANS. 2017. *Cow slaughter: Calcutta Beef Dealers' Association to meet Kolkata civic body over change in timings.* 11 April. Accessed February 25, 2019. https://zeenews.india.com/kolkata/cow-slaughter-calcutta-beef-dealers-association-to-meet-kolkata-civic-body-over-change-in-timings-1995124.html.

4. Ray, Saikat. 2017. *Supply falls, Kolkata shuts India's first fully automated abattoir.* 31 May. Accessed February 25, 2019. https://timesofindia.

indiatimes.com/city/kolkata/supply-falls-kmc-shuts-indias-first-fully-automated-abattoir/articleshow/58918700.cms.

5. PETA India. October 2005. *Investigative Report on Transport and Slaughter Conditions for Animals Used for Meat and Leather in Tamil Nadu, India*. Mumbai: PETA India.

6. Manikandan, M. 2017. *Slaughterhouse turns tipplers' den*. 1 January. Accessed February 25, 2019. http://www.newindianexpress.com/states/tamil-nadu/2017/jan/01/slaughterhouse-turns-tipplers-den-1554947.html.

7. n.d. *State Level Bankers' Committee, Tamil Nadu*. Accessed February 25, 2019. http://www.slbctn.com/Industries.aspx.

8. Parker, Miriam. 2000. *Best Practices*.

9. Linning, Stephanie. 2016. *Halal-slaughtered animals are 'dying in agony' because of 'Muslim ignorance' over pre-slaughter stunning, say experts*. 24 October. Accessed February 25, 2019. https://www.dailymail.co.uk/news/article-3866340/Animals-dying-agony-halal-meat-Muslim-ignorance-pre-slaughter-stunning-causing-needless-pain-say-experts.html.

10. Gripper (BSc MRCVS), John, and Miriam Parker. 2000. *Transport and Slaughterhouse Conditions in India*. World Society for the Protection of Animals.

11. Subramaniam, A. (2018, August 14). *Pottery Town slaughter house hopes for improvements, as BBMP wakes up*. Retrieved from Citizen Matters: http://bengaluru.citizenmatters.in/slaughter-house-frazer-town-bangalore-abattoir-etp-bbmp-kspcb-27004.

12. The Hindu. 2009. *Harohalli residents are against slaughterhouse: P.G.R. Sindhia*. 26 March. Accessed February 25, 2019. https://www.thehindu.com/todays-paper/tp-national/tp-karnataka/Harohalli-residents-are-against-slaughterhouse-P.G.R.-Sindhia/article16648512.ece.

13. z.top, Tony. 2013. *The Brutal Barbarian Way of Killing Farms Animals in Kerala (India)*. 30 January. Accessed February 25, 2019. https://www.youtube.com/watch?v=4Po-3nGuJ08.

14. Praveen, M.P. 2014. *Captive bolt pistol still greek to abattoirs that wield hammers*. 2 July. Accessed February 25, 2019. https://www.thehindu.com/todays-paper/tp-national/tp-kerala/captive-bolt-pistol-still-greek-to-abattoirs-that-wield-hammers/article6168533.ece.

15. —.2013. *Abattoirs told to replace hammers with bolt pistol.* 26 November. Accessed February 25, 2019. https://www.thehindu.com/todays-paper/ tp-national/tp-kerala/abattoirs-told-to-replace-hammers-with-bolt-pistol/article5392280.ece.

16. PETA US. 1999–2000. *Report on the Transport and Slaughter Conditions of Indian Cattle Used for Meat and Leather Export.* PETA US.

17. PETA India. n.d. *Deonar Abattoir: Report on the Failure of Government and of Management to Meet Humane, Hygiene, Religious and Legal Standards for Slaughter and Animal Handling.* PETA India.

18. PETA India. 2016. *Video: Animals Electrocuted at Ghazipur Slaughterhouse.* 21 September. Accessed February 26, 2019. https:// www.petaindia.com/blog/video-animals-electrocuted-ghazipur-slaughterhouse/.

19. Agricultural and Processed Food Products Export Development Authority (APEDA). n.d. *Approved Indian Abattoirs-Cum-Meat Processing Plants/Stand Alone Abattoirs.* Accessed February 26, 2019. http://apeda.gov.in/apedawebsite/Announcements/PLANTS-1-APPROVED-INDIAN-ABATTOIRS.pdf.

Chapter 11: Fish Used for Food

1. International Vegetarian Union (IVU). n.d. *Europe: early 20th Century, Franz Kafka (1883-1924).* Accessed February 28, 2019. https://ivu.org/ history/europe20a/kafka.html.

2. Brown-Heidenreich, Sophia. 2017. *Full-scale reform: Berkeley bans fish as prizes at carnivals.* 22 October. Accessed March 2, 2019. http:// www.dailycal.org/2017/10/22/full-scale-reform-berkeley-bans-fish-as-prizes-at-carnivals/.

3. Reuters. 2005. *Rome bans 'cruel' goldfish bowls.* 25 October. Accessed March 2, 2019. https://www.abc.net.au/news/2005-10-26/rome-bans-cruel-goldfish-bowls/2132214.

4. Trgovich, Marti. 2016. *Goldfish Actually Don't Belong In Bowls.* 8 July. Accessed March 2, 2019. https://www.thedodo.com/goldfish-bowl-1911460513.html.

5. Wedderburn, Pete. 2016. *Do single goldfish get lonely?* 25 July. Accessed March 3, 2019. https://www.telegraph.co.uk/pets/news-features/do-single-goldfish-get-lonely/.

6. Guilford, Gwynn. 2016. *The future is here: People are now eating more farmed fish than wild-caught fish.* 14 July. Accessed January 26, 2019. https://qz.com/730794/the-future-is-here-people-are-now-eating-more-farmed-fish-than-wild-caught-fish/.

7. Fishcount.org.uk. n.d. *Fish count estimates.* Accessed December 17, 2019. http://fishcount.org.uk/fish-count-estimates.

8. Kaneka, Toshiko, and Carl Haub. 2018. *How Many People Have Ever Lived on Earth?* 9 March. Accessed March 2, 2019. https://www.prb.org/howmanypeoplehaveeverlivedonearth/.

9. Guilford, Gwynn. 2016. *The future is here: People are now eating more farmed fish than wild-caught fish.* 14 July. Accessed January 26, 2019. https://qz.com/730794/the-future-is-here-people-are-now-eating-more-farmed-fish-than-wild-caught-fish/.

10. Ministry of Agriculture & Farmers Welfare, Government of India. 2017. *India becomes second largest fish producing country in the world: Shri Radha Mohan Singh.* 21 November. Accessed March 2, 2019. http://pib.nic.in/newsite/PrintRelease.aspx?relid=173699.

11. Essere Animali. 2018. *Allevamenti Intensivi Di Pesci: Prima Indagine In Europa.* 18 October. Accessed March 2, 2019. https://www.youtube.com/watch?time_continue=10&v=wImDWAA_ALc.

12. Bollard, Lewis. 2018. *Fish: The Forgotten Farm Animal.* 18 January. Accessed March 2, 2019. https://www.openphilanthropy.org/blog/fish-forgotten-farm-animal.

13. Sneddon, Lynne U. 5 September 2003. 'The evidence for pain in fish: the use of morphine as an analgesic.' *Applied Animal Behaviour Science* Vol. 83(2): 153–162.

14. Jabr, Ferris. 2018. *It's Official: Fish Feel Pain.* 8 January. Accessed March 2, 2019. https://www.smithsonianmag.com/science-nature/fish-feel-pain-180967764/.

15. ibid.

16. Bekoff, Dr Marc. 2014. *Fish Are Sentient and Emotional Beings and Clearly Feel Pain.* 19 June. Accessed March 2, 2019. https://www.psychologytoday.com/gb/blog/animal-emotions/201406/fish-are-sentient-and-emotional-beings-and-clearly-feel-pain.

17. Brown, C. 2015. 'Fish intelligence, sentience and ethics.' *Animal Cognition* 18(1): 1–17.

18. Guardian Staff. 2018. *Crayfish becomes online hero by detaching claw to escape boiling soup.* 3 Jun. Accessed March 2, 2019. https://www.theguardian.com/world/2018/jun/03/crayfish-becomes-online-hero-by-detaching-claw-to-escape-boiling-soup.

19. Hooper, Ben. 2017. *Crab climbs out of pot, switches off hot plate.* 19 September. Accessed March 2, 2019. https://www.upi.com/Odd_News/2017/09/19/Crab-climbs-out-of-pot-switches-off-hot-plate/7111505841136/.

20. Stelling, Tamar. 2014. *Do lobsters and other invertebrates feel pain? New research has some answers.* 10 March. Accessed March 2, 2019. https://www.washingtonpost.com/national/health-science/do-lobsters-and-other-invertebrates-feel-pain-new-research-has-some-answers/2014/03/07/f026ea9e-9e59-11e3-b8d8-94577ff66b28_story.html?noredirect=on&utm_term=.d18d3c12873f.

21. Stelling, Tamar. 2014. *Do lobsters and other invertebrates feel pain? New research has some answers.* 10 March. Accessed March 2, 2019. https://www.washingtonpost.com/national/health-science/do-lobsters-and-other-invertebrates-feel-pain-new-research-has-some-answers/2014/03/07/f026ea9e-9e59-11e3-b8d8-94577ff66b28_story.html?noredirect=on&utm_term=.d18d3c12873f.

22. Walsh, Bryan. 2013. *Do Crabs Feel Pain? Maybe — and Maybe We Should Rethink Eating Them.* 18 January. Accessed March 2, 2019. http://science.time.com/2013/01/18/do-crabs-feel-pain-maybe-and-maybe-we-should-rethink-eating-them/.

23. Cressey, Daniel. 2013. *Experiments reveal that crabs and lobsters feel pain.* 7 August. Accessed March 2, 2019. http://blogs.nature.com/news/2013/08/experiments-reveal-that-crabs-and-lobsters-feel-pain.html.

24. Wallace, David Foster. 2004. *Consider the Lobster.* August. Accessed March 2, 2019. http://www.gourmet.com.s3-website-us-east-1.amazonaws.com/magazine/2000s/2004/08/consider_the_lobster.html.

25. Pollack, Hilary. 2015. *How An Octopus Feels When It's Eaten Alive.* 7 November. Accessed March 2, 2019. https://munchies.vice.com/en_us/article/vvxzzx/how-an-octopus-feels-when-its-eaten-alive.

26. Malik, Wajeeha. 2016. *Inky's Daring Escape Shows How Smart Octopuses Are.* 14 April. Accessed March 2, 2019. https://news.nationalgeographic.com/2016/04/160414-inky-octopus-escapes-intelligence/.

27. Hunt, Elle. 2017. *Alien intelligence: the extraordinary minds of octopuses and other cephalopods.* 28 March. Accessed March 2, 2019. https://www.theguardian.com/environment/2017/mar/28/alien-intelligence-the-extraordinary-minds-of-octopuses-and-other-cephalopods.

28. *The Telegraph.* 2008. *Otto the octopus wreaks havoc.* 31 October. Accessed March 2, 2019. https://www.telegraph.co.uk/news/newstopics/howaboutthat/3328480/Otto-the-octopus-wrecks-havoc.html.

29. Puschmann, Sarah B. 2017. *Are Octopuses Smart?* 18 August. Accessed March 2, 2019. https://www.livescience.com/60168-how-smart-are-octopuses.html.

30. Hunt, Elle. 2016. *Do you care about animals? Then you really shouldn't eat octopus.* 26 May. Accessed March 2, 2019. https://www.theguardian.com/commentisfree/2016/may/26/do-you-care-about-animals-then-you-really-shouldnt-eat-octopus.

31. Hooper, Rowan. 2017. *Cephalopods show signs of intelligence.* 23 September. Accessed March 2, 2019. https://www.japantimes.co.jp/news/2017/09/23/national/science-health/cephalopods-show-signs-intelligence/#.XHquIoj7TIW.

32. Lee, Jane J. 2015. *Watch Jumbo Squid Speak by 'Flashing' Each Other.* 21 January. Accessed March 2, 2019. https://news.nationalgeographic.com/news/2015/01/150121-humboldt-jumbo-squid-crittercam-animal-ocean-science/.

33. Main, Douglas. 2014. *Squids And Other Invertebrates Can Probably Feel Pain.* 11 March. Accessed March 2, 2019. https://www.popsci.com/article/science/squids-and-other-invertebrates-can-probably-feel-pain.

34. E. Vivekanandan, V. V. Singh and J. K. Kizhakudan. 10 August 2013. 'Carbon footprint by marine fishing boats of India.' *Current Science* Vol. 105(3): 361–66.

35. Kaieteur News. 2011. *Seventy percent of world's fish species fully exploited, depleted – UN.* 10 October. Accessed March 2, 2019. https://www.kaieteurnewsonline.com/2011/10/10/seventy-percent-of-world%E2%80%99s-fish-species-fully-exploited-depleted-un/.

36. Goudarzi, Sara. 2006. *Study: Marine Species Collapse by 2048.* 2 November. Accessed March 2, 2019. https://www.livescience.com/4288-study-marine-species-collapse-2048.html.

37. Srinivasan, Meera. 2017. *Sri Lanka bans bottom-trawling.* 7 July. Accessed March 2, 2019. https://www.thehindu.com/news/national/tamil-nadu/sri-lanka-bans-bottom-trawling/article19227034.ece.

38. Greenpeace. n.d. *Bottom trawling.* Accessed March 2, 2019. https://www.greenpeace.org.uk/what-we-do/oceans/overfishing/bottom-trawling/.

39. Shark Savers. 2012. *Shark Fin Trade Myths and Truths: BYCATCH.* Accessed March 2, 2019. http://www.sharksavers.org/files/8613/3185/9956/Shark_Bycatch_FACT_SHEET_Shark_Savers.pdf.

40. Amanda Keledjian, Gib Brogan, Beth Lowell, Jon Warrenchuk, Ben Enticknap, Geoff Shester, Michael Hirshfield and Dominique Cano-Stocco. March 2014. *Wasted Catch: Unsolved Problems in US Fisheries.* Oceana. http://oceana.org/sites/default/files/reports/Bycatch_Report_FINAL.pdf.

41. PETA US. n.d. *Commercial Fishing: How Fish Get From the High Seas to Your Supermarket.* Accessed March 2, 2019. https://www.peta.org/issues/animals-used-for-food/factory-farming/fish/commercial-fishing/.

42. Dubsky, Eoin. 2011. *The harsh reality of longline fishing.* 18 November. Accessed March 2, 2019. https://www.greenpeace.org/usa/the-harsh-reality-of-longline-fishing/.

43. Werner, T. B., S. Northridge, K.M. Press, and Young N. 2015. 'Mitigating bycatch and depredation of marine mammals in longline fisheries.' *ICES Journal of Marine Science: Journal du Conseil* 72(5): 1576–1586.

44. PETA US. n.d. *Commercial Fishing: How Fish Get From the High Seas to Your Supermarket.* Accessed March 2, 2019. https://www.peta.org/issues/animals-used-for-food/factory-farming/fish/commercial-fishing/.

45. Rao, G.S. 2010. 'Current status and prospects of fishery resources of the Indian.' *Coastal Fishery Resources of India: Conservation and Sustainable* 1-13.

46. PETA US. n.d. *Commercial Fishing: How Fish Get From the High Seas to Your Supermarket.* Accessed March 2, 2019. https://www.peta.org/

issues/animals-used-for-food/factory-farming/fish/commercial-fishing/.

47. TRAFFIC. 2016. *Indian Ocean sharks at risk from deepwater gillnets.* 26 May. Accessed March 3, 2019. https://www.traffic.org/news/indian-ocean-sharks-at-risk-from-deepwater-gillnets/.

48. Chatterjee, Badri. 2017. *Purse seine fishing nets banned across Maharashtra from Jan 1, fishermen allege violations.* 2 January. Accessed March 3, 2019. https://www.hindustantimes.com/mumbai-news/purse-seine-fishing-nets-banned-across-maharashtra-from-jan-1-fishermen-allege-violations/story-yIU0lQATApQ7UMYnh41HAP.html.

49. Mackenzie, Willie. 2010. *When purse-seining goes bad.* 18 May. Accessed March 3, 2019. https://www.greenpeace.org/archive-international/en/news/Blogs/makingwaves/when-purse-seining-goes-bad/blog/11803/.

50. Chatterjee, Badri. 2017. *Purse seine fishing nets banned across Maharashtra from Jan 1, fishermen allege violations.* 2 January. Accessed March 3, 2019. https://www.hindustantimes.com/mumbai-news/purse-seine-fishing-nets-banned-across-maharashtra-from-jan-1-fishermen-allege-violations/story-yIU0lQATApQ7UMYnh41HAP.html.

51. Paleontological Research Institution. n.d. *Filter Feeding.* Accessed March 3, 2019. https://www.priweb.org/index.php/education/education-projects-programs/under-siege-marine-life-vs-the-gulf-oil-spill/lifestyles/filter-feeding.

52. Seafood Watch. n.d. *Fishing & Farming Methods.* Accessed March 3, 2019. https://www.seafoodwatch.org/ocean-issues/fishing-and-farming-methods.

53. Kesharwani, Sadhna, K.K. Dube, and Rizwana Khan. 2017. 'Effect of Profenofos on Rohu Fish (Labio rohita): A Fish Widely Cultivated In Rural Areas of India.' *International Journal of Current Microbiology and Applied Sciences* 6(5): 1889–1893.

54. Food and Agriculture Organization of the United Nations. n.d. *National Aquaculture Sector Overview: India.* Accessed March 3, 2019. http://www.fao.org/fishery/countrysector/naso_india/en.

55. Loria, Joe. 2018. *Italian Animal Rights Group Exposes Fish Suffocating at Factory Farms.* 19 October. Accessed March 3, 2019. https://mercyforanimals.org/italian-animal-rights-group-exposes-fish.

56. Gandhi, Maneka. 2018. *Fish breeding often involves use of antibiotics, chemicals which harm human health and alter ecosystem.* 12 February. Accessed March 3, 2019. https://www.firstpost.com/india/fish-breeding-often-involves-use-of-antibiotics-chemicals-which-harm-human-health-and-alter-ecosystem-4347227.html.

57. Doshi, Vidhi. 2017. *Kolkata: the city that eats fish reared on sewage.* 25 January. Accessed March 3, 2019. https://www.theguardian.com/sustainable-business/2017/jan/25/kolkata-west-bengal-india-cites-fish-farming-sewage-food-demand-real-estate.

58. Serrano, Pilar Hernández. 2005. *Responsible use of antibiotics in aquaculture.* Rome: Food and Agriculture Organization of the United Nations.

59. Deccan Chronicle. 2017. *Andhra Pradesh: Usage of antibiotics in aquaculture worrisome.* 10 October. Accessed March 3, 2019. https://www.deccanchronicle.com/lifestyle/pets-and-environment/101017/andhra-pradesh-usage-of-antibiotics-in-aquaculture-worrisome.html.

60. Patnaik, Santosh. 2018. *NFDB to educate aquaculture farmers on antibiotics overdose.* 9 July. Accessed March 3, 2019. https://www.thehindu.com/news/cities/Visakhapatnam/nfdb-to-educate-aquaculture-farmers-on-antibiotics-overdose/article24367592.ece.

61. Oaklander, Mandy. 2014. *There Are Antibiotics In Your Fish.* 22 October. Accessed March 3, 2019. http://time.com/3531828/antibiotics-fish-seafood/.

62. Oaklander, Mandy. 2014. *There Are Antibiotics In Your Fish.* 22 October. Accessed March 3, 2019. http://time.com/3531828/antibiotics-fish-seafood/.

63. University of Waterloo. 2018. *Vaccines not protecting farmed fish from disease.* 22 January. Accessed March 3, 2019. https://eurekalert.org/pub_releases/2018-01/uow-vnp011918.php.

64. Compassion in World Farming (CIWF). 2008. *The Welfare of Farmed Fish.* July. Accessed March 3, 2019. https://www.ciwf.org.uk/media/3818654/farmed-fish-briefing.pdf.

65. Bollard, Lewis. 2018. *Fish: The Forgotten Farm Animal.* 18 January. Accessed March 2, 2019. https://www.openphilanthropy.org/blog/fish-forgotten-farm-animal.

66. Vidal, John. 2017. *Salmon farming in crisis: 'We are seeing a chemical arms race in the seas'.* 1 April. Accessed March 3, 2019. https://www. theguardian.com/environment/2017/apr/01/is-farming-salmon-bad-for-the-environment.

67. Tørud, Brit, and Tore Håstein. 2008. 'Skin lesions in fish: causes and solutions.' *Acta Veterinaria Scandinavica* 50(Suppl 1): S7.

68. Hays, Brook. 2016. *Study: Farm-raised salmon suffer from depression.* 25 May. Accessed March 3, 2019. https://www.upi.com/Science_News/2016/05/25/Study-Farm-raised-salmon-suffer-from-depression/5391464194628/.

69. Compassion in World Farming (CIWF). 2008. *The Welfare of Farmed Fish.* July. Accessed March 3, 2019. https://www.ciwf.org.uk/media/3818654/farmed-fish-briefing.pdf.

70. Seafood Watch. n.d. *Aquaculture: Pollution and Disease.* Accessed March 3, 2019. https://www.seafoodwatch.org/ocean-issues/aquaculture/pollution-and-disease.

Chapter 12: The Unsustainability of Eating Animals

1. Gates, Bill. 2015. *Is There Enough Meat for Everyone?* 21 April. Accessed March 3, 2019. https://www.gatesnotes.com/Books/Should-We-Eat-Meat?WT.mc_id=04_21_2015_Vaclav_HuffingtonPostImpact&WT.tsrc=HuffingtonPostImpact.

2. *India Today.* 2019. *Avni killed in self-defence? Think again, says probe report.* 6 December. Accessed March 9, 2019. https://www.indiatoday.in/india/story/avni-killing-probe-report-lapses-asghar-ali-1403934-2018-12-06.

3. Ashar, Meet. 2018. *Avni was tagged 'man-eater' without proper evidence; authorities behind her 'ruthless killing' must be brought to book.* 6 November. Accessed March 9, 2019. https://www.firstpost.com/india/avni-was-tagged-man-eater-without-proper-evidence-authorities-behind-her-ruthless-killing-must-be-brought-to-book-5511101.html.

4. *Times of India.* 2018. *Celebs support 'Let Avni Live' campaign.* 22 October. Accessed March 9, 2019. https://photogallery.indiatimes.com/events/mumbai/celebs-support-let-avni-live-campaign/articleshow/66318646.cms.

5. Firstpost. 2018. *'Let Avni Live': Twitterati unite to save 'man-eater' tigress T1 after Maharashtra forest dept issues shoot-at-sight orders.* 4 October. Accessed March 9, 2019. https://www.firstpost.com/india/let-avni-live-twitterati-unite-to-save-man-eater-tigress-t1-after-maharashtra-forest-dept-issues-shoot-at-sight-orders-5314281.html.

6. Goswami, Dev. 2018. *Hunt for man-eating tiger Avni sparks chorus for presidential pardon.* 12 October. Accessed March 9, 2019. https://www.indiatoday.in/india/story/maharashtra-avni-tiger-hunt-presidential-pardon-1366831-2018-10-12.

7. Sutter, John D. 2016. *We have 20 years—at the very most—to prevent mass extinction.* 27 October. Accessed March 9, 2019. https://edition.cnn.com/2016/10/27/opinions/sutter-wwf-sixth-extinction/.

8. WWF. n.d. *How many species are we losing?* Accessed March 9, 2019. http://wwf.panda.org/our_work/biodiversity/biodiversity/.

9. Yong, Ed. 2018. *Wait, Have We Really Wiped Out 60 Percent of Animals?* 31 October. Accessed March 9, 2019. https://www.theatlantic.com/science/archive/2018/10/have-we-really-killed-60-percent-animals-1970/574549/.

10. Hance, Jeremy. 2015. *How humans are driving the sixth mass extinction.* 20 October. Accessed March 9, 2019. https://www.theguardian.com/environment/radical-conservation/2015/oct/20/the-four-horsemen-of-the-sixth-mass-extinction.

11. Sutter, John D. 2016. *We have 20 years—at the very most—to prevent mass extinction.* 27 October. Accessed March 9, 2019. https://edition.cnn.com/2016/10/27/opinions/sutter-wwf-sixth-extinction/.

12. Machovina, Brian, Kenneth J. Feeley, and William J. Ripple. 1 December 2015. 'Biodiversity conservation: The key is reducing meat consumption.' *Science of The Total Environment* Volume 536, 419–431.

13. Morell, Virginia. 2015. *Meat-eaters may speed worldwide species extinction, study warns.* 11 August. Accessed March 9, 2019. http://www.sciencemag.org/news/2015/08/meat-eaters-may-speed-worldwide-species-extinction-study-warns.

14. The World Bank. 2013. *India: Climate Change Impacts.* 19 June. Accessed March 9, 2019. http://www.worldbank.org/en/news/feature/2013/06/19/india-climate-change-impacts.

316 *Notes*

15. IANS. 2017. *Retreating monsoon worst in 140 years; TN declares drought as 144 farmers die.* 11 January. Accessed March 9, 2019. https://www. thenewsminute.com/article/retreating-monsoon-worst-140-years-tn-declares-drought-144-farmers-die-55567.

16. Watts, K. (2019, June 19). *Water crisis: Day Zero arrives in Chennai.* Retrieved from Health Issues India: https://www.healthissuesindia. com/2019/06/19/water-crisis-day-zero-arrives-in-chennai/.

17. Murphy, P. P., & Mezzofiore, G. (2019, June 20). *Chennai, India, is almost out of water. Satellite images show its nearly bone-dry reservoirs.* Retrieved from CNN: https://edition.cnn.com/2019/06/20/world/chennai-satellite-images-reservoirs-water-crisis-trnd/index.html.

18. ANI. (2019, June 20). *21 Indian Cities Will Run Out Of Groundwater By 2020: Report.* Retrieved from NDTV: https://www.ndtv.com/india-news/21-indian-cities-will-run-out-of-groundwater-by-2020-report-2056129.

19. Verisk Maplecroft. 2013. *31% of global economic output forecast to face climate change risks by 2025.* 30 October. Accessed March 9, 2019. https://www.maplecroft.com/insights/analysis/global-economic-output-forecast-faces-high-or-extreme-climate-change-risks-by-2025/.

20. The World Bank. 2013. *India: Green growth is necessary and affordable for India, says new World Bank Report.* 17 July. Accessed March 9, 2019. http://www.worldbank.org/en/news/press-release/2013/07/17/india-green-growth-necessary-and-affordable-for-india-says-new-world-bank-report.

21. Press Trust of India. 2018. *Climate Change Could Shave Off 2.8% Of India's GDP By 2050: World Bank.* 29 June. Accessed March 9, 2019. https://www.ndtv.com/india-news/climate-change-could-shave-off-2-8-of-indias-gdp-by-2050-world-bank-1874988.

22. Mohan, Vishwa. 2014. *Climate change may lead India to war: UN report.* 1 April. Accessed March 9, 2019. https://timesofindia.indiatimes.com/home/environment/global-warming/Climate-change-may-lead-India-to-war-UN-report/articleshow/33034504.cms.

23. Hemalatha, K. (2019, August 27). *Thefts, Fights and Murder: Water Scarcity is Making Chennai an Angry City.* Retrieved from The Weather

Channel: https://weather.com/en-IN/india/news/news/2019-08-27-chennai-water-crisis-drought-encroachment.

24. TNN. (2019, June 7). *Man murdered in fight over drawing of water from public tap.* Retrieved from Times of India: https://timesofindia.indiatimes.com/city/chennai/man-murdered-in-fight-over-drawing-of-water-from-public-tap/articleshow/69684042.cms.

25. Sattiraju, Nikitha. 2017. *The ignored side of the Cauvery debate.* 21 March. Accessed March 9, 2019. https://yourstory.com/2017/03/ignored-side-cauvery-debate/.

26. Nierenberg, Danielle. 2011. *Global Meat Production and Consumption Continue to Rise.* 13 October. Accessed March 9, 2019. http://www.worldwatch.org/system/files/Global%20Meat%20Production%20and%20Consumption%20Continue%20to%20Rise.pdf.

27. Compassion in World Farming. n.d. *Strategic Plan 2013-2017: For Kinder, Fairer Farming Worldwide.* Surrey: Compassion in World Farming.

28. Cowspiracy. n.d. *The Facts.* Accessed March 9, 2019. http://www.cowspiracy.com/facts/.

29. Carus, Felicity. 2010. *UN urges global move to meat and dairy-free diet.* 2 June. Accessed March 9, 2019. https://www.theguardian.com/environment/2010/jun/02/un-report-meat-free-diet.

30. 2014. In *Adventures in the Anthropocene: A Journey to the Heart of the Planet We Made,* by Gaia Vince, 250. London: Chatto & Windus.

31. Bera, Sayantan. 2017. *India home to 23.4% of world's hungry, 51% women are anemic: UN report.* 15 September. Accessed March 9, 2019. https://www.livemint.com/Politics/8BBA9K4GHvpSvXR0ps602O/India-home-to-234-of-worlds-hungry-51-women-are-anemic.html.

32. Water.org. n.d. *India's water and sanitation crisis.* Accessed March 9, 2019. https://water.org/our-impact/india/.

33. Herrero, Mario, Petr Havlík, Hugo Valin, An Notenbaert, Mariana C. Rufino, Philip K. Thornton, Michael Blümmel, Franz Weiss, Delia Grace, and Michael Obersteiner. December 2013. 'Global livestock: Biomass use, production, & GHG.' *Proceedings of the National Academy of Sciences of the United States of America* 110(52): 20888–20893.

34. Water Footprint Network. n.d. *Water footprint of crop and animal products: a comparison.* Accessed March 9, 2019. https://waterfootprint. org/en/water-footprint/product-water-footprint/water-footprint-crop-and-animal-products/.

35. MacDonald, Mia, and Sangamithra Iyer. 2012. *Veg or Non-Veg? India at the Crossroads.* Brooklyn, New York: Brighter Green.

36. Sansoucy, R. n.d. *Livestock–a driving force for food security and sustainable development.* Accessed March 9, 2019. http://www.fao. org/3/v8180t/v8180t07.htm.

37. Holt-Giménez, Eric. 2012. *We Already Grow Enough Food for 10 Billion People... and Still Can't End Hunger.* 8 May. Accessed March 9, 2019. https://www.commondreams.org/views/2012/05/08/we-already-grow-enough-food-10-billion-people-and-still-cant-end-hunger.

38. Thornton, Philip, Mario Herrero, and Polly Ericksen. November 2011. *Livestock and climate change.* Nairobi: International Livestock Research Institute. https://cgspace.cgiar.org/bitstream/handle/10568/10601/ IssueBrief3.pdf.

39. Greenpeace International. 1 June 2009. *Slaughtering the Amazon.* Greenpeace International.

40. Mackintosh, E. (2019, August 23). *The Amazon is burning because the world eats so much meat.* Retrieved from CNN: https://edition.cnn. com/2019/08/23/americas/brazil-beef-amazon-rainforest-fire-intl/ index.html.

41. Bain, M. (2019, August 30). *The Amazon fires prompt H&M, Vans and Timberland to stop buying Brazilian leather.* Retrieved from Quartz: https://qz.com/1698612/amazon-fires-prompt-vans-timberland-to-stop-buying-brazilian-leather/.

42. Mackintosh, E. (2019, August 23). *The Amazon is burning because the world eats so much meat.* Retrieved from CNN: https://edition.cnn. com/2019/08/23/americas/brazil-beef-amazon-rainforest-fire-intl/ index.html.

43. Asner, Gregory P. n.d. *Measuring Carbon Emissions from Tropical Deforestation: An Overview.* Accessed March 9, 2019. https://www.edf. org/sites/default/files/10333_Measuring_Carbon_Emissions_from_ Tropical_Deforestation–An_Overview.pdf.

44. Fraser, Barbara. 2014. *Report: Forests may play bigger role in rainfall than estimated.* 10 April. Accessed March 9, 2019. https://forestsnews. cifor.org/22060/report-forests-may-play-bigger-role-in-rainfall-than-estimated?fnl=en.
45. Gerber, P.J., H. Steinfeld, B. Henderson, A. Mottet, C. Opio, J. Dijkman, A. Falcucci, and G. Tempio. 2013. *Tackling Climate Change Through Livestock: A Global Assessment of Emissions and Mitigation Opportunities.* Rome: Food and Agriculture Organization of the United Nations (FAO).
46. Food and Agriculture Organization of the United Nations (FAO). 2006. *Livestock a major threat to environment.* 29 November. Accessed March 9, 2019. http://www.fao.org/newsroom/en/news/2006/1000448/index. html.
47. Lean, Geoffrey. 2006. *Cow 'emissions' more damaging to planet than CO2 from cars.* 10 December. Accessed March 9, 2019. https://www. independent.co.uk/environment/climate-change/cow-emissions-more-damaging-to-planet-than-co2-from-cars-427843.html.
48. Mims, Christopher. 2010. *Defusing the Methane Greenhouse Time Bomb.* 5 February. Accessed March 9, 2019. https://www.scientificamerican. com/article/defusing-the-methane-time-bomb/.
49. Sharma, Betwa. 2012. *India, World's Largest Livestock Owner, Balks at Farming Gas Curbs in Doha.* 5 December. Accessed March 9, 2019. https://india.blogs.nytimes.com/2012/12/05/india-worlds-largest-livestock-owner-balks-at-farming-gas-curbs-in-doha/.
50. Singh, S. 2018. *Methane from Indian livestock adds to global warming.* 17 January. Accessed March 9, 2019. https://www.scidev.net/asia-pacific/livestock/news/methane-from-indian-livestock-adds-to-global-warming.html.
51. Chhabra, Abha, K.R. Manjunath, Sushma Panigrahy, and J.S. Parihar. March 2013. 'Greenhouse gas emissions from Indian livestock.' *Climatic Change* Volume 117(1–2): 329–44.
52. Chacko, C.T., Gopikrishna, V. Padmakumar, Shailendra Tiwari, and Vidya Ramesh. 2008. *Livestock in the changing landscape in India; its environmental, social and health consequences and responses.* A case study, Hyderabad: Intercooperation Delegation-India.

53. Lean, Geoffrey. 2006. *Cow 'emissions' more damaging to planet than CO2 from cars*. 10 December. Accessed March 9, 2019. https://www.independent.co.uk/environment/climate-change/cow-emissions-more-damaging-to-planet-than-co2-from-cars-427843.html.

54. US Environmental Protection Agency. May 2004. *Risk Assessment Evaluation for Concentrated Animal Feeding Operations*. Cincinnati: US Environmental Protection Agency.

55. Anderson, Kip, and Keegan Kuhn. 2015. *The Sustainability Secret: Rethinking Our Diet to Transform the World*. Chapter 5. San Rafael: Insight Editions.

56. Graham, Jay P., and Keeve E. Nachman. 2010. 'Managing waste from confined animal feeding operations.' *Journal of Water and Health*, 646–70.

57. Ross, Daniel. 2019. *Factory Farms Pollute the Environment and Poison Drinking Water*. 20 February. Accessed March 10, 2019. https://www.ecowatch.com/factory-farms-drinking-water-pollution-2629508815.html.

58. Foodprint. n.d. *What Happens to Animal Waste?* Accessed March 10, 2019. https://foodprint.org/issues/what-happens-to-animal-waste/#easy-footnote-bottom-1-1324.

59. Murawski, John. 2018. *Hurricane Florence Bathed North Carolina in Raw Sewage. New Figures Show It Was Even Worse Than We Thought*. 27 December. Accessed March 10, 2019. http://www.govtech.com/em/disaster/Hurricane-Florence-Bathed-North-Carolina-in-Raw-Sewage-New-Figures-Show-it-was-Even-Worse-than-we-Thought.html.

60. Philpott, Tom. 2013. *Mysterious Poop Foam Causes Explosions on Hog Farms*. 15 May. Accessed March 10, 2019. https://www.motherjones.com/food/2013/05/menace-manure-foam-still-haunting-huge-hog-farms/.

61. Scheer, Roddy, and Doug Moss. n.d. *What Causes Ocean 'Dead Zones'?* Accessed March 10, 2019. https://www.scientificamerican.com/article/ocean-dead-zones/.

62. US Environmental Protection Agency. n.d. *Nutrient Pollution*. Accessed March 10, 2019. https://www.epa.gov/nutrientpollution/problem.

63. Murawski, John. 2018. *Hurricane Florence Bathed North Carolina in Raw Sewage. New Figures Show It Was Even Worse Than We Thought.* 27 December. Accessed March 10, 2019. http://www.govtech.com/em/disaster/Hurricane-Florence-Bathed-North-Carolina-in-Raw-Sewage-New-Figures-Show-it-was-Even-Worse-than-we-Thought.html.

64. Louisiana State University. 2018. *Gulf of Mexico 'dead zone' forecasted to exceed the size of Connecticut.* 7 June. Accessed March 10, 2019. https://www.sciencedaily.com/releases/2018/06/180607120724.htm.

65. J&K State Pollution Control Board. n.d. *CHAPTER 5: Slaughterhouse Waste and Dead Animals.* Accessed March 10, 2019. http://jkspcb.nic.in/WriteReadData/userfiles/file/Slaughter%20houses/Report%20by%20Ministry%20of%20Urban%20dev_%20Deptt_.pdf.

66. US Environmental Protection Agency. n.d. *Nutrient Pollution.* Accessed March 10, 2019. https://www.epa.gov/nutrientpollution/problem.

67. The World Bank. 2012. *India Groundwater: a Valuable but Diminishing Resource.* 6 March. Accessed March 10, 2019. https://www.worldbank.org/en/news/feature/2012/03/06/india-groundwater-critical-diminishing.

68. *The Times of India* (Kochi). 2014. *Kaloor slaughterhouse unscientific and unhygienic: PCB tells high court.* 8 July. Accessed March 10, 2019. http://epaperbeta.timesofindia.com/Article.aspx?eid=31811&articlexml=Kaloor-slaughterhouse-unscientific-and-unhygienic-PCB-tells-high-08072014003033.

69. Singh, Abha Lakshmi, Saleha Jamal, Shanawaz Ahmad Baba, and Md. Manirul Islam. 2014. 'Environmental and Health Impacts from Slaughter Houses Located on the City Outskirts: A Case Study.' *Journal of Environmental Protection* Volume 5(6), Article ID: 46296.

70. Scarborough, Peter, Paul N. Appleby, Anja Mizdrak, Adam D.M. Briggs, Ruth C. Travis, Kathryn E. Bradbury, and Timothy J. Key. July 2014. 'Dietary greenhouse gas emissions of meat-eaters, fish-eaters, vegetarians and vegans in the UK.' *Climatic Change* Volume 125(2): 179–92.

71. University of Oxford. 2016. *Veggie-based diets could save 8 million lives by 2050 and cut global warming.* 22 March. Accessed March 10, 2019.

http://www.ox.ac.uk/news/2016-03-22-veggie-based-diets-could-save-8-million-lives-2050-and-cut-global-warming.

72. Carrington, Damian. 2016. *Study reveals greater climate impacts of 2C temperature rise.* 21 April. Accessed March 10, 2019. https://www.theguardian.com/environment/2016/apr/21/study-reveals-greater-climate-impacts-of-2c-temperature-rise-heatwaves.

73. AFP. 2016. *Global warming set to pass 2C threshold in 2050: report.* 29 September. Accessed March 10, 2019. https://phys.org/news/2016-09-global-2c-threshold.html.

Chapter 13: The Price We Pay

1. Gandhi, Mahatma. 2014. *Healthy Living According to Gandhi.* New Delhi: Orient Publishing.

2. Mittal, Dr Amit. 2017. *Increasing heart attacks in young Indians.* 3 January. Accessed March 10, 2019. https://timesofindia.indiatimes.com/life-style/health-fitness/every-heart-counts/increasing-heart-attacks-in-young-indians/articleshow/56295257.cms.

3. Thomas, Maria. 2017. *It's time Indians take the risk of heart disease very, very seriously.* 16 November. Accessed March 10, 2019. https://qz.com/india/1129834/heart-attacks-and-related-diseases-are-killing-more-indians-than-ever-before/.

4. Mitra, Sounak. 2016. *Are Indians smoking fewer cigarettes.* 23 July. Accessed March 10, 2019. https://www.livemint.com/Industry/9pLAJk1eEmZTdjJGqeQBDJ/Are-Indians-smoking-fewer-cigarettes.html.

5. Forks Over Knives. n.d. *The Forks Over Knives Diet.* Accessed March 10, 2019. https://www.forksoverknives.com/what-to-eat/.

6. Chiorando, Maria. 2018. *Plant-Based Doctors Tell The Government To 'Ditch Dairy' With Sign Outside White House.* 16 August. Accessed March 10, 2019. https://www.plantbasednews.org/post/plant-based-doctors-tell-government-ditch-dairy-sign-white-house.

7. Dr Esselstyn's Prevent and Reverse Heart Disease Program. n.d. *About the Book.* Accessed March 10, 2019. http://www.dresselstyn.com/site/books/prevent-reverse/about-the-book/.

8. Physicians' Committee for Responsible Medicine. n.d. *Tackle Diabetes with a Plant-Based Diet.* Accessed March 10, 2019. https://www.pcrm.org/health-topics/diabetes.

9. LeBlanc, Alberta. 2016. *Learning New Tricks.* 24 February. Accessed March 10, 2019. https://prime.peta.org/2016/02/learning-new-tricks.

10. LeBlanc, Robbie, interview by Poorva Joshipura. 2018. *Interview regarding Alberta LeBlanc* (7 April).

11. Sharan. n.d. *Testimonials.* Accessed March 10, 2019. https://sharan-india.org/testimonials/.

12. Shenoy, Sonali. 2016. *She has the recipe to reverse diabetes.* 30 July. Accessed March 10, 2019. http://www.newindianexpress.com/cities/chennai/2016/jul/30/She-has-the-recipe-to-reverse-diabetes-945868.html.

13. IANS. 2016. *Heart attack kills one person every 33 seconds in India.* 18 May. Accessed March 10, 2019. https://www.business-standard.com/article/news-ians/heart-attack-kills-one-person-every-33-seconds-in-india-116051801086_1.html.

14. —. n.d. *Cardiovascular disease.* Accessed March 10, 2019. https://www.who.int/cardiovascular_diseases/en/.

15. Mishra, Nikita. 2016. *World Heart Day: 20-Somethings Can Also Die From a Heart Attack.* 28 September. Accessed March 10, 2019. https://fit.thequint.com/health-news/alert-20-somethings-are-not-too-young-to-die-from-a-heart-attack-2.

16. Ahmad, Omair. 2009. *'India Is The Impotence Capital Of The World'.* 26 January. Accessed March 10, 2019. https://www.outlookindia.com/magazine/story/india-is-the-impotence-capital-of-the-world/239548.

17. Physicians Committee for Responsible Medicine (PCRM). 2005. *Impotence Predicts Heart Disease.* 22 December. Accessed March 10, 2019. https://www.pcrm.org/news/health-nutrition/impotence-predicts-heart-disease.

18. Sharma, Radha. 2013. *Now, Erectile Dysfunction afflicts more men below 30 years.* 7 July. Accessed March 10, 2019. https://timesofindia.indiatimes.com/home/science/Now-Erectile-Dysfunction-afflicts-more-men-below-30-years/articleshow/20951362.cms.

19. Pandian, Jeyaraj Durai, and Paulin Sudhan. 2013. 'Stroke Epidemiology and Stroke Care Services in India.' *Journal of Stroke* 15(3): 128–134.
20. Malik, Rakesh. 2016. *India is the diabetes capital of the world!* 28 January. Accessed February 7, 2019. https://timesofindia.indiatimes.com/lifestyle/health-fitness/health-news/India-is-the-diabetes-capital-of-the-world/articleshow/50753461.cms.
21. CADI (Coronary Artery Disease among Asian Indians) Research Foundation. n.d. *Hypertension in India.* Accessed March 10, 2013. http://www.cadiresearch.org/topic/hypertension/hypertension-india.
22. Nikose, Sunil, Pradeep Singh, Sohael Khan, Mridul Arora, Shounak Taywade, Mahendra Gudhe, and Swapnil Gadge. 2015. 'Prevalence of Osteoporosis in Female Population in Rural Central India [By Calcaneal Ultrasound].' *Journal of Women's Health Care* 4, 262.
23. Gandhi, Ajeet Kumar, Pavnesh Kumar, Menal Bhandari, Bharti Devnani, and Goura Kishor Rath. 2016. 'Burden of preventable cancers in India: Time to strike the cancer epidemic.' *Journal of the Egyptian National Cancer Institute* 29, 11–18.
24. IANS. 2016. *Why does obesity cause diabetes? Indian scientists just found an explanation.* 7 September. Accessed March 10, 2019. https://www.hindustantimes.com/health-and-fitness/why-does-obesity-cause-diabetes-indian-scientists-just-found-an-explanation/story-M2ExSvGoD4DjjSodszeVrL.html.
25. Pandit, Sadaguru. 2016. *17 million obese children in India by 2025: International journal.* 11 October. Accessed March 10, 2019. https://www.hindustantimes.com/mumbai-news/17-million-obese-children-in-india-by-2025-international-journal/story-vTSZnYhFIWTjgKwSg5J2AL.html.
26. Raj, Manu. 2012. 'Obesity and cardiovascular risk in children and adolescents.' *Indian Journal of Endocrinology and Metabolism* 16(1): 13–19.
27. Umer, Amna, George A. Kelley, Lesley E. Cottrell, Peter Giacobbi Jr., Kim E. Innes, and Christa L. Lilly. 2017. 'Childhood obesity and adult cardiovascular disease risk factors: a systematic review with meta-analysis.' *BMC Public Health* 17: 683.

28. Mittal, Dr Amit. 2017. *Increasing heart attacks in young Indians*. 3 January. Accessed March 10, 2019. https://timesofindia.indiatimes. com/life-style/health-fitness/every-heart-counts/increasing-heart-attacks-in-young-indians/articleshow/56295257.cms.

29. Janakiram, Karthik. 2016. *Kerala Just Imposed A 14.5% 'Fat Tax' On All Fast Food Chains*. 8 July. Accessed March 10, 2019. https://www. scoopwhoop.com/Kerala-Has-Imposed-A-145-Fat-Tax-On-All-Fast-Food-Chains-Serving-Fatty-Food/#.8bqagitue.

30. Karlsen, Micaela. 2012. *Meeting Protein Needs Simply by Eating*. 7 November. Accessed March 10, 2019. https://www.forksoverknives. com/meeting-protein-needs-simply-by-eating/#gs.0w4sma.

31. Oliveira, Dr Rosane. 2015. *Getting Clarity About Calcium*. 21 May. Accessed March 10, 2019. https://www.forksoverknives.com/milk-myth-why-you-dont-need-dairy-for-calcium/#gs.0w4hmx.

32. American Egg Board. n.d. *Yes, It Really is Incredible–The Indisputably Potent Protein Eggs Supply*. Accessed March 10, 2019. https://www.aeb. org/food-manufacturers/why-eggs/white-papers/real-eggs-not-all-proteins-are-created-equal.

33. Jacob, Aglaee. 2018. *Do Nut Butters Count as Proteins or Fats?* 19 December. Accessed March 10, 2019. https://healthyeating.sfgate.com/ nut-butters-count-proteins-fats-2177.html.

34. Stoll, Dr Scott. 2013. *Yes, Plants Have Protein*. 15 January. Accessed March 10, 2019. https://webcache.googleusercontent.com/ search?q=cache:L_zmoVAofeAJ:https://www.wholefoodsmarket.com/ blog/whole-story/yes-plants-have-protein+&cd=11&hl=en&ct=clnk& gl=uk.

35. US Department of Health and Human Services. 2016. *What are good sources of calcium?* 1 December. Accessed March 10, 2019. https://www. nichd.nih.gov/health/topics/bonehealth/conditioninfo/sources.

36. Physicians' Committee for Responsible Medicine (PCRM). n.d. *Calcium and Strong Bones*. Accessed March 11, 2019. https://www.pcrm.org/ good-nutrition/nutrition-information/health-concerns-about-dairy/ calcium-and-strong-bones.

37. —. n.d. *Vegetarian Starter Kit*. Accessed March 11, 2019. http://support. pcrm.org/site/DocServer/Vegetarian_Start_Kit.pdf?docID=261.

38. —. n.d. *Lowering Cholesterol with a Plant-Based Diet*. Accessed March 11, 2019. https://www.pcrm.org/good-nutrition/nutrition-information/lowering-cholesterol-with-a-plant-based-diet.

39. Salazar, Tessa R. 2016. *Dietary cholesterol linked to increased breast cancer risk*. 9 July. Accessed March 11, 2019. https://business.inquirer.net/211723/dietary-cholesterol-linked-to-increased-breast-cancer-risk?utm_expid=.XqNwTug2W6nwDVUSgFJXed.1.

40. Physicians' Committee for Responsible Medicine (PCRM). n.d. *Cholesterol and Heart Disease*. Accessed March 11, 2019. https://bragg.com/healthinfo/features/cholesterol_heart.html.

41. Patel, Devang. 2014. *Sunday ho ya monday roz khao ande By Devang Patel*. 19 July. Accessed March 11, 2019. https://www.youtube.com/watch?v=-B-UF-tuMgg.

42. Physicians' Committee for Responsibile Medicine (PCRM). n.d. *Health Concerns with Eggs*. Accessed March 11, 2019. https://www.pcrm.org/good-nutrition/nutrition-information/health-concerns-with-eggs.

43. —. 2016. *Studies Link Eggs to Stroke, Diabetes, Heart Disease, Cancer*. 2 November. Accessed March 11, 2019. https://www.pcrm.org/news/blog/studies-link-eggs-stroke-diabetes-heart-disease-cancer.

44. —. n.d. *Lurking Beneath the Shell: Health Concerns With Eggs*. Accessed March 11, 2019. http://www.greenwichpuremedical.com/images/pdfdownloads/Eggs-fact-sheet.pdf.

45. *Forks Over Knives*. 2011. Directed by Lee Fulkerson.

46. Lanou, Amy Joy. May 2009. 'Should dairy be recommended as part of a healthy vegetarian diet? Counterpoint.' *The American Journal of Clinical Nutrition* Volume 89(5): 1638S–1642S.

47. Barnard, Dr Neal. n.d. *Milk and Prostate Cancer: The Evidence Mounts*. Accessed March 11, 2019. http://thefoodconnection.org.uk/milk_and_prostate_evidence.pdf.

48. Physicians' Committee for Responsible Medicine (PCRM). 2007. *Health Concerns About Dairy Products*. April. Accessed March 11, 2019. http://www.afa-online.org/docs/faq_dairy.pdf.

49. Physicians' Committee for Responsible Medicine (PCRM). 2007. *Health Concerns About Dairy Products*. April. Accessed March 11, 2019. http://www.afa-online.org/docs/faq_dairy.pdf.

50. Sharda, Shailvee. 2015. *Three out of four Indians have no milk tolerance: Study.* 11 March. Accessed March 11, 2019. https://timesofindia. indiatimes.com/city/lucknow/Three-out-of-four-Indians-have-no-milk-tolerance-Study/articleshow/46522488.cms.

51. Aptaclub. n.d. *Signs and symptoms of lactose intolerance in babies.* Accessed March 11, 2019. https://www.aptaclub.co.uk/baby/diet-and-nutrition/allergies-and-food-intolerance/lactose-intolerance-in-babies.html.

52. Mayo Clinic. n.d. *Milk allergy.* Accessed March 11, 2019. https://www. mayoclinic.org/diseases-conditions/milk-allergy/symptoms-causes/syc-20375101.

53. Physicians' Committee for Responsible Medicine (PCRM). 2007. *Health Concerns About Dairy Products.* April. Accessed March 11, 2019. http://www.afa-online.org/docs/faq_dairy.pdf.

54. US Food and Drug Administration. n.d. *Eating Fish: What Pregnant Women and Parents Should Know.* Accessed March 11, 2019. https:// www.fda.gov/Food/ResourcesForYou/Consumers/ucm393070.htm.

55. Centre for Science and Environment (CSE). 2010. *Mercury Pollution of India.* 8 January. Accessed March 11, 2019. https://www.cseindia.org/mercury-pollution-of-india-439.

56. Physicians' Committee for Responsible Medicine (PCRM). n.d. *Fish.* Accessed March 12, 2019. http://www.shamanicspring.com/fish_report.pdf.

57. World Health Organization (WHO). 2015. *WHO's first ever global estimates of foodborne diseases find children under 5 account for almost one third of deaths.* 3 December. Accessed March 12, 2019. https://www. who.int/en/news-room/detail/03-12-2015-who-s-first-ever-global-estimates-of-foodborne-diseases-find-children-under-5-account-for-almost-one-third-of-deaths.

58. Centers for Disease Control and Prevention. n.d. *Campylobacter (Campylobacteriosis).* Accessed March 12, 2019. https://www.cdc.gov/campylobacter/index.html.

59. National Research Council of the National Academies. n.d. *How to Make Sure the Ground Beef You Serve Is Safe.* Accessed March 12, 2019. https://www.nap.edu/resource/13069/Ground-Beef-Fact-Sheet.pdf.

60. Ipatenco, Sara. n.d. *Diseases From Pork That Pass to Humans.* Accessed March 12, 2019. https://www.livestrong.com/article/555801-diseases-from-pork-that-pass-to-humans/.

61. Physicians Committee for Responsible Medicine (PCRM). 2017. *Cheese Causes Foodborne Illness Deaths.* 10 March. Accessed March 12, 2019. https://www.pcrm.org/news/news-releases/cheese-causes-foodborne-illness-deaths.

62. Centers for Disease Control and Prevention (CDC). 2018. *Antibiotic Resistance, Food, and Food-Producing Animals.* 8 November. Accessed March 12, 2019. https://www.cdc.gov/features/antibiotic-resistance-food/index.html.

63. Worley, Heidi. 2014. *Water, Sanitation, Hygiene, and Malnutrition in India.* 23 September. Accessed March 12, 2019. https://www.prb.org/india-sanitation-malnutrition/.

64. Ahuja, D.K. (2019, September). Review of State Mid-Day Meal Schemes by PETA India.

65. Government of Madhya Pradesh. n.d. *Weekly Menu of Mid-Day Meal.* Accessed March 12, 2019. https://slideplayer.com/slide/7627136/.

66. Dr Kiran Ahuja. (2019, September). *Why Midday Meals Should be Entirely Plant Powered.* PETA India.

67. Vesanto, Melina, Winston Craig, and Susan Levin. 2016. 'Position of the Academy of Nutrition and Dietetics: Vegetarian Diets.' *Journal of the Academy of Nutrition and Dietetics* 116: 1970–1980.

68. Physicians Committee for Responsible Medicine (PCRM). 2013. *Ask Dr. Neal Barnard: Do I need vitamin B12?* 19 December. Accessed March 12, 2019. https://www.youtube.com/watch?v=QyTjS80Dyk0.

69. Physicians' Committee for Responsible Medicine (PCRM). n.d. *Vitamin B12: A Simple Solution.* Washington DC: PCRM.

70. Gallagher, James. 2013. *Vegetarians 'cut heart risk by 32%'.* 30 January. Accessed January 19, 2019. https://www.bbc.co.uk/news/health-21258509.

71. Key, T.J., P.N. Appleby, E.A. Spencer, R.C. Travis, A.W. Roddam, and N.E. Allen. 2009 May. 'Cancer incidence in vegetarians: results from the European Prospective Investigation into Cancer and Nutrition

(EPIC-Oxford).' *The American Journal of Clinical Nutrition (AJCN)* 89(5): 1620S–1626S.

72. Tantamango-Bartley, Yessenia, Karen Jaceldo-Siegl, Jing Fan, and Gary Fraser. 2013. 'Vegetarian Diets and the Incidence of Cancer in a Low-Risk Population.' *Cancer Epidemiology, Biomarkers & Prevention* 22(2): 286–94.

73. Godman, Heidi. 2015. *Vegetarian diet linked to lower colon cancer risk.* 11 March. Accessed March 12, 2019. https://www.health. harvard.edu/blog/vegetarian-diet-linked-to-lower-colon-cancer-risk-201503117785.

74. Tonstad, S., K. Stewart, K. Oda, M. Batech, R.P. Herring, and G.E. Fraser. 2013 April. 'Vegetarian diets and incidence of diabetes in the Adventist Health Study-2.' *Nutrition, Metabolism & Cardiovascular Diseases* 23(4): 292–99.

75. HuffPost. 2013. *Vegetarians Slimmer Than Meat-Eaters, Study Finds.* 10 May. Accessed March 13, 2019. https://www.huffpost.com/entry/ vegetarians-slimmer-meat-eaters-weight_n_4039441?ir=India.

Chapter 14: The Myth of Humane Production

1. Newkirk, Ingrid. 2013. *Let's Face It: There Is No Such Thing as Humane Meat.* 26 February. Accessed March 6, 2019. https://www. huffingtonpost.com/ingrid-newkirk/humane-meat_b_2765996.html.

2. Associated Press. 2015. *Dalmatians, dogs with collars spotted at China's dog meat festival.* 22 June. Accessed March 6, 2019. https://nypost. com/2015/06/22/restaurants-doing-brisk-business-at-chinese-dog-meat-festival/.

3. Sky News. 2013. *China: Animal Campaigners Expose Puppy Trade.* 12 September. Accessed March 6, 2019. https://news.sky.com/story/ china-animal-campaigners-expose-puppy-trade-10434560.

4. Last Chance for Animals. 2016. *Animal slaughter 2016: Pets Dogs Clubbed to Death for Chinese Restaurants.* 18 October. Accessed March 6, 2019. https://www.youtube.com/watch?v=C406IVEPqF4.

5. PETA Asia. n.d. *Exposed: Chinese Dog-Leather Industry.* Accessed March 6, 2019. http://action.petaasia.com/ea-action/action?ea.client. id=110&ea.campaign.id=32734.

6.   Winter, Stuart. 2018. *Yulin dog eating festival: 3000 dogs skinned alive, blow-torched then served-up as food.* 24 May. Accessed March 6, 2019. https://www.express.co.uk/news/nature/964194/Yulin-news-dog-eating-festival-China-animal-abuse-numbers-blow-torch.

7.   Ibrahim, Farid M. 2018. *Dogs and cats blow-torched alive at Indonesia 'extreme' market despite promised ban.* 11 September. Accessed March 6, 2019. https://www.abc.net.au/news/2018-09-11/dogs-and-cats-burnt-alive-at-extreme-market-in-indonesia/10222240.

8.   Compassion in World Farming (CIWF). n.d. *Know Your Labels.* Accessed March 6, 2019. https://www.ciwf.com/your-food/know-your-labels/.

9.   Kailing, Ken. 2012. *Grass-Fed vs. Feedlot Beef – What's the difference?* 31 January. Accessed March 6, 2019. http://www.goodfoodworld.com/2012/01/grass-fed-vs-feedlot-beef-whats-the-difference/.

10. UK Department for Environment, Food & Rural Affairs and Animal and Plant Health Agency. 2012. *Eggs: trade regulations.* 8 October. Accessed March 8, 2019. https://www.gov.uk/guidance/eggs-trade-regulations#egg-marking.

11. Sentience Institute. 2017. *Survey of US Attitudes Towards Animal Farming and Animal-Free Food October 2017.* 20 November. Accessed March 8, 2019. https://www.sentienceinstitute.org/animal-farming-attitudes-survey-2017.

12. Hickman, Martin. 2012. *The 'good food' stamp barely worth the label it's printed on.* 1 May. Accessed March 8, 2019. https://www.independent.co.uk/life-style/food-and-drink/news/the-good-food-stamp-barely-worth-the-label-its-printed-on-7697854.html.

13. Quinn, Sue. 2015. *What are the most ethical eggs you can buy?* 15 February. Accessed March 8, 2019. https://www.telegraph.co.uk/foodanddrink/foodanddrinkadvice/11411975/What-are-the-most-ethical-eggs-you-can-buy.html.

14. Noble Foods. n.d. *Noble Foods taps into Britains growing appetite for speciality eggs.* Accessed March 8, 2019. https://www.noblefoods.co.uk/noble-foods-taps-into-britains-growing-appetite-for-speciality-eggs/.

15. —.n.d. *Corporate Social Responsibility.* Accessed March 8, 2019. https://www.noblefoods.co.uk/corporate-social-responsibility/.

16. Southern, Keiran. 2017. *Firm behind Happy Egg Co 'also keeps 4.3m hens in cages where they only have the floorspace of a piece of A4 paper to themselves for its Big & Fresh range'.* 10 October. Accessed March 8, 2019. https://www.dailymail.co.uk/news/article-4965500/Free-range-egg-firm-slammed-use-caged-hens.html.

17. UK Department for Environment, Food and Rural Affairs. 2019. *United Kingdom Egg Statistics - Quarter 4, 2018.* 31 January. Accessed March 8. https://assets.publishing.service.gov.uk/government/uploads/system/uploads/attachment_data/file/775055/eggs-statsnotice-31jan19.pdf.

18. Viva!!. n.d. *Viva!! investigates: The Happy Egg Company.* Accessed March 8, 2019. https://www.Viva!.org.uk/what-we-do/happy-egg-company.

19. Animal Aid. 2008. *Animal suffering exposed on 'Freedom Food' farm.* 2 July. Accessed March 8, 2019. https://www.animalaid.org.uk/animal-suffering-exposed-freedom-food-farm/.

20. Viva!! 2008. *'Freedom Foods Turkeys' Covered in Blood.* Accessed March 8, 2019. https://www.Viva!.org.uk/what-we-do/our-work/turkeys/moorfield-poultry-farm-freedom-food.

21. Parkes, Kate. 2013. *Why McDonald's Move to 100% Freedom Food Pork Is a Big Deal for Animal Welfare.* 23 April. Accessed March 8, 2019. https://www.huffingtonpost.co.uk/kate-parkes/mcdonalds-animal-welfare_b_3132180.html?guccounter=1.

22. Panther, Lewis. 2013. *Semi-paralysed and slumped in their own waste yet these pigs live on a Freedom Food farm.* 1 September. Accessed March 8, 2019. https://www.mirror.co.uk/news/uk-news/semi-paralysed-slumped-waste-yet-pigs-2241928.

23. Armstrong, Laura. 2011. *Sickening Scenes at Freedom Food Pig Farm.* 18 September. Accessed March 8, 2019. https://www.mirror.co.uk/news/world-news/sickening-scenes-at-freedom-food-pig-1700710.

24. RSPCA. (2019, October 1). *RSPCA welfare standards.* Retrieved from https://science.rspca.org.uk/sciencegroup/farmanimals/standards.

25. Animal Aid. 2009. *Three workers suspended and CCTV installed in organic abattoir following cruelty allegations.* 11 December. Accessed March 9, 2019. https://www.animalaid.org.uk/three-workers-

suspended-cctv-installed-organic-abattoir-following-cruelty-allegations/.

26. Consumer Reports. n.d. *American Humane Association.* Accessed March 9, 2019. https://mercyforanimals.org/files/American-Humane-Association-Consumer-Reports.pdf.

27. Mercy for Animals. n.d. *Don't Buy the Lie.* Accessed March 9, 2019. http://www.americanhumanescam.com/learnmore.php.

28. Whole Foods Market. n.d. Accessed March 9, 2019. https://www.wholefoodsmarket.com/company-info.

29. PETA US. n.d. *Whole Foods 'Happy Meat' Supplier Exposed.* Accessed March 9, 2019. https://investigations.peta.org/whole-foods-humane-meat-exposed/.

30. Gallo, A. C. n.d. *Our Meat: No Antibiotics, Ever.* Accessed March 9, 2019. https://www.wholefoodsmarket.com/blog/whole-story/our-meat-no-antibiotics-ever-0.

31. Mayo Clinic. n.d. *Salmonella infection.* Accessed March 9, 2019. https://www.mayoclinic.org/diseases-conditions/salmonella/symptoms-causes/syc-20355329.

32. PETA US. n.d. *PETA Exposes This Cage-Free 'Chicken Disneyland' as Hell for Hens.* Accessed March 9, 2019. https://www.peta.org/blog/chicken-disneyland-hell-hens/.

33. Carter, Dom. 2015. *Welcome to Banksy's sinister twist on Disneyland.* 21 August. Accessed March 9, 2019. https://www.creativebloq.com/street-art/welcome-banksys-sinister-twist-disneyland-81516388.

34. DW. 2018. *Undercover videos of organic chicken farms can be aired.* 10 April. Accessed March 9, 2019. http://www.dw.com/en/undercover-videos-of-organic-chicken-farms-can-be-aired/a-43320605.

35. Nainer, Nahla. 2018. *India's first brand of free range eggs ensures humane treatment of the birds.* 15 March. Accessed March 9, 2019. https://www.thehindu.com/life-and-style/food/indias-first-brand-of-free-range-eggs-ensures-humane-treatment-of-the-birds/article23261238.ece.

36. Happy Hens Farm. n.d. *Animal Welfare.* Accessed March 9, 2019. http://www.thehappyhensfarm.com/our-hens/.

37. Nainer, Nahla. 2018. *India's first brand of free range eggs ensures humane treatment of the birds.* 15 March. Accessed March 9, 2019. https://www.

thehindu.com/life-and-style/food/indias-first-brand-of-free-range-eggs-ensures-humane-treatment-of-the-birds/article23261238.ece.

38. Ray, C. Claiborne. 2016. *How Many Eggs Does a Chicken Lay in Its Lifetime?* 18 April. Accessed March 9, 2019. https://www.nytimes.com/2016/04/19/science/how-many-eggs-does-a-chicken-lay-in-its-lifetime.html.

39. Economic Times. 2018. *Rajasthan government plans safari to educate people about cows.* 28 June. Accessed March 9, 2019. https://economictimes.indiatimes.com/news/politics-and-nation/rajasthan-government-plans-safari-to-educate-people-about-cows/articleshow/64775065.cms.

40. Food and Agriculture Organization of the United Nations (FAO). n.d. *Statistical Yearbook of the Food and Agricultural Organization for the United Nations.* Accessed March 9, 2019. http://www.fao.org/3/i3138e/i3138e07.pdf.

41. Harkinson, Josh. 2014. *Slaughter-Free Milk Is Great for Cows, But Not the Environment.* 21 July. Accessed March 9, 2019. https://www.motherjones.com/environment/2014/07/downside-no-kill-dairies/.

42. Singh, S. 2018. *Methane from Indian livestock adds to global warming.* 17 January. Accessed March 9, 2019. https://www.scidev.net/asia-pacific/livestock/news/methane-from-indian-livestock-adds-to-global-warming.html.

43. Reese, Jacy. 2018. *There's no such thing as humane meat or eggs. Stop kidding yourself.* 16 November. Accessed March 9, 2019. https://www.theguardian.com/food/2018/nov/16/theres-no-such-thing-as-humane-meat-or-eggs-stop-kidding-yourself.

Chapter 15: Making the Transition

1. Tolstoy, Leo. 1997. *A Calendar of Wisdom.* New York: Scribner.

2. Sharma, Charu. 2017. *'Vegetarianism Will Be The New Trend'.* 31 July. Accessed March 3, 2019. https://www.franchiseindia.com/restaurant/Vegetarianism-will-be-the-New-Trend.9777.

3. Clear, James. 2014. *How Long Does it Actually Take to Form a New Habit (Backed by Science).* 4 June. Accessed March 4, 2019. https://www.huffpost.com/entry/forming-new-habits_n_5104807.

4. Forks Over Knives. n.d. *Forks Over Knives: The Documentary Feature.* Accessed March 4, 2019. https://www.forksoverknives.com/the-film/.

5. What the Health. n.d. Accessed March 5, 2019. http://www. whatthehealthfilm.com/.

6. Newkirk, Ingrid. n.d. *What Is Animal Liberation? Philosopher Peter Singer's Groundbreaking Work Turns 40.* Accessed March 5, 2019. https://www.peta.org/about-peta/learn-about-peta/ingrid-newkirk/ animal-liberation/.

7. Penguin. n.d. *The Animals' Agenda.* Accessed March 5, 2019. https:// www.penguin.com.au/books/the-animals-agenda-9780807027608.

8. Vegan Outreach. n.d. *Vegan Mentor Program.* Accessed March 5, 2019. https://veganoutreach.org/vegan-mentorship-program/.

9. Loria, Joe. 2016. *13 Inspiring Celebrity Quotes on Why Veganism Is the Bomb.* 11 August. Accessed March 5, 2019. https://mercyforanimals. org/13-inspiring-celebrity-quotes-on-why-veganism.

INDEX

bone marrow aplasia, 76
Bong Joon Ho, 252
Bonnie (baby cow), 53–54
bottom trawling, 186–87
bottom-dwelling species, 189
Bowser, Paul R., 176
Braithwaite, Victoria, 180–81
Brambell, Roger, 40
branding of animals, 110–11
Bratanova, Boyka, 20
Brazilian Amazon, 203–04
'breed standards', 104
breeding for unnatural physical
     traits, 111–14
breeding technologies, 119
Briefrel, Roland, 154
Brighter Green, 202, 203, 204
British Blacktail eggs, 235
British Royal Society for the
     Prevention of Cruelty to
     Animals (RSPCA), 235–37,
     242, 244
     Freedom Food scheme
         (changed to RSPCA
         Assured), 236–38, 242
broiler chickens, 113–17, 118,
     155
broiler farming, 100, 101
Brown, Culum, 13, 181
buffaloes, 4–6, 14, 31, 205
     destined for slaughter, 140,
         141–42
     protected from slaughter in
         some of the Indian states,
         72
bulls used for work, 123–24, 125,
     134

depression, 129–31
     pushed beyond their physical
         limits, 126–27 slaughter,
         169–70
     torturous events like fairs,
         races, fights etc, 131–34
bullfighting, 132, 135
Bureau of Indian Standards (BIS),
     90, 148
     Code of Practice for Poultry
         Housing, 100
Bureau of Investigative
     Journalism, 46
Burger King, 36, 51
Burnbrae Farms, 239
Butterball, 239
'bycatch', 186–87

'cage layer fatigue', 95
Cal-Maine, 239
calves allowed to die, 64–65
camels, 205
Cameron, James, 251
Campbell, T. Colin, 85, 213, 223
campylobacter, 227
cancer in animals, 112, 128, 130
cancer in humans, 213, 214, 229,
     230
     breast cancer, 85, 224
     ovarian cancer, 85, 224
     prostate cancer, 85, 221, 223,
         224, 227
cannibalism, 59, 95–96
Capaul, Armin, 107
carbon footprint, xxiii
Cardiovascular diseases, 218–20,
     230

ACKNOWLEDGEMENTS

For being a visionary and my mentor for all things animal rights, Ingrid Newkirk. For your unwavering belief in me, for standing by me when animal abusers are burning me in effigy, and for always pushing me to do more, Soum. For introducing me to animal rights, Natalie Hawkins. For suggesting I write this book, Debasri Rakshit. For editing this book and your guidance, Siddhesh Inamdar. For keeping me going, my agent, Kanishka Gupta. For recognizing the importance of publishing this book, HarperCollins. For instilling in me that values matter, mom and dad. For being the sensible one so that I can be the daring one, Megha. For your compassion for all and for providing comic relief, Neil. For being companions and teachers, Mehboob, Tim and Mil. For providing me support, joy and much-needed breaks, all of my wonderful friends. For sharing your experiences for this book and for being world-class veterinarians, Dr Manilal Valliyate and Dr Naresh Upreti. For your bravery, commitment and for exposing cruelty to animals, PETA India investigators, Animals Now, and everyone else through whom we know what really happens to animals for meat, milk and eggs.

For motivating me every day with your compassion, intelligence, strategy, persistence, dedication and victories for animals, the incredible PETA India and staff of PETA affiliates around the globe. For letting me tag along and everything you do for bulls and your tremendous animal rescues and other hands-on work with animals, the Animal Rahat staff. For showing us plants save lives, Dr Neal Barnard, Dr Caldwell Esselstyn, Dr Nandita Shah and all of the other health professionals who prescribe eating plant-based. For fighting the good fight, my colleagues at other animal protection groups. For contributing to our knowledge, all of the scientists, documentary filmmakers, authors, sanctuary workers and others through whom we know more about animals, the environment or eating for good health. For making the world a kinder place, everyone who puts out water for a stray.

ABOUT THE AUTHOR

Poorva Joshipura has been raising awareness on the plight of animals used for food and other industries across the globe for over twenty years. Her work to expose the mistreatment of animals has taken her to animal markets, slaughter floors, inside laboratories and other places where animals are commonly abused. She has also overseen or been involved in the work of other investigators who have documented the handling of animals at egg, fish and dairy farms, in transport, circuses and more.

Her award-winning efforts to help animals has also led her to courtrooms and inside corporate boardrooms, government offices and newsrooms. She is the current senior vice president of International Operations with PETA Foundation, a European affiliate of US-based People for the Ethical Treatment of Animals, a member of the board of directors for PETA India, former chief executive officer of PETA India and former co-opted member of the Animal Welfare Board of India, a statutory body which operates under the Ministry of Environment, Forests and Climate Change, Government of India. Campaigns Poorva has led through PETA India and other

PETA affiliates span helping stop cruelty to animals used for food, clothing, experimentation and entertainment in countries around the world.

These campaigns have been widely covered by Indian, European, and other major news agencies. Poorva is a regular guest on television news and radio shows through which she encourages viewers and listeners to take action to help animals. She spends most of her time between London, Mumbai and Delhi.